ORGANIC NO-TILL FARMING

ADVANCING NO-TILL AGRICULTURE — CROPS, SOILS, EQUIPMENT

ORGANIC NO-TILL FARMING

ADVANCING NO-TILL AGRICULTURE — CROPS, SOILS, EQUIPMENT

JEFF MOYER

ACRES U.S.A.
AUSTIN, TEXAS

Organic No-Till Farming

Acres U.S.A.
P.O. Box 91299
Austin, Texas 78709 U.S.A.
(512) 892-4400 • fax (512) 892-4448
info@acresusa.com • www.acresusa.com

Printed in the United States of America

Publisher's Cataloging-in-Publication

Moyer, Jeff, 1955-
Organic no-till farming / Jeff Moyer. Austin, TX, ACRES U.S.A., 2011
xiv, 204 pp., 28 cm.
Includes Index
Includes Bibliography
ISBN 978-1-60173-017-6 (trade)

1. Organic farming. 2. Cropping systems – no-till. 3. Agriculture – soil improvement. 4. Farm machinery. 5. Alternative agriculture. I. Moyer, Jeff, 1955- II. Title.

S604.M69 2011 631.58

Photo on page 51 courtesy of Doug Thompson.

ACKNOWLEDGEMENTS

With any endeavor of this nature, there are many people who have contributed to its creation. To all those folks – farmers, researchers, collaborators and partners, I'd like to acknowledge their tremendous contribution. Without their expertise and inspiration the work and information discussed in this book would never have come to light. I am indebted to all who have shaped my thinking and my work over the past 34 years.

I will always be grateful to George Kuepper, formerly with ATTRA (National Sustainable Agriculture Information Service), who first suggested I write this book as a way of both documenting the lifetime of effort that went into this system design and to serve as an outreach vehicle to carry the important message of organic no-till to farmers and folks who can best put it to work in their own fields. I am also grateful to Ardie (Ardath) Rodale for inspiring me to get started by simply saying, "You can do it" and "just start by writing one page." Thank you.

To all the organic farmers who blazed the trail ahead of me, I owe my deepest appreciation. While I might consider myself a pioneer in the world of organic farming, having been working in the field for over 34 years, many have gone before me. Blazing new trails is never easy work and theirs was no exception. Ridicule and distain was all part of their daily lives as they forged ahead with the knowledge that building healthy soil is the true key to a successful and sustainable food system.

I also want to thank all the conservationists, environmentalists and ecologists who set the tone for the science needed to move the practices discussed in this book from the pages of esoteric documents to the laboratories and field trials. They too were willing to make giant leaps of faith based on the ideas and inspirations seen in natural systems and working to translate them into food production systems. Without their leadership the world of "organic production" would still be viewed as nothing more than an interesting side note in American agriculture rather than the science-based programs being conducted at land grant and USDA research stations across the country.

I'd be terribly remiss if I didn't pay special thanks to all the staff members of Rodale Institute, past and present, who have supported and enabled this work, added to it, and encouraged my efforts. Without their efforts the information in this book could not have been developed and presented here. The farm operations team has worked tirelessly conducting field trials and adding their expertise to the system design. The research team over many years has labored to solve problems, expand the horizons of what is possible and lead the way in collecting mountains of data to document the successes and failures as we moved the projects forward. Also, thanks to the administration that supported all this work with resources – without which none of this would be possible.

And finally I need to thank my neighbor and farmer/fabricator extraordinaire, John Brubaker who translated the ideas and requirements for that first roller/crimper, made from raw steel found in the salvage yard, into the tool we all know as the Rodale Roller/Crimper. This isn't the first project we teamed up on and hopefully it won't be the last. John's engineering mind and technical skills reach far beyond my own. He is a true farmer/builder for whom no idea seems too strange or challenge too difficult to tackle.

This book would never have come to life if it wasn't for the dedicated efforts of Erika Jensen. She used her unique talent for prodding me and pulling out information and then helping to organize the information into, well, this book. She was a constant source of energy, eager to take on the many tasks and challenges I asked her to accept.

Erika Jensen

Erika is a market gardener with ten years of experience. She specializes in vegetable, herb and cut flower crops. The family farm also produces certified organic crops such as corn, soybeans, oats, barley and wheat. Erika is an educator as well as a grower, and has experience with public speaking, writing, and organizing classes and workshops. Erika has a BA in English from Bates College, and has completed two years of organic farming internships, as well as Master Gardener core training.

Erika is also the author of 45 articles on organic farming and gardening. She has written for such publications as *Organic Gardening, New Farm, Northern Gardener, The Organic Broadcaster, Wisconsin Trails, Growing for Market, The Herb Quarterly*, and *Countryside* & *Small Stock Journal.* The articles cover a wide range of topics, including vegetable, herb and flower production, irrigation, soil building, and new techniques for farmers.

To Fred, Anne and the team at Acres U.S.A. who saw in this work the potential to reach out to farmers and researchers, to inspire and challenge them to rethink how we can manage the soil with systems free from herbicides – thank you.

And finally to Gretchen, my wife, and to my family who are always there to help and support my work, the biggest thank you of all.

–Jeff Moyer

CONTENTS

INTRODUCTION

First, I am not a professional author. Yes, I have had the opportunity to write many articles over the years related to my work in organic agriculture. I am also not a professional educator. Yet, I have had many occasions to teach and train farmers, gardeners, and policy makers about the many benefits of a food system based on organic and regenerative principles.

While most of my work has been done right here in Southeastern Pennsylvania, colleagues around the world have proven these systems can easily be transferred to other regions, other soils, and many different crop rotations because they are based on sound biological principals. Working for Rodale Institute has afforded me countless points of contact with some of the best agricultural minds in the world who were and are eager to share their knowledge, experience and energy.

Many people ask how I became interested in the concepts of organic no-till. The answer is really fairly simple. As organic farmers we spend a great deal of time, energy and resources working to improve the health of our soils. Feeding the microbes, cycling the nutrients, building the organic matter content, and working with crop rotations, only to see much of that work destroyed by the negative effects of tillage just didn't seem right. It isn't hard to imagine yourself as an earthworm on plowing day. So it became part of my mission to design biological practices that would lead us to a no-till system where biology replaced chemistry. The concepts of organic no-till were born from the idea that if we could manage cover crops, in a sense, growing a mulch right in the field where cash crops are to be planted, we could indeed eliminate tillage within certain points in the crop rotation. Because organic farmers and gardeners have few tools to help in their weed management strategies, tillage has taken center stage in their implementation arsenal. Primary tillage and secondary tillage to get seeds or transplants started must then be followed by several more tillage operations in the form of cultivation activities to remove or bury weeds. This has led to two problems – overtillage and limitations for larger-scale operations in their transition away from herbicides and toward organic systems.

What has been most exciting is that almost as many conventional farmers as organic farmers have begun to adopt these concepts and are using cover crops to suppress weeds, then using a roller/crimper to terminate their growth. By using the roller/crimper instead of chemicals to terminate their growth, farmers are able to delay termination by many weeks – leading to increased biomass production, greater nitrogen fixation, and more soil organic matter formation. These practices have not only opened the door for larger numbers of farmers to include cover crops in their production systems but they have sped up the process of farm land transitioning to organic production.

The purpose of this book is to introduce farmers, researchers and others to organic no-till and to inspire and challenge them to implant these practices on their own operations. It will give them practical information about a number of different topics, including getting started, an introduction to the technology, troubleshooting problems, cover crops, and scientific research results from around the world. Overall, the book aims to be farmer-friendly, with simple, clear language and an honest approach to the possibilities and challenges of organic no-till. It has brought together information from many collaborating researchers all of whom are pioneers in this technology who have shared their experiences here.

The concept of organic no-till provides great potential for agricultural change, through the use of cover crops and reduction of synthetic herbicides, while giving organic farmers what they need in terms of weed management and soil building practices. Both organic and conventional farmers alike will benefit from learning about this exciting new technology.

Every farmer who reads this book will be introduced to a system of farming with cover crops that will completely change the way they view their farm. They'll be able to visualize how cover crops actually become the primary crop they grow, shifting their imagination and energy from cash crops to the cover crops leading to no-till systems that not only help manage weeds but improve the health of their soil. Then the production of marketable crops becomes almost a by-product of a soil-building program.

–Jeff Moyer

ABOUT THE AUTHOR

Jeff Moyer has been working in the field of organic agriculture all of his adult life. Over the past 28 years he has been the farm manager/director for the prestigious Rodale Institute located in Southeastern Pennsylvania. At the Rodale Institute farm, Moyer conducts his own research and manages the day-to-day workings of the farm operations department.

As part of his responsibilities at the Rodale Institute, he is also an educator with significant experience in both written and verbal communications. He is often asked to speak on issues related directly to his research and work, presenting on numerous diverse topics from compost production to growing organic apples and on food production systems in general. For over four years, he wrote a monthly article titled "From One Farm to Another" for Rodale's New Farm (an online webzine reaching 60,000 farmers and interested individuals per month). He is often quoted in the media on organic issues.

Moyer's interest in agriculture began while growing up on a small farm in Pennsylvania where his family grew and produced much of the food they consumed. Though his college experience was in forestry, land surveying, and construction technology, his desire to participate in the organic movement of the '70s led him to the Rodale Institute. Because of his conviction that organic farmers could benefit from reduced tillage technologies, he has worked for 20 years on designing equipment specifically for the management of cover crops. The result is equipment that will not only reduce the tillage necessary to grow crops organically, but will also cut down on energy consumption and sequester more carbon in the soil.

Moyer is both well connected and well respected in the organic farming community. He currently chairs the United States Department of Agriculture's National Organic Standards Board and serves as an advisor on organic issues to the Secretary of Agriculture. Jeff is also a founding board member of Pennsylvania Certified Organic, a private non-profit certification agency. He serves (and has served) as a member of several other committees and boards: the Governor of Pennsylvania's steering committee for Farms in Transition, Pennsylvania State University's Organic Research Advisory Board, Walmart's 2006 Sustainability ANSI Standards Committee, Leonardo Academy's Sustainable Ag Board, the board of Pennypack Farm, and the 2003-2010 advisory board to the Pennsylvania State University's Department of Crops and Soils. He is also a past president and current member of the Northeast Society of Agricultural Research Managers.

Moyer also manages Sky Hollow Farm, a small farm of his own where he and his family have lived for over 30 years. Here he maintains 52 acres of crops and woodland to raise beef cattle, hay, grains, and now as his son Orin takes over – pastured poultry.

ABOUT RODALE INSTITUTE

Rodale Institute is a 501(c)(3) nonprofit organization creating organic farming global solutions from the ground up. Soil scientists and a cooperating network of researchers have documented that organic farming techniques offer the best solution to global warming and famine. Rodale Institute was founded in Pennsylvania in 1947 by organic pioneer J.I. Rodale. The Rodale Institute's Farming Systems Trial is the longest-running U.S. study comparing organic and conventional farming techniques. It is the basis for practical training to thousands of farmers in Africa, Asia and the Americas.

The Rodale Institute findings clearly show that a global organic transformation will mitigate greenhouse gas emissions in our atmosphere and restore soil fertility.

The Rodale Institute mission is to improve the health and well-being of people and the planet.

Visionary J.I. Rodale who moved to rural Pennsylvania in the late 1930s where he was able to realize his keen personal interest in farming created the Rodale Institute. He learned about the organic food-growing concepts being promoted by Lady Eve Balfour and Sir Albert Howard and theorized that to preserve and improve our health we must restore and protect the natural health of the soil. Developing and demonstrating practical methods of rebuilding natural soil fertility became J.I. Rodale's primary goal after World War II created a sudden shortage of nitrogen fertilizer, as it was diverted to making munitions – exposed the natural nutrient poverty of the nation's soil. In 1947, J.I. Rodale founded the Soil and Health Foundation, forerunner to the Rodale Institute. He also created publications including *Health Bulletin*, *Organic Farming and Gardening* and *Prevention* magazines.

The concept of "organic" was simple but revolutionary in the post World War II era. Manure, cover crops and crop mixtures had been standard practices throughout history, but chemical fertilizers, pesticides, herbicides, artificial ingredients, preservatives and additives for taste and appearance in the post war years rapidly changed agriculture. As J.I. Rodale communicated the idea of creating soil, rich in nutrients and free of contaminants however, people began to listen and acceptance grew. "Organics is not a fad," J.I. wrote in 1954. "It has been a long-established practice – much more firmly grounded than the current chemical flair. Present agricultural practices are leading us downhill."

After J.I. Rodale died in 1971, his son Robert (Bob) expanded the farm and health-related research with the purchase of a 333-acre farm near Kutztown, Pennsylvania. With his wife Ardath, Robert established what is now the Rodale Institute and an era of scientific research began. In 1961, John Haberern was hired by Robert Rodale as a book editor for Rodale Press. John would later become the Institute's president. Powerful testimony by Bob, John, farmers and scientists, who swore by their sustainable methods, convinced the U.S. Congress to include funds for regenerative agriculture in the 1985 Farm

Bill. Today, federal, state and local governments, land-grant universities and other organizations nationwide are pursuing organic and regenerative agriculture research and education programs.

When Robert Rodale died in a traffic accident in 1990, while in Moscow, Ardath Rodale became the Institute Chairman and their son Anthony became Vice-Chairman. Anthony and his wife Florence developed outreach efforts for children during their period of active program involvement before Anthony became an international ambassador for the Rodale Institute. Board member Paul McGinley became co-chair of the board with Ardath in 2005. Following Ardath's death in 2009, Maria Rodale became board co-chair and the tradition of deep family involvement with the Institute's goals and mission continues.

Timothy J. LaSalle became the first CEO of the Institute in July 2007, bringing decades of experience in academic, agricultural and non-profit leadership to the task. Under his leadership, the Institute champions organic solutions for the challenges of global climate change, better nutrition in food, famine prevention and poverty reduction.

In 2010 the Rodale Institute entered a new phase of operation – refocusing on core capacities and structure that will ultimately reenergize the team as a search is underway for a new CEO. The strength of the Rodale Board and family leadership has led to a reshaping of the organization's goals that will allow the farm to be the true embodiment of the mission and vision of the Rodale Institute – that scientific research continues to be the cornerstone of efforts to document the impact of organic farming systems on human and environmental health.

CHAPTER 01 NO-TILL BASICS

▶ ORGANIC NO-TILL — WHAT IS IT?

It is the hope and dream of many organic farmers to limit tillage, increase soil organic matter, save money, and improve soil structure on their farms. Organic no-till can fulfill all these goals. Many organic farmers are accused of over-tilling the soil. Tillage is used for pre-plant soil preparation, as a means of managing weeds, and as a method of incorporating fertilizers, crop residue, and soil amendments. Now, armed with new technologies and tools based on sound biological principles, organic producers can begin to reduce or even eliminate tillage from their system.

Organic no-till is both a technique and a tool to achieve farmer's objectives of reducing tillage and improving soil organic matter. It is also a whole farm system. While there are many ways the system can be implemented, in its simplest form organic no-till includes the following elements: annual or winter annual cover crops that are planted in the fall, overwintered until mature in the spring, and then killed with a special tool called a roller/crimper. After the death of the cover crop, cash crops can be planted into the residue with a no-till planter, drill or transplanter. Whether you grow agronomic or horticultural crops, this system can work on your farm, and we'll show you how to get started with this exciting new technology.

These techniques and tools can work equally well on both conventional (farms based on chemically based practices) and organic farms (farms that follow the USDA's definition of organic). Organic no-till is a rotational tillage system that combines the best aspects of no-till while satisfying the requirements of the USDA organic regulations. It is not necessarily a continuous no-till system but one that may include some tillage in rotation, especially

The author pulling back the killed cover crop to show no-till mulch in action with corn seedlings.

to establish the cover crops. After cash crops are planted, no further tillage or cultivation is generally needed, and this greatly reduces the required field operations. While organic farmers typically work the field several times just to get the crop in the ground, organic no-till farmers can get by with as few as two field operations: rolling the cover crop and planting the cash crop in one pass, and then harvesting the cash crop. By reducing the number of field operations, farmers can save on fuel and time – all the while building up their soil.

Cover crops are the cornerstone of weed management and soil building – so much so that they become as important as the cash crop. Most organic farmers know something about cover cropping, but with organic no-till you'll get a chance to sharpen your skills. If you are managing a chemically based operation you can still take advantage of these tools and use cover cropping on your farm. Winter annuals like rye and hairy vetch are common examples, but summer planted buckwheat, field peas, many small grains, and annual legumes are also a possibility. A later chapter on cover crops will tell you more about which cover crops can be killed by rolling and when. Our rule of thumb is simple: if you can step on the plant and it dies, then you can kill it with a roller/crimper. This means that plants like alfalfa or perennial weeds are not good candidates for rolling. When seeded at the correct time during the fall, these cover crops will get started by developing an extensive root system and growing a small amount of vegetative matter. During the winter, the cover crops will either continue to grow slowly (in warmer climates) or essentially remain dormant (in the north). There are several benefits to a winter cover crop, including erosion control, nutrient cycling, and microbial habitat in the root zone.

During spring, the cover crops jump to life and really put on biomass. Then they can be killed with the roller/crimper as they reach the peak of their life cycle. With the winter annuals commonly used in the system, this corresponds to the period when they are entering their reproductive phase. For example, with winter rye, the correct time to roll the cover crop is when the rye is in "anthesis" or producing pollen. With hairy vetch, the vetch should be at least 75 percent in bloom, but 100 percent bloom is even better. An annual crop typically allocates 20 to 30 percent of its resources toward the process of flowering and seed production. In addition, enzymatic changes at this time cause the plant to begin to senesce, or start the process of aging and breakdown prior to death. During this phase of the plant's life cycle, it is much more vulnerable, and can be effectively killed by the roller/crimper.

The roller/crimper is a specialized tool designed by John Brubaker and myself and tested at the Rodale Institute. It works by rolling the cover crop plants in one direction, crushing them, and crimping their stems. The roller/crimper can be front mounted on a tractor, while a no-till planter, drill or transplanter brings up the rear, planting directly into the rolled cover crop. Or the roller can be pulled in a separate pass. Since the system is based on biology and mechanics, it is scale neutral – suitable for use on either small or large farms. The roller/crimper can be pulled behind a tractor, a horse, or even by hand depending on the scale of the operation. While other tools, such as a stalk chopper, rolling harrows, and mowers have been used for this purpose; the roller/crimper has several advantages over other tools. It has been specially designed for organic no-till, and performs its function exceptionally well.

Provided that the cover crop is thick enough, the field will take care of itself for the rest of the season. The mashed cover crops provide a mulch layer for the cash crop, both preventing the growth of weeds, but also breaking down gradually during the season to provide a long-term slow release of nutrients.

▶ PROFILES OF CEREAL GRAINS

Rye: 6,000-8,000 lbs/acre dry weight, C:N ratio of 40:1

Barley: 4,000-5,000 lbs/acre dry weight, C:N ratio of 20:1

Wheat: 5,000-6,000 lbs/acre dry weight, C:N ratio of 35:1

To achieve adequate weed control, the cover crop should be planted at a high rate and produce approximately 2.5 tons of dry matter per acre. For this reason, only certain kinds of cover crops, ones that yield a high amount of biomass, work well for the no-till system. It's also important to select cover crops with a carbon to nitrogen ratio higher than 20:1. The higher the ratio, the more carbon, and the more slowly the crop will break down. This will provide a consistent weed management barrier through the season. These topics will be explained in more detail further in this book.

After harvest, the killed cover crops can be disked under and the next round of cover crops is planted for the following season. Thus, the crop year begins in the fall with planning for the following year. For this reason, organic no-till requires considerable long-term planning.

Principles of Organic No-Till

Organic no-till rests on three fundamental principles: a) soil biology powers the system; b) cover crops are a source of fertility and weed management; and c) tillage is limited, and best described as rotational tillage. In both the goals and ideology, organic no-till is very similar to other kinds of organic farming. These include soil building with organic matter and soil biology, managing weeds, insects and diseases through diverse and non-chemical means, and achieving

▶ THE ROLLER/CRIMPER

HOW IT WORKS:

- Crushes the cover crops
- Crimps the stems of the cover crops every seven inches

DESIGN FEATURES:

- Front mounted on the tractor
- Chevron pattern maximizes downward force while keeping the tractor on a straight course
- Drum can be filled with water to increase weight
- Easy to maintain with fewer bearings and areas where cover crops can become jammed

The Rodale Institute roller/crimper in action.

general plant health through soil health and good management practices. However, organic no-till uses different methods to achieve those goals. Much more emphasis is placed on cover cropping, which replaces tillage and cultivation as a means of soil building and managing weeds.

Maximize your natural soil biology & minimize synthetic chemical inputs

In organic no-till, as with all types of organic agriculture, biology replaces chemistry. This means that organic farmers let the soil organisms do the work of facilitating nitrogen fixation, improving nutrient cycling, as well as enhancing soil structure and texture. These soil organisms include macroorganisms like earthworms and as well as microorganisms like soil bacteria and fungi. Organic no-till goes one step further than the current technology offered in organic systems. By providing nearly year-round cover and limiting tillage, the soil biology is given a chance to thrive and power the system that is the organic farm.

Chemistry, as used by conventional agriculture, has some fundamental problems. When we say chemistry we mean synthetic products such as man-made fertilizers and pesticides. Conventional no-till is closely tied to herbicide use, since this is the primary means of weed control. Typically, as tillage is reduced herbicide management is increased in an attempt to control weeds. Although some surface residues are generated from no-till, they are not enough to provide consistent weed control. This dependence on herbicides generates a host of problems, from resistant weeds to the destruction of beneficial insects. Genetically modified crops (GMOs) are also commonly used in a conventional no-till system since the marriage of herbicide resistant crops and ag chemicals has been a consistent theme. There are a number of concerns about GMOs – they may cause allergic reactions in sensitive individuals, they can cross pollinate with non-GMO crops, and there is an increased dependence on chemical herbicides and pesticides. GMOs also prevent farmers from saving their own seed since these technologies are all patented. None of these technologies are currently allowed under the USDA organic standards.

Cover crops are the key

Cover crops are an essential part of any organic system but are especially crucial to the success of no-till in an organic operation. Instead of relying on chemical fertilizers to boost crop production, organic no-till depends on the cover crops to provide the nutrition needs of the cash crop. Legumes, such as hairy vetch, can provide enough nitrogen to satisfy all of the needs of high demand crops like corn. Soybeans, which can produce much of their own nitrogen, are grown in rotation following rye or another grass crop that has the ability to produce large amounts of carbon, providing a slow breakdown and release of nutrients. Of course, the nutrients from the cover crops are not available immediately. They are partially available the first year and partially available in successive years. If your soil is low in organic matter, or if you have not farmed organically before, it may take a while to build up the "bank account" in the soil. Think of it as putting money in the bank. You're investing in your soil, and as time progresses you will be able to cash in on the interest from your account. Since cover crops are key to the success of the system, it is vitally important to make sure that seeds are well established through proper timing of seeding and good pre-plant soil preparations.

Cover crops, as well as amendments like manure and compost, are merely the fuel that makes the engine run. Soil life is the "engine" and does the heavy work of breaking down the cover crop and releasing the nutrients. This includes microorganisms like fungi and bacteria as well as macroorganisms like earthworms and various insects. These organisms are constantly at work – feeding on organic matter, breaking it down into smaller and smaller pieces, and releasing nutrients that plants can use. In an interesting symbiosis, the plants expend quite a bit of energy (perhaps 10 percent) producing root exudates in the form of simple carbohydrates, which nurture and protect the microorganisms. The fungi and bacteria, in turn, physically extend the root system of the plant and help it to absorb nutrients from the soil. In addition to providing access to nutrients, fungi benefit the soil structure by producing glomalin, a carbonatious substance that acts like a glue and holds soil particles together in aggregates. The final product of the breakdown of soil organic matter is humus, a relatively stable product that persists in the soil, sequestering carbon for years without much change. The dynamic system of the soil food web constantly needs recharging; it is cover crops that do the job in organic no-till.

Cover crops perform another important function, and that's helping us manage weeds. When grown for this purpose they are sometimes called "smother crops." Organic no-till can help break weed cycles in a number of different ways. First, since the soil is never left bare, weeds will always have competition, either from the growing cover crop or from the combination of the killed cover crop residue and the cash crop. Biennial weeds, which do much of their growing in fall and winter and bloom and set seed in the early spring, are effectively controlled by winter cover crops. By the time annual weeds germinate in early to mid-spring, the cover crops are already established, robbing weeds of access to water and sunlight. Some cover crops, like rye, suppress weed growth at this point with allelopathic effect, a kind of chemical warfare that goes on underneath the soil. Many annual weeds are small-seeded and are particularly vulnerable to allelopathic effects. Perennial weeds are the most difficult to manage in an organic no-till. Farmers often rely on tillage to disturb the root systems of perennial weeds and reduce their stored carbohydrate and this is all still possible with this technology. However cover crops in combination with tillage can provide an effective measure of control here. Cover crops can interrupt the life cycle of perennials by providing competition. In the organic no-till system the cover crops are often rolled before perennials have a chance to go to seed. And since organic no-till is a system that makes use of rotational tillage, as well as crop rotations, there are multiple opportunities to take action against various weeds.

After the cover crops are rolled they provide an effective means of weed protection. In order to provide control the cover crop needs to provide 100 percent coverage of the bare ground. That's right – 100 percent. This is because every place that sunlight touches the soil, weeds can grow. Organic no-tilled fields are not likely to be completely weed-free. However, weeds are more likely to grow between rows where they will cause less competition. Also, weeds tend to grow later in the season after the crops are up and growing. With organic no-till, you may want to do a small amount of spot weeding for the few weeds that make it through the mulch layer.

Limited tillage

Like conventional no-till, organic no-till maintains that tillage is essentially harmful to the soil and should be limited or eliminated. Tillage is harmful to soils because it stimulates the breakdown of soil organic matter, sometimes at a very rapid rate. It can also physically damage the soil structure, breaking down soil aggregates and structural elements like infiltration channels. Tillage often inverts the soil, causing disturbance to soil life. Organic no-till addresses a criticism often aimed at organic agriculture – that it uses too much tillage, as well as involves cultivation that also disturbs the soil. Vegetable farmers, especially, may till the soil several times a year as they plant multiple crops and use cultivation to manage annual weeds.

Problems that arise from tillage are familiar to most farmers. Plowpan, or layers of compaction, is one problem. Crop roots have difficulty penetrating through compacted soil, as does water, resulting in problems with runoff and soil erosion. A general decline in soil structure may also be evident. Good soil is only made up of about 50 percent solid matter. The other half is water and soil air spaces. In order to maintain this composition, pore structure as well as infiltration channels from plant roots and earthworm burrows are very important. While tillage may have negative effects on some aspects of soil management, data collected on long-term research trials at Rodale Institute, and replicated around the country, have shown consistently that soils using organic methods sequester more carbon than conventionally farmed soils. This is true even when the conventional systems implemented conservation tillage practices and the organic systems depended on tillage to manage weeds. This data supports the argument for the adoption of an organic approach

Seedling corn emerging through killed cover crop mulch.

to soil management. However, when coupled with a true reduction in tillage, the system has the potential to build the organic matter content more rapidly, improve the quality of the organic matter, and sequester even greater amounts of carbon.

Reduced tillage, on the other hand, maintains soil structure – which is as important to growing good crops as fertility. An organic farm can maximize its potential only with the development of good pore structure, soil aggregates and decreased bulk density. A good soil structure is important for many reasons. Water infiltration is improved and erosion is reduced. Plants are able to grow healthy and extensive root systems thereby increasing crop yields, disease resistance, and drought tolerance.

The goal of conservation tillage is to provide at least 30 percent soil coverage from plant residues. Benefits of conservation tillage include lower soil erosion, fewer inputs, better water and air quality, better quality soil, and increased availability of water for crop production. A combination of cover cropping and conservation tillage works well, maximizing the benefits of each. As organic farmers work towards implementing conservation tillage principles, many have experienced increased weed pressure. That is because most conservation or reduced tillage practices evolved under chemical-based systems. Organic farmers must balance the need to reduce tillage and the need to improve the health of their soils with weed management strategies.

Organic no-till utilizes what can best be described as rotational tillage. Rotational tillage balances the benefits of a no-till system with a limited tillage system. In rotational tillage, tillage occurs at strategic times during the cropping year and during the rotation when it will cause the least damage to soil structure and give us the greatest gain to the system.

To preserve soil structure, non-inversion tillage is far preferable to inversion tillage. In inversion tillage, layers of soil may be mixed up, for example in moldboard plowing. With non-inversion tillage, like disking or chisel plowing, the soil layers remain primarily unchanged, though air is introduced and compaction layers may be broken up. However, while non-inversion tillage is more compatible with the principles of good agricultural practices, weed pressures can increase in an organic system. In an organic no-till system we have been able to balance the need for tillage with the desire for reduced tillage by creating a system of rotational tillage. In some years we use tillage here and in other years we don't.

Why till in a no-till system? Primarily, it's to incorporate crop residue left on the surface of the soil after the cash crops have been harvested, to incorporate perennial hay crops like grass sod or alfalfa, or to establish cover crops themselves. Shallowly incorporating these residues makes it easier to prepare a good seedbed for the next crop. Chisel plowing may also be used to alleviate compaction, deepening the soil bed for roots and increasing water and availability of nutrients. However, it's best to be aware that these reduced tillage tools were designed to work in concert with chemical herbicides. Tillage can also be useful to incorporate manure, compost and other amendments, and to manage perennial weeds.

Introduction to the Benefits of Organic No-Till

Organic no-till can help your farm in a number of different ways. Although these will be examined further in chapter 2, the following will serve as an introduction to the main points.

Increase soil organic matter

Organic no-till can help to build soil organic matter year-round. Cover crops can provide a huge contribution of organic matter both through their roots and through their leaves and stems. Organic no-till is an intensive system that requires at least 2.5 tons of dry matter per acre to be effective. Cover crops are grown to their full potential, instead of being tilled in at an earlier growth stage. This means, in general, that the organic matter will be higher in carbon and lower in nitrogen, making for long-lasting benefits for soils and crops.

Provide year-round cover for the soil

In organic no-till, cover crops are generally planted whenever cash crops aren't present, especially in the fall, overwintered, then killed, and left in place. This provides nearly year-round cover for the soil, in addition to erosion control. Covering the soil increases infiltration, reduces evaporation, stabilizes soil temperatures, provides habitat for soil life, and reduces soil crusting. If your farm is in an area with partial or consistent snow cover during the winter, the cover crop produces a natural snow fence that reduces blowing and drifting snow.

Reduced erosion

A consistent cover crop also reduces much of the erosion associated with tillage farming. Cover crops reduce erosion from both wind and rainfall. The roots of the cover crop stabilize soil and reduce runoff, while the aboveground portion of the plant protects the soil against the destructive force of raindrops. In an organic no-till system, actively growing cover crops (or the rolled and killed cover crops) are in place during key times when erosion can occur, including spring melt, winter thaws, and summer storms. The benefits are clear, too, for water quality. Because of reduced erosion cover crops can reduce water pollution due to soil loss, nutrients, or agricultural chemicals. As soil tilth improves, so does stability.

Capture, hold and stabilize nutrients for the cash crop

Many cover crops are excellent scavengers of nitrogen as well as other nutrients. Sometimes they are referred to as "catch crops" when describing this function. The best cover crops for this purpose are cereal grains like barley, wheat, rye and oats. Rye, in particular, can scavenge 25 to 100 percent of residual nitrogen from cornfields. As covers are rolled down and begin to decompose, this nitrogen begins to be available for use by the subsequent cash crops. Cover crop roots can also forage deeper in the soil, bringing calcium and potassium up from untapped soil layers. Cover crops may also capture phosphorus, hold it in a stable form, and then release it for use by cash crops. Buckwheat is one of the best covers for this purpose. Unlike chemical fertilizers, organic amendments are more likely to provide a slow release of nutrients. Although nutrient leaching can still occur, it is much less likely with soils that are high in organic matter.

Increase biological activity, both in the soil and aboveground

Organic no-till increases diversity on the farm by providing year-round habitat and minimizing soil disturbance. In the soil, cover crops provide roots that nourish microorganisms and stabilize organic matter. As the roots of the cover crop decompose, they become a food source for the microorganisms and earthworms as well as many other forms of microbial life. Aboveground, beneficial insects benefit from both the habitat and nectar sources. The diversity supported by an actively growing cover crop increases the number of competitors for pest insects, which may lessen their severity. Because the roller/crimper technology reduces or eliminates the need for herbicides, it is easier to establish habitats, within the field or along border areas that encourage beneficial insect populations. This can mitigate many pest insect problems.

Crop rotation

Cover crops provide many of the benefits of a crop rotation: recharging the nutrients in the soil, breaking pest and disease cycles, building soil, and reducing weed pressure. In addition to rotating cash crops, rotating the cover crops can help increase the complexity and intensity of crop rotations.

Reduce field operations

With the roller/crimper mounted on the front of the tractor (as described later in more detail) field operations are greatly reduced when compared to organic plow-tillage systems. Conventional as well as organic farmers can achieve similar benefits when the roller/crimper and cover crops are used together. In organic no-till, the yearly field operations can be as few as two passes. One pass to roll the cover crop (while planting in the same pass) and another to harvest the crop. Additional field operations may be used at other points in the rotation to establish the cover crops; however, these crops generally don't require any cultivation to manage weeds. With a regular organic system, as many as nine or ten field operations are needed to prepare the seedbed, plant the crop, and cultivate it. Reducing these operations will save time, money and possibly make some farm equipment obsolete.

Energy savings

Organic no-till provides significant energy savings. Fuel is conserved due to the reduced number of field operations. According to some estimates, up to 80 percent of fuel is conserved by converting to no-till. Organic no-till can also eventually eliminate the need for conventional nitrogen fertilizer (that is produced using natural gas), as well as herbicides and the energy required for their production. With the current high cost of energy and no relief in sight for the near future, this should be a very attractive benefit to farmers. In addition, there are obvious advantages to society as a whole. The cost of other petrochemical products is likely to go up as well. Conventional producers can realize many of these energy savings as well. In addition, just by cutting inputs like herbicides and pesticides, conventional farmers can improve their bottom line.

Provide non-chemical weed management

For organic farmers, weed management is ranked as the number one challenge in most surveys. Organic no-till can help by both breaking weed cycles and by providing in situ mulch through much of the growing season. This approach works well to manage small-seeded annual weeds. However, persistent perennial weeds can be difficult to eliminate.

Although this list of benefits is fairly comprehensive, it's a mistake to think that organic no-till can do it all, or that it can eliminate all the challenges on your farm. Just like any farm tool or technology, it has to be used in the right way – with skill and thoughtful attention to detail. This book will provide a realistic assessment of the possibilities as well as the challenges of organic no-till.

No-Till Caveats

Organic no-till can work in a variety of different situations, but there are a few things to keep in mind. These issues will be addressed at different points in the book, but it is helpful to have them summarized in a concise fashion here.

Nitrogen tie-up

Organic no-till changes the way nitrogen cycles. During the decomposition process nitrogen can become temporarily less accessible to plants. This is especially true if you are working with very dry soil conditions – there could be a nitrogen tie-up early in the season if your cover is a cereal grain. There may also be nitrogen tie-up if you choose to till in mature cover crops, particularly cereal grains. If you use a legume cover crop this is much less likely to happen.

Water use

Water needs for some cover crops can be heavy, especially for rye. If you farm in an arid location, or if you depend on spring runoff and rain for your crop establishment, the cover crop may compete with your cash crop by taking up much of the available water, leaving less than adequate supplies for subsequent crops. The good news is that over time no-till can help considerably with water conservation by improving the general health of your soils and by building the soil organic matter content.

Insufficient biomass

A poor stand of cover crops doesn't work well for the organic no-till system. If establishment is inadequate for any reason, the farmer must realistically assess the cover crop. Then he or she must either decide to continue as planned, choose to perform a tillage operation, or (in the case of a conventional farm) spray herbicide for weed control.

Rolling too early

Another common mistake is rolling too early. It can be very tempting to roll the cover crop before it is mature (especially when your neighbors have already planted and you're still waiting to plant), resulting in a poor kill with the roller/crimper. Cover crops that do not completely die can provide competition for the cash crop, robbing it of nutrients and moisture.

Problems with planting cash crops

Some experimentation may be needed to make sure your planter is working correctly. Common difficulties include: the planter does not cut through the cover crop, the planter does not provide good seed to soil contact, or the planter's depth wheels ride up, making it difficult to get the seed well placed in the furrow.

Delayed planting

Because you'll have to wait while cover crops mature in the spring to kill them effectively, you may have to delay planting your cash crop beyond your normal calendar date. You may want to source cover crop varieties that mature earlier, or varieties that are better suited to your particular location. If you live in a northern climate, your planting window in the spring may be very tight. Summer cover cropping may be a better option for northern farmers depending on where you live. Consider the specific traits you need for your operation, and then search for varieties that express these traits.

Cooler soils

Cover crops can shade the soil resulting in cooler soils in the spring. Crops that like hot temperatures, such as tomatoes, eggplant and peppers, may get a slow start. However, soils temperatures will also be more even and moderated year-round, which can be an advantage. Once rolled and crimped, cover crops can maintain cooler, moister soil conditions that will protect crops during hot, dry periods later in the season.

Getting Started

Here are some suggestions about how to get started – without planting a single seed. The following ideas will help you become a successful organic no-till farmer, while managing the risks of adjusting to a new system.

Reading and learning

Find out as much as you can about which cover crops do well in your area. This might include talking to other organic and no-till farmers, taking advantage of resources available at your local Extension office, and following up by consulting reference guides.

Source local seed

Locally adapted cover crop seed will give you an edge, providing a crop that's already adapted to your area. These will be less likely to winterkill and may perform better on your farm. Since it may take some time to track down a local source, you should begin early. This is especially true for organic seed since quantities may be limited.

Test plot

With organic no-till, perhaps the biggest source of risk comes from transitioning to a new management system and a completely new technology. During the first couple of years, the learning curve may be fairly steep. It's a good idea to start with a small, experimental area or test plot on your farm.

Assess your farm

The checklist at the end of this book will help you realistically assess the challenges you'll experience as you transition to organic no-till.

Resources

Baker, C.J. et al. *No-Tillage Seeding in Conservation Agriculture,* 2nd Edition. Cambridge, U.K.: CAB International, 2007.

Balkcom, Kipling, A. Clark, W. Reeves and H. Schomberg. "Managing Cover Crops in Conservation Tillage Systems" in *Managing Cover Crops Profitably*, 3rd edition. Beltsville, MD: Sustainable Agriculture Network, 2007.

Ingham, Elaine, A. Moldenke, and C. Edwards. *Soil Biology Primer.* Ankeny, IL: The Soil and Water Conservation Society, 2000.

Schonbeck, Mark. "Cover Cropping: On-Farm, Solar-powered Soil Building." Virginia Association for Biological Farming, 2006. *www.vabf.org/infosheets/1.06.pdf.*

Sustainable Agriculture Network. *Managing Cover Crops Profitably*, 3rd edition. Beltsville, MD, 2007.

Wilson, Dave. "Choosing Cover Crops for Organic No-till Soybeans." The New Farm, 2005. *http://newfarm.rodaleinstitute.org/depts/weeds/features/1005/weeds_dw.shtml.*

CHAPTER 02 THE ORGANIC NO-TILL FARM

▶ WHOLE FARM PLANNING FOR YOUR TRANSITION TO ORGANIC NO-TILL

The organic farm operates as a system, and the success of the organic farm is largely dependent on how the farmer designs and implements the system. The term "system" refers to an imposed structure of crop rotations, crop variety selections, planting and harvest timetables, and other components, but it also refers to the ability to cultivate naturally occurring systems. These include managing water, soil nutrient cycles, farm biodiversity, and habitat for beneficial insects just to name a few of the components. Organic farmers are not only stewards of the earth, but also innovative managers of the on-farm resources available to them. Given these methods, organic farmers will want to think about how no-till technology could fit into the picture of the whole farm. In some cases, no-till can significantly reduce management responsibilities; in other areas, farmers will need to develop additional skills and knowledge before converting to no-till practices.

The Basics: Three to Consider Before You Start

We'll start with three crucial planning items: rotations, timing issues, and equipment.

Rotations

A conversion to no-till will require a shift in how you think about your rotations. The primary change is adjusting to the idea that the cover crops in the rotation are actually the most important component in the cropping cycle. New opportunities or "niches" for cover crops can be found by arranging and re-arranging your crops in a diverse rotation. Many of these opportunities will be found by the addition of fall-planted cover crops, although there are some options for summer cover crops as well. In general, the shift to using more cover crops should bring greater flexibility in terms of rotations. Although a corn-soybeans rotation could be used continuously if cover crops were grown each winter, more diverse rotations are included here, since they maximize many benefits such as weed control.

Here is an exercise that will help you work through possible rotation shifts without going through the experience of hard knocks to see how things might play out in the field. Start by writing the name of each cash crop in your rotation on a 3x5 note card. Next lay them out on the kitchen table in the sequence in which you typically plant them. This could be a very simple rotation of only two or three crops or a very complex rotation utilizing many crops. Once you have them chronologically organized, place them under the headings of what season of the year they are planted. For example, corn would be a late spring planted crop; winter wheat is typically planted in mid-fall and so on. This arrangement should begin to point to opportunities for places in the rotation when the soil resource is not utilized to its maximum and where cover crops might fit into the picture.

Examples might be when wheat is harvested in the summer giving you an opportunity to start a cover crop of hairy vetch in late August, when potatoes are dug in late summer affording time for a rye cover, or in early spring when field peas could be planted before an early summer planting of broccoli or soybeans.

The accompanying tables are some sample rotations just to get you thinking about how your own crop rotations might allow for additional cover crop plantings.

Timing issues

As with all things in life, timing is everything. This couldn't be truer when it comes to organic no-till. If you are a farmer, you already know that time management and exploiting windows of opportunity at key times of the year are one of the crucial factors for success. With organic no-till, there are some additional deadlines to monitor. We'll examine some of the timing issues for rye and hairy vetch as a means of introducing important concepts that you can apply to other cover crops. More information about the best cover crop planting and rolling dates is explained in chapter 7, Cover Crops: The Foundation of Organic No-Till. Of course, experimentation is the best way to determine the best dates for your region and for your own farm.

Fall planting of cover crops

In order to achieve the targeted amount of biomass for the following year, cover crops usually need to be planted as early as possible after the preceding cash crop has been harvested. If you farm in the north, this may be a very tight deadline, depending on weather, soil moisture, and other factors.

FALL RYE Rye is the most cold tolerant of all cereal grains, so it is a good choice for planting after late harvested field crops with an excellent chance for overwintering. This cover crop can establish itself in very cool soil temperatures. Although it will germinate at 34 F., it requires temperatures of at least 38 F. for vegetative growth. Once rye is established, it is very cold tolerant, and will survive temperatures as low as −28 F. It will also serve as a snow break; this enhances its ability to overwinter, since consistent snow cover will moderate soil temperatures. If interseeded with other cover crops such as hairy vetch or crimson clover, it may also improve their survival by acting as a nurse crop, protecting the less cold tolerant plants. Rye will only winterkill if its crown is

▶ SAMPLE ROTATIONS

Rotation one: Grain/Forage

This rotation is a typical one used in the United States corn belt. The alfalfa in years four, five and six provides a rest from the grain segment of the rotation, breaking pest cycles and providing a significant N contribution. Since this is not a continuous no-till system, manure or compost can be incorporated in the fall before the cover crop is planted. In this proposed rotation corn, soybeans and rye can all be planted without the use of primary tillage.

Year one

Spring: Corn; Vetch precedes the corn in the rotation (Year six), which provides much of the N needed for the corn.

Fall: Rye; Rye is planted as soon as the corn has been harvested.

Year two

Spring: Soybeans; Rye is rolled in early June and soybeans are planted into the killed residue.

Fall: Rye; This rye is strictly for winter cover if you plan to grow oats in year three. Alternatively, you can skip the oats, grow the rye to full maturity, and save your own seed.

Year three

Spring: Oats; Oats can be harvested for grain or cut for early forage. If harvested for grain, straw can be baled.

Fall: Winter Wheat/Alfalfa; Winter wheat is planted in the fall, underseeded with alfalfa or frost seeded in late winter. (If there is no desire for a hay crop in the rotation, you can skip the alfalfa and proceed to planting hairy vetch in early fall following wheat harvest).

Year four

Alfalfa; Winter wheat is harvested in July and the alfalfa continues to grow.

Year five

Alfalfa; Alfalfa is harvested for hay.

Year six

Alfalfa/vetch; two to three cuttings are taken off the alfalfa during the summer. In the fall the alfalfa is tilled under and vetch is planted as a winter cover crop. Repeat.

Rotation two: Vegetables

This rotation is an eight year rotation based on one used by Eliot Coleman in the book *The New Organic Grower*. Depending on your latitude, additional crops may be squeezed in during the summer or fall. Again, this is not a continuous no-till system — tillage performed in the fall, with manure or compost incorporated at that time. If desired, grains and legumes may be grown together for additional nitrogen with a carbon boost. For beginners, it's easier to manage same species plantings.

Year one

Spring: Sweet Corn; In the rotation, vetch precedes corn and provides adequate N.

Fall: Rye/Vetch mix; Vetch replaces some of the N lost with sweet corn, rye provides adequate biomass for weed management.

Year two

Spring: Potatoes; Potatoes are planted 5 inches deep into a raised bed. Cover crop killed two weeks later.

Fall: Rye; Squash (Year three) has comparatively low N needs, so the next cover planted is rye.

damaged. It is more likely to die from flooding, frost heaving and iced-over fields. In hardiness zones 3-7, rye should be planted in late summer to mid-fall. In zones 8 and higher, it can be planted from fall to mid-winter. Rye's powerful allelopathic effects are strongest in young plants, so planting rye in a timely manner is one way to combat biennial weeds or late germinating annual weeds.

If your fall planting windows are very tight, you might experiment with overseeding. Recently, some experiments have been done with soybean, corn and cotton that allow rye to be planted as early as September 1. Rye can be aerial seeded or broadcast into corn at the silking and tasseling stage or using the same method, seeded into soybean at leaf yellowing, but before leaf drop or defoliation. However, drilling rye is still the best means of making sure that you have good seed to soil contact and establish an adequate stand. Broadcast seeding, by contrast, depends on having adequate soil moisture. If conditions are less than ideal, you may get a poor stand, which will not provide enough biomass for good weed suppression in the following year.

▶ SAMPLE ROTATIONS, CONTINUED

Year three

Spring: Summer Squash; A planting of summer squash is transplanted into killed rye in early June.

Late Summer: Buckwheat; After summer squash, a quick smother crop of buckwheat is planted for additional weed suppression and phosphorus uptake.

Year four

Spring: Radishes; An early planting of radishes is direct seeded into winterkilled buckwheat in April. Crop is conventionally cultivated. A mid-summer lettuce planting could follow, with supplemental nitrogen.

Fall: Rye; Beans (Year five) have relatively low N needs, so the next cover crop is rye.

Year five

Spring: Snap Beans; Rye is rolled in early June, and beans are direct seeded into the killed cover crop.

Fall: Vetch; Tomatoes (Year six) have relatively high N needs, so the next cover crop is vetch.

Year six

Spring: Tomatoes; Vetch is rolled in June, and tomatoes are transplanted into the killed residue.

Fall: Oats; Peas (Year seven) have relatively low N requirements, so the next cover crop is oats.

Year seven

Spring: Peas; Peas are direct seeded into the winterkilled oat residue. Conventional cultivation is used.

Fall: Vetch; Cabbage, the next crop in the rotation, is a heavy feeder, so vetch is planted to supply its N needs.

Year eight

Spring: Cabbage; Cabbage is transplanted into the killed vetch.

Fall: Vetch; Vetch is planted again to supply the needs of the following sweet corn crop, and the rotation begins again.

FALL HAIRY VETCH Like rye, hairy vetch has excellent winter hardiness through zone 4b as long as you have winter snow cover, and your seed variety is adapted to local conditions. Many cover crops of the same species and variety can be grown across a wide segment of the country. Look for seed grown in a similar climate, because it will have better cold tolerance. Vetch can be planted in combination with grasses such as oats, rye or wheat for a nurse crop and winter protection (in the case of oats they will winterkill leaving the vetch to grow in spring). Plant vetch 30 to 45 days before a killing frost for a good winter annual crop. The cover grows slowly in fall, but picks up the pace early in the spring, smothering weeds and generating considerable biomass. Fall growth may be slow if daytime temperatures are below 60 F. If planted by mid-September in the Northeast, vetch can yield 100 pounds of available nitrogen by the following spring fixing a total of over 200 pounds of total nitrogen.

Select a higher seeding rate if you are planting later in the fall or in adverse conditions, which may reduce germination. If there is adequate soil moisture, vetch can be overseeded into soybeans at the leaf yellowing stage. Vetch can also be interseeded into sunflower or corn at last cultivation, after the plants reach 12-15 inches tall. Late season vegetables can also be overseeded with vetch, but the small plants may not tolerate heavy traffic from harvesting, including foot traffic. Moisture is critical to the success of a broadcast seeding; as with rye, drilling is much preferable.

▶ FALL PLANTING SUGGESTIONS FOR VETCH

From the *Northeast Cover Crop Handbook*

Zone 7: August 15-October 10

Zone 6: August 10-September 20

Zone 5: August 1-September 10

Zone 4: July 15-September 10 (mixed results)

Spring cover crop rolling and cash crop planting

Another set of planting deadlines confronts us in the spring. In order for organic no-till to work correctly, farmers will need to wait until the cover crop is in its reproductive phase. It can be difficult to wait while all the other farmers in your neighborhood are planting, but waiting for the proper maturity phase of the cover crop is absolutely necessary for the system to work correctly. If you don't delay until the cover crop is mature, you run the risk of the cover crop re-growing and becoming a weed. Just like the fall planting deadlines, the spring deadlines are highly variable due to fluctuations in weather conditions, so it's difficult to make a prediction or generalization for individual locations. Here's the key factor for success: you must time your planting of the cash crop based on the maturity of the cover crop – even if that means delaying the planting date. Cover crop variety selection and planting date can greatly affect, positively or negatively, the date when reproductive maturity arrives. It's best to research these issues before you begin – preferably a year in advance.

Every farmer should be a researcher. Yes, we need our scientific institutions to lead the way in taking many of the risks we as farmers cannot afford to take. When it comes to fine tuning the system, we all need to experiment to see what works, when it works and most importantly where it fits into our system. Try some small areas of the cover crops you think might fit into your system just to get a feel for how they might work, when to plant them and when they mature in your specific location on your soils and fields.

SPRING RYE Rye grows and matures very quickly in the spring. Rye is a long-day plant. Flowering is triggered by 14 hours of daylight and daytime temperatures of at least 40 F. If you don't happen to know when 14 hours of daylight occurs in your area, there are a number of different tools online to make the task easier. Search for the phrase "hours of day length" and you'll find a number of free calculator tools. Environmental conditions also affect maturity considerably.

Maturity date also varies according to variety. Unfortunately, rye breeding has been in decline during the past century, and very few new varieties have been released since the 1970s. New breeding and more experimentation needs to be conducted in order to find earlier maturing cultivars or cultivars that produce more biomass. Some on-farm experimentation with popular varieties for your area could provide a starting point and is highly recommended.

Rye needs to be rolled down at anthesis, when it is starting to shed pollen. In Pennsylvania, this usually occurs in late May to early June. You should be able to see the pollen on the outside of the seed head.

At this stage, the seeds are not viable and will not become a weed problem once the rye is crimped. If rolling is delayed until the rye grain is too mature it could continue to ripen, reseed itself, and compete with your cash crop for resources like water and nutrients. Varieties can differ widely in the amount of time it takes to go from anthesis to mature grain, from 32 to 61 days, according to the Germplasm Information Network.

With a roller/crimper front mounted on your tractor and a planter on the back, you can roll and plant in one step. This saves time, energy and fuel. However, there are a couple of considerations that may delay your planting date. First, especially with rye, soil moisture may be an issue. Rye has a reputation for drying out the soil, and you may want to wait for 7-14 days to let the soil moisture recharge after killing the cover crop. Of course, with wet soil conditions, this won't be an issue. Rye does have a few things on its side: it can hold snow over winter, which generates some moisture; it can actually help dry out fields in the spring that are traditionally low and wet. Plus, it has an early maturity date compared with some other cover crops.

Rye is an excellent choice for weed suppression for another reason – it has an allelopathic effect on other plants. Rye has several different compounds that inhibit the germination and growth of surrounding plants, especially grasses (like other small grains or even corn). However, the allelopathic effect can present a problem when you are planting your cash crop. Generally, this is a concern with smaller seeds, such as cotton, lettuce or carrots. Larger-seeded crops like soybeans are not usually set back, although it may be advantageous to select larger-seeded varieties. The beneficial effects of the rye cover crop, such as improved infiltration and increased organic matter, outweigh any detrimental effects from the allelopathic compounds. On the other hand, if you'd like to try strip tillage with small-seeded vegetables, it's best to wait for several weeks to let the allelopathic effect wear off.

SPRING HAIRY VETCH Bloom stage is the primary factor to consider when timing the mechanical killing of hairy vetch. The vetch should be at full-bloom or a minimum of 75 percent before rolling. Bloom time is determined by cultivar, day length (photoperiod), and temperature during the spring of the year. At full bloom some of the lower flowers may already have begun to form seed pods. You'll need to roll before these pods have time to form mature seeds. At the Rodale Institute, hairy vetch usually reaches full bloom in late May to early June. Again, it may be hard to wait, but timing is critical to the success of the system. Rolling at the full-bloom stage will ensure adequate kill by the roller/crimper. Variety selection, origin of the seed, and cover crop planting date all can impact the flowering time.

Besides an adequate kill, there are some other reasons to delay killing vetch. A later rolling date will ensure that the hairy vetch will supply adequate biomass for both weed suppression, as well as the nitrogen needed for the corn or other cash crop. The aboveground biomass that makes up the rolled mat controls the weeds until the corn can start to grow enough to form its leafy canopy, shading out weeds that eventually break through the mat. In studies done in Maryland, an early kill date actually decreased corn yields. Because the residue was less substantial and the mulch layer was thinner, the crop did not have as much protection against moisture loss later in the season. By contrast, late April or early May kill dates consistently resulted in higher corn yields. The same has been found to be true at experiments done at Rodale, as the following tables will illustrate.

During experiments at the Rodale Institute, we learned a lot about the importance of timing the rolling/planting operation properly. As you can see from the adjacent tables, the vetch had higher levels of nitrogen as well as biomass. On the first two rolling dates (May 30 and June 7) the hairy vetch was not yet mature enough to kill with the roller/crimper. By May 30 (the vetch was at 55 percent bloom) and by June 7 the vetch was at 65 percent bloom. These two roll dates had 45 percent and 28 percent re-growth respectively. Since the hairy vetch did not adequately kill after roll down on the first two rolling dates, the re-growth resulted in inadequate matting for weed suppression. The hairy vetch rolled at the two later dates (June 14 and June 21) when the hairy vetch was at 100 percent bloom were effectively killed by the roller/crimper. Weed suppression was also satisfactory. The first two dates had increased weed dry matter levels of 6,318 and 10,403 lbs./acre respectively compared to 2,657 and 1,206 lbs./acre at the two later planted dates. (see table)

The later planted corn performed better for another reason. The plantings on June 14 and June 21 emerged late enough to avoid the peak of the cutworm population. As a result, there was less damage to these corn seedlings. The black cutworm (*Agrotis ipsilon*) – the cutworm moth in

▶ HAIRY VETCH COMPARISON OF (LBS./ACRE N) IN ABOVEGROUND BIOMASS *(Calculated as lbs./acre dry matter x % tissue analysis)*

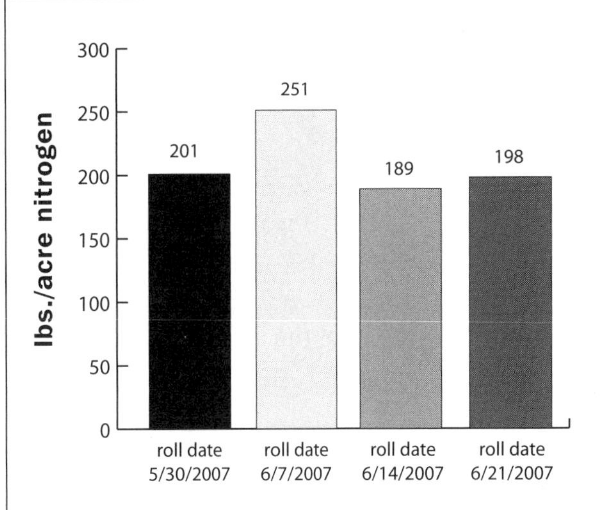

The highest gain in nitrogen was on the June 7 roll date. However, the best corn yields were from plantings later in the month.

▶ HAIRY VETCH BIOMASS VS. ROLL DATE

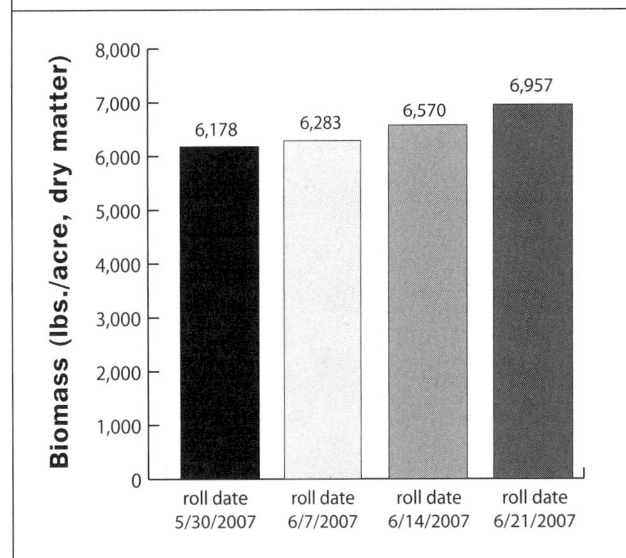

Biomass from the hairy vetch continued to increase through the last roll date, on June 21.

TOTAL WEED BIOMASS VS. ROLLING DATE

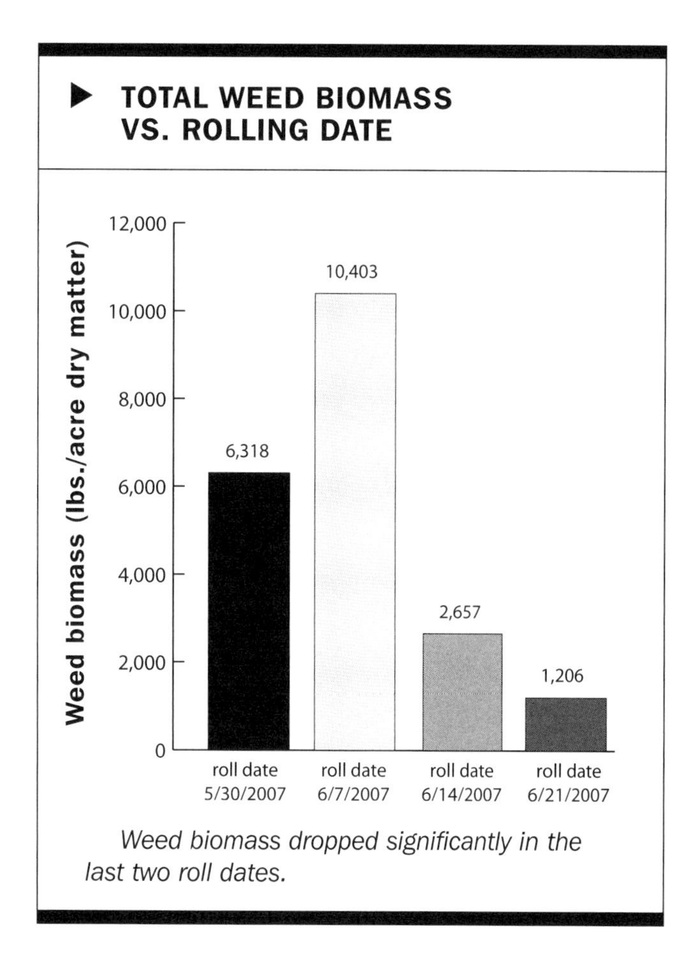

Weed biomass dropped significantly in the last two roll dates.

NO-TILL CORN YIELDS
(The Rodale Institute, Field 14-15, Berks County, Pennsylvania)

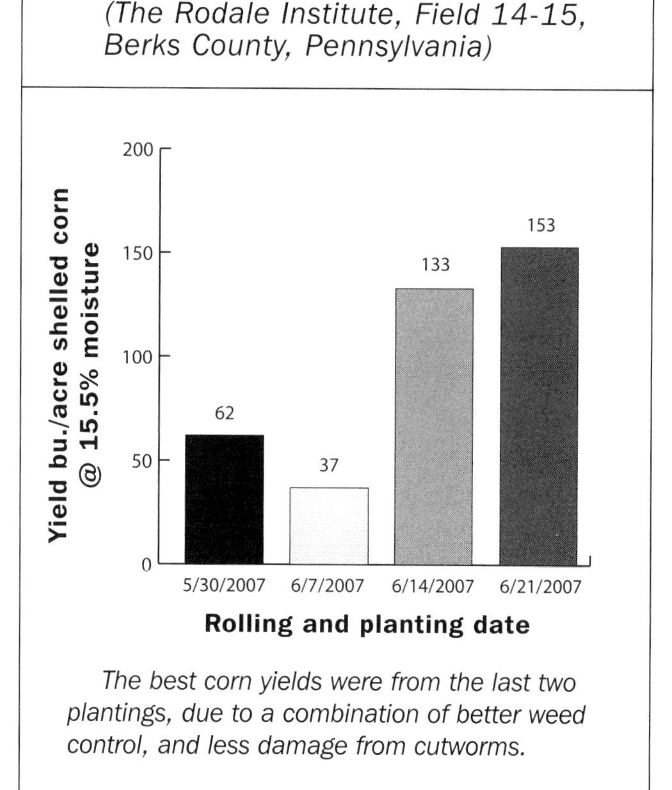

The best corn yields were from the last two plantings, due to a combination of better weed control, and less damage from cutworms.

its caterpillar stage – has been a major pest of our organic no-till corn was seen only in certain years and in certain fields. Some moths may overwinter but most of the population comes from adult moths blown into the area with storms during April and May. Moths fall out of the storm front, laying eggs where they land in the early spring, usually before the corn is planted. Living cover crops are natural sites for egg deposition by cutworm moths.

Just how much did planting date affect the corn populations? Let's take a look at the numbers. On all four dates, corn was no-till planted at a rate of 36,624 seeds per acre. With a 95 percent germination rate, the optimum stand we could expect would be 34,792 plants per acre. The two earlier plantings (May 30 and June 7) sustained heavy cutworm damage, with plant stands of 15,616 and 7,569 respectively per acre. On the two later dates (June 14 and June 21) the results were much improved, with stands of 27,998 and 29,991 respectively per acre. Not surprisingly, the first two plantings had lower yields, 62 and 37 bushels per acre, respectively. Significantly higher yields of 133 and 153 bushels per acre were achieved from the second two plantings respectively. (see above table)

To sum up, decreased corn population due to cutworm damage and increased weed pressure due to the inadequate kill of the hairy vetch were the contributing factors leading to the decreased yields in the two early dates of planting. Timing of planting in relation to bloom stage of hairy vetch and seasonal cutworm populations will be the major considerations for successful organic no-till corn production.

Hairy vetch and winter survival

Winter survival of the hairy vetch cover crop is of foremost importance for farmers located in northern latitudes. Sub-freezing temperatures during the winter can cause serious stand losses in northern states, even in southeastern Pennsylvania.

Although extremeness of winters may vary from year to year, farmers should select cold tolerant types of hairy vetch to hedge against harsh winter conditions that can lead to a failure to overwinter. Winter survival of hairy vetch can be one of the most important determinants of successful biomass production the following spring (and of subsequent crop yields during the growing season). In the organic no-till corn system, adequate cover crop biomass production is necessary for adequate weed control and nitrogen production, making all other considerations secondary to cover crop survival.

At the Rodale Farm during the winter of 2006-2007 we trialed two different varieties of hairy vetch that had originated in Nebraska and Oregon. The results of the trial helped us to learn a lot about the importance of the seed origin. The winter of 2006-2007 began mildly and the fall growth of both varieties produced about 1,000 lbs./acre of biomass (dry weight) before going dormant for winter. Then in February, the Oregon seed origin labeled "Early Cover" hairy vetch winterkilled, due to harsh winter conditions. We had little snow cover to provide insulation for the cover crop. To make matters worse, early February temperatures dropped as low as 0 F. and in mid-February we recorded low temps of 4 F. Afterwards temperatures warmed up above freezing, but dropped as low as 0 F. again by mid-March. We learned that the variety that originated in Nebraska was much better suited to our climate, probably because it was adapted to colder conditions.

▶ 'PURPLE BOUNTY' HAIRY VETCH

The use of hairy vetch has been constrained by a lack of cultivars that combine the traits of early flowering and winter hardiness sufficient for winter survival in the northern states. As a result of this evaluation and the data collected, a new variety was released in 2007 and is going through a seed increase program. It should be available in commercial quantities in 2009. 'Purple Bounty' was bred to provide a cultivar that flowers early and survives winter in the northern United States.

The breeder's supply of seeds for 'Purple Bounty' are maintained by the Sustainable Agricultural Systems Laboratory, Animal and Natural Resources Institute, USDA-ARS, Beltsville, Maryland. 'Purple Bounty' seed is also deposited in the National Plant Germplasm System where it will be available for research purposes, including development and commercialization of new cultivars. Protection for 'Purple Bounty' is being sought under the Plant Variety Protection Act.

No-till equipment

If you are converting to a no-till system, you will need to consider adding some additional equipment to your line up. The two most important pieces you'll need are a no-till planter and a roller/crimper. If you already farm no-till or own a no-till planter, you may need to modify your planter in order to plant through the thick layer of killed cover crop. There will be more information about this topic in chapters 4 and 5, but here is a brief summary of what you'll need to think about.

ROLLER/CRIMPER Roller/crimpers based on the Rodale design can be purchased through I & J Manufacturing in Gap, Pennsylvania. Visit their company website at *www.croproller.com.* They can also be made by a local fabricator, or build your own from free plans which can be downloaded at *www.rodaleinstitute.org/notill_plans.* Rollers vary in cost depending on size and complexity of design, for example hydraulic folding. If you would like to mount your roller/crimper on the front of your tractor, you'll need to consider purchasing a special front 3-point hitch although some folks have modified a loader frame to handle the task.

NO-TILL PLANTER Most no-till planters will work for organic no-till, but you may need to modify your planter to optimize your success. These modifications may include adding weights to supply downward pressure, and using cast iron closing wheels to press through the mulch and close the seed slot. You might also consider foam markers to help you determine the location of the planter passes. In addition, your planter will need to be well maintained with sharp coulters.

NO-TILL TRANSPLANTER If you are a vegetable farmer, your transplanter will likely not be able to handle the heavy residues associated with organic no-till, especially in dry conditions when the soil is harder. The sub-surface tiller-transplanter (SSTT), designed by Ron Morse, is one tool you can investigate.

NO-TILL GRAIN DRILL Even small grains or soybeans can be established without tillage at various points in the crop rotation. New no-till grain drills are well designed to handle the conditions you'll find with the roller/crimper system. You should investigate models that are designed for heavy residue management.

Some of your other equipment, such as tillage equipment, may become obsolete over time, but don't sell it yet. This equipment will be important during the transition period, and to incorporate manure or compost during the fall. Remember, the organic no-till system is based on rotational tillage. It includes no-till planting within the rotation, but may also include plow till, disking and other tillage activities to build a well-rounded weed management plan.

No-Till Can Help, With Some Caveats

Organic no-till systems can help you manage a number of important factors, such as soil nutrients, weeds, pests and disease, energy and even your time. However, there are a few considerations to take into account before you get started.

Nutrient management

Organic no-till depends on cover cropping for weed management, but it can also help substantially with nutrient management. Your crops' nitrogen needs can be addressed through the inclusion of legumes in your rotation. And because the soil's organic matter stores nutrients in a bio-available form, you will be building a store of nutrients that will last for years to come. Fertilizers, compost and manure will be more difficult to incorporate and may need to be applied at alternate times when tillage fits into the rotation. On fields you plan to no-till, manure or compost can best be applied in the fall when the cover crops are planted. This might lead to manure management concerns during the winter and spring. This is an opportunity to plan around the system's limitations. You might consider composting as a way to store your manure in a more stable form. Let's take a look at more detailed information on how organic no-till will affect your nutrient management.

Decrease nitrogen leaching

The peak leaching season is during the late fall to early spring, when the surface of the soil is most often left bare. With organic no-till, the soil surface is almost always covered. Rye is an excellent nitrogen scavenger, and keeps it immobilized for later use by cash crops. Cover crops also improve infiltration of rainwater, resulting in greatly reduced leaching.

Increase naturally produced nitrogen

Nitrogen in the organic no-till system comes not only from cover crop legumes in the rotation, but also from the biological decomposition of fresh residues and soil organic matter. By using legumes in the rotation (hairy vetch, peas, annual clovers or another legume), these systems can sequester tremendous amounts of nitrogen. The losses commonly experienced with chemically based nitrogen sources, are greatly lessened by using slow release, biologically sourced nitrogen. Once the soil organic matter is built up, little supplemental nitrogen, if any, is needed in these cover crop-based no-till systems. At the Rodale Institute, our only other source of nitrogen for our grain production fields comes from an application of compost once every five to seven years at the rate of 10 tons/acre, and from alfalfa hay in the rotation. This enables farmers to cut costs on purchased inputs, whether they are using conventional or organic fertilizers.

But here's the caveat: if you are transitioning to organic production, you may need to add supplementary fertilizer at first in order to get things going. If your soil organic matter is high you may need little or no supplementary fertilizer. If your soil organic matter is lower, you may need to supplement, especially at certain times of the year. Multiple applications are better than a single, early season application. Ron Morse, of Virginia Tech, who works with no-till vegetables, recommends sidedressing with feathermeal as well as fertigating with fish fertilizer or kelp to get these high value crops started.

Enhance phosphorus and potassium availability

Cover crops can pull nutrients, such as potassium and calcium, up from deeper soil layers, which increase their availability for cash crops. Cover crops can also make phosphorus more available and prevent leaching.

Slow release of nutrients

In these cover crop-based no-till systems residues are from mature plants. Consequently, some (like rye) are higher in carbon than in nitrogen. They are also not tilled into the soil, where they would more readily decompose. The cover crop residues then take time to break down, which means a slow release of nutrients, and longer-term weed management from the mulch.

Food source for microorganisms

No-till provides an ongoing feast for microorganisms, by providing fresh decomposing residues year round. It also offers undisturbed habitat and refuge for the microorganisms. Since green living roots are in the soil for a large percentage of the year, arbuscular mycorrhizal fungi flourish in these systems. Arbuscular mycorrhizal fungi enable your cash crops to forage for nutrients and water more effectively, because they double or triple the plant's root zone. We'll discuss this in greater detail later in the book.

Crop rotation

The cover crop plantings add complexity to the crop rotation, which helps with nutrient management, breaking of pest and weed cycles, building both the content and quality of soil organic matter, and improving the bio-diversity of your soil.

Time management

Less time spent in the field tilling and cultivating means more time spent on other projects you need to get done – and there's always a long list, right? Perhaps you could spend more time marketing your products. Or you could spend more time on equipment maintenance, reducing the risk of breakdowns in the field. However, until you have several seasons under your belt as a no-till farmer, you may spend more time initially on building your skills. Here are some ways that no-till can save you time.

Instead of several field operations for tillage, planting, cultivation and harvesting, organic no-tillage generally requires only one pass through the fields for rolling and planting, and one pass for harvesting. Up to 60 percent fewer person hours are used with no-tillage systems compared with tillage.

Organic no-till also offers flexibility in terms of harvest windows. With the high amount of residue from the killed cover crops you'll be able to get back into the fields more quickly after a heavy rainfall. The residue soaks up water like a sponge, improves infiltration, and slows runoff. Since the soil structure is improved it will stand increased traffic with less compaction and structural damage. This is true whether the harvesting is a machine operation or done by hand. Imagine harvesting pumpkins or tomatoes while walking on a thick mat of rye instead of bare soil.

You may also spend less time irrigating, due to the improved water-holding capacity of the soil, and reduced evaporation. An improvement in soil structure can bring an improvement in your crop's root system, allowing it to access water more effectively. A general rise in soil organic matter will help with water management as well. These same mulches that suppress weeds will prevent evaporation of water from the soil by protecting the soil from the sun. At the same time, any rain that does fall will be captured within the mulch allowing it to slowly percolate into the soil profile. In some situations the cover crop may actually increase the need for irrigation. For example, in arid climates where irrigation is the primary source of crop production water you may need to rethink your irrigation habits. Cover crops will need valuable water to germinate and grow. Some cover crops pull water out of the soil (such as rye) while others hold moisture in the soil (legumes).

With less machinery, you'll spend less time on maintenance. The roller/crimper is designed to be low-maintenance with fewer bearings and places where cover crop residue can collect and jam. In fact, it is our experience that a fresh coat of paint every few years is all our roller/crimper needs. However, the planting equipment must be well maintained since it is required to perform under difficult conditions.

▶ **CORN: TILLAGE VS. NO-TILL**

Till	No-Till
• plow & till	• roll & plant
• plow	• harvest
• disc	= 160 bu./acre
• pack	
• plant	
• rotary hoe	
• cultivate	
• harvest	
= 143 bu./acre	

No-till, a two-step organic corn production system — just plant and harvest! The above list of field operations clearly depicts how changing your management plans, such as not plowing, can save many hours of field work without sacrificing yield or income.

Weed management

We know from decades of garden experience, mulches can be utilized to prevent annual weeds from germinating. We also know that we need to use thick heavy mulches if we want season-long protection from weed infestation. Until now it has been impractical to mulch large acreage due to expenses of time and materials. But by growing the mulch right in the field and using state-of-the-art planting equipment we're now able to accomplish this feat with ease, saving both time and money over conventionally tilled systems.

Since crops have a mulch of killed cover crop around them, weed management is considerably easier in a no-till system. In contrast, a conventional till system without a mulch layer, will have many weeds that germinate and grow right along with your cash crop. Weeds will be found uniformly distributed through the entire field. The ones between the rows can be removed or buried by cultivation. However, in-row weeds are difficult to remove.

By contrast, in an organic no-till system weeds will generally be found between the rows rather than in the row. This reduces the competition between crop plants and weeds. The few weeds that emerge from the cover crop mat will grow fast and large, making the field appear weedy. Sometimes (depending on the crop) farmers will want to hand weed their fields to provide better control, and to keep any escaping weeds from going to seed.

Also, without the constant soil disturbance found in the conventionally tilled system, there is less movement of weed seeds in the soil profile. They tend to stay on the surface where they are less likely to germinate and are vulnerable to predation or weathering. However, nature is quick to react to any changes we impose on her. As tillage is reduced there may be a shift in the dominant weed species, from fewer annual weeds to more perennials. Systems that are dependent on chemical herbicides tend to generate resistant weeds, which can cause serious problems. On the other hand, organic no-till and rotational tillage relies on a natural system of checks and balances that keeps weeds manageable in the long term. For this reason we still use tillage in our systems at Rodale Institute to prevent perennial weeds from getting a foothold.

The weed management you're able to achieve with organic no-till partially depends on the residual allelopathic effects of the cover crop. Rye, sorghum-sudangrass, oats and barley are some of the cover crops with the highest allelopathic effects. Although the chemical compounds that cause the allelopathy are strongest in growing plants, they persist in the killed residue for several weeks until they leach into the soil and are broken down by microorganisms. Meanwhile, they provide weed management when the cash crop is at its most vulnerable stage. Allelopathic effects from cover crops can eliminate the need for a post-emergent herbicide. Cover crop varieties can vary widely

▶ CORN YIELD INCREASES IN WEEDED PLOTS IN 2003 & 2004 AT THE RODALE INSTITUTE

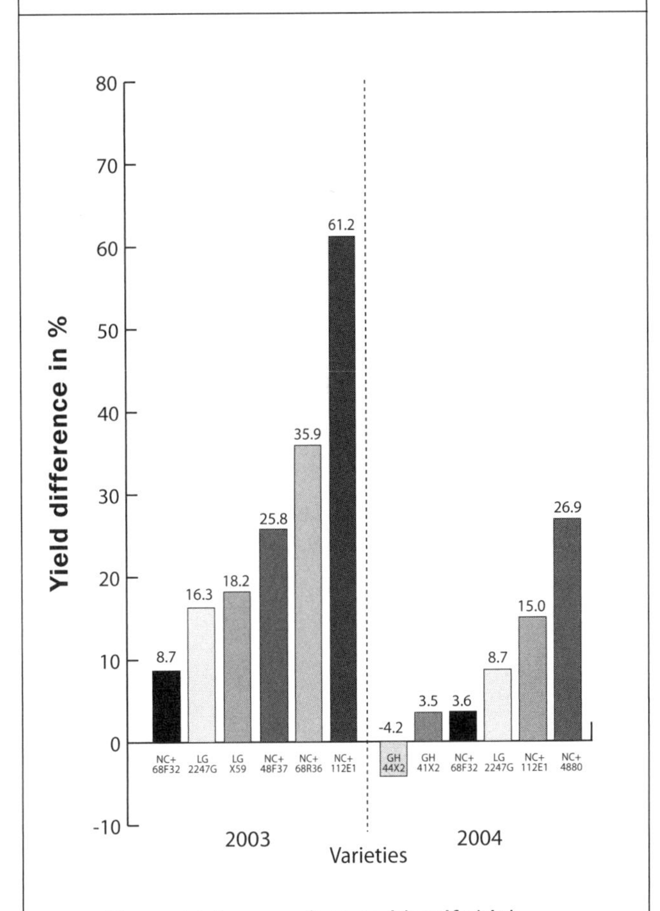

These trials were done to identify high yielding, food-grade corn varieties that experience less than a 10 percent yield loss under weed pressure. The best performing corn variety was NC+ 68F32 which had yield losses below that limit for two years in a row. (LG=Limagrain, GH=Great Harvest)

in their allelopathic effect. The cultivars 'Bonel', 'Maton' and 'Elbon' were found to be the best rye cultivars for allelopathic use.

If you are an organic farmer, you may have noticed that organic crops compete more strongly with weeds than conventional crops, allowing organic crops to produce good yields despite weed pressure. There are a number of factors that may be involved. For example, the fertility sources on conventional and organic farms are different. Weeds may be more aggressive and grow faster with synthetic fertilizers that provide a quick release of nutrients. Soil organic matter on organic farms is often higher, leading to more consistent soil moisture. It's likely that this makes crops more competitive with weeds over the course of the season. Finally, organic farmers often plant their corn later in the spring when the soil has warmed, since they cannot use treated seed. The corn not only germinates, but also grows more quickly under these conditions, competing well with the weeds.

According to the Rodale Institute's integrated weed management farm trials, there are substantial differences in how corn and soybean varieties tolerate weeds. In experiments done in 2003-2004, corn yield differences between hand weeded and non-hand weeded areas ranged from 0-46 bushels/acre. Weeds did not affect some varieties at all, while others suffered losses of up to 60 percent. For this reason, it might be beneficial to choose varieties that are more weed tolerant for your organic no-till transition. To learn more about these studies visit the New Farm website at *http://newfarm.rodaleinstitute.org/depts/weeds/features/0905/weeds_rs.shtml* and don't hesitate to try some on-farm experimentation using your own varieties.

Pests and diseases

As you transition to organic no-till, pest populations will shift as well. Some pest populations will decrease, and in some cases will get worse, depending on your situation. With more surface residue, some pests like slugs or cutworms can become a problem. However, with greater crop diversity, additional habitat, and fewer chemicals, beneficial insects may take care of most of the difficulty. Rye, and especially vetch, are cover crops that encourage beneficial insects. You might manage the problem by including hedgerows and permanent habitat for these beneficials so that they have a refuge during the crop transitions. The following is a discussion of some of the factors that come into play with organic no-till.

Cover crop environment

No-till brings considerable change to the farm ecosystem. The absence of soil disturbance as well as more surface residues creates a better habitat for insects, pests and predators, but also encourages the soil biology to thrive. The biggest changes are likely to occur in the first year after conversion to no-till. Slugs, which appreciate a high-humidity environment with lots of cover, can be a common pest in no-till systems. Slugs will feed on the freshly planted seeds as well as young plants. Other pests to be aware of include cutworms, as we have already discussed. While some pests may become a problem, no-till may also increase the population of beneficial insects resulting in no net gains in pest numbers.

Biodiversity effects

Biodiversity refers to crops, weeds, livestock, pollinators, beneficial insects and soil microorganisms. As we build a diverse community of plants and animals, we also nurture a more diverse community of pest-fighting beneficial insects. Many of the strategies for increasing diversity will sound familiar to no-till farmers: planting cover crops, varying crop rotations, including a variety of plant species, and reducing or eliminating tillage. There's no doubt that no-till creates a more varied ecosystem for insects, both beneficials and pests. During the summer, beneficials are protected by a combination of plant residues and living crops. This often results in an expansion of generalist insects that may attack several different kinds of pest insects. In one cotton field in South Georgia, 120 different species of ants, spiders and arthropods were observed where residues were left in place and no insecticides were used.

Beneficial insects

Living cover crops can help beneficial insects and spiders in a number of ways. They provide habitat, moisture, and a source of food. Organic no-till is especially beneficial for insects because the system retains the residue on the soil surface, ensuring that the insects and spiders can maintain their presence in the area. They'll be on hand when crops begin to germinate and grow, when pests often do the most harm. Colorado potato beetles, cucumber beetles and aphids are examples of pests that can be partially controlled by beneficial insects that thrive in the no-till system. Of course, many insecticides kill beneficials as well as pest insects, so it is important to intervene with a spray only as a last resort when a clear economic loss is predicted. This is true whether you are an organic or conventional grower.

Farmscaping

Farmscaping is an ecological approach to pest management. Hedgerows, insectary plants, cover crops and water reservoirs are some of the features used to attract beneficial insects as well as birds, bats and spiders. Cover crops that encourage beneficial insects include buckwheat, sweet clover, fava (faba) beans, vetch, red clover, white clover, mustards and cowpeas. In general, permanent systems (like orchards) are more hospitable environments for beneficials, whereas annual systems (like row crops) are more challenging. Those growing annual crops should consider introducing a permanent component into their fields, such as a hedgerow or managed irrigation ditches to provide year-round habitat.

Organic no-till provides a nice balance to some of the problems associated with annual crops. With less soil disturbance and overwintered cover crops, beneficial insect populations and soil microbes are more likely to remain stable over time. Reducing soil disturbance benefits insects considerably, since about three-quarters of all insects spend some part of their life in the soil. Spiders and ground beetles, in particular, benefit from mulches or fields with high residue. An overwintering habitat with a more moderate environment is especially important. Ground beetles also eat weed seeds, and may make a contribution to reducing the weed seed bank.

Water management

Organic no-till can improve water management for the long term. Water cycling is enhanced by the steady addition of green manures to your farm's soil. Soil organic matter works like a sponge to soak up moisture, and then slowly releases it.

Conservation tillage systems conserve water since they do not disturb the soil as much as conventional tillage. During no-till planting, only a very small zone is disturbed for planting the seeds. Water is also conserved throughout the growing season since cultivation is not necessary. Traditional till organic farming requires farmers to disturb the soil several times during the growing season and with each disturbance, some water is lost.

Infiltration rates are also higher in rotational tillage systems. Rainfall is slowed and absorbed more readily due to higher surface residues, earthworm burrows, increased pore space in soils, and plant root holes. In organic no-till, the thick mat of the killed cover crop expands the benefits during that point in the tillage rotation. Except during a major rainfall event or on steep slopes, you can expect the infiltration rate to be near one hundred percent.

Organic matter improves the retention of soil moisture considerably. For each one percent increase in soil organic matter, the available water-holding capacity in the soil increases 3.7 percent by volume. Of course, the difference will only be noticed over time, as your soil will improve very gradually. But even small differences in soil organic matter can translate to substantial long-term benefits. Organic no-till builds organic matter more quickly than many other systems, because it allows the cover crop to mature and accumulate significant amounts of carbon. This breaks down more slowly than greener, succulent foliage.

▶ THE NATIONAL ATLAS OF THE UNITED STATES PRECIPITATION COMPILED BY THE U.S. DEPARTMENT OF THE INTERIOR AND THE U.S. GEOLOGICAL SURVEY

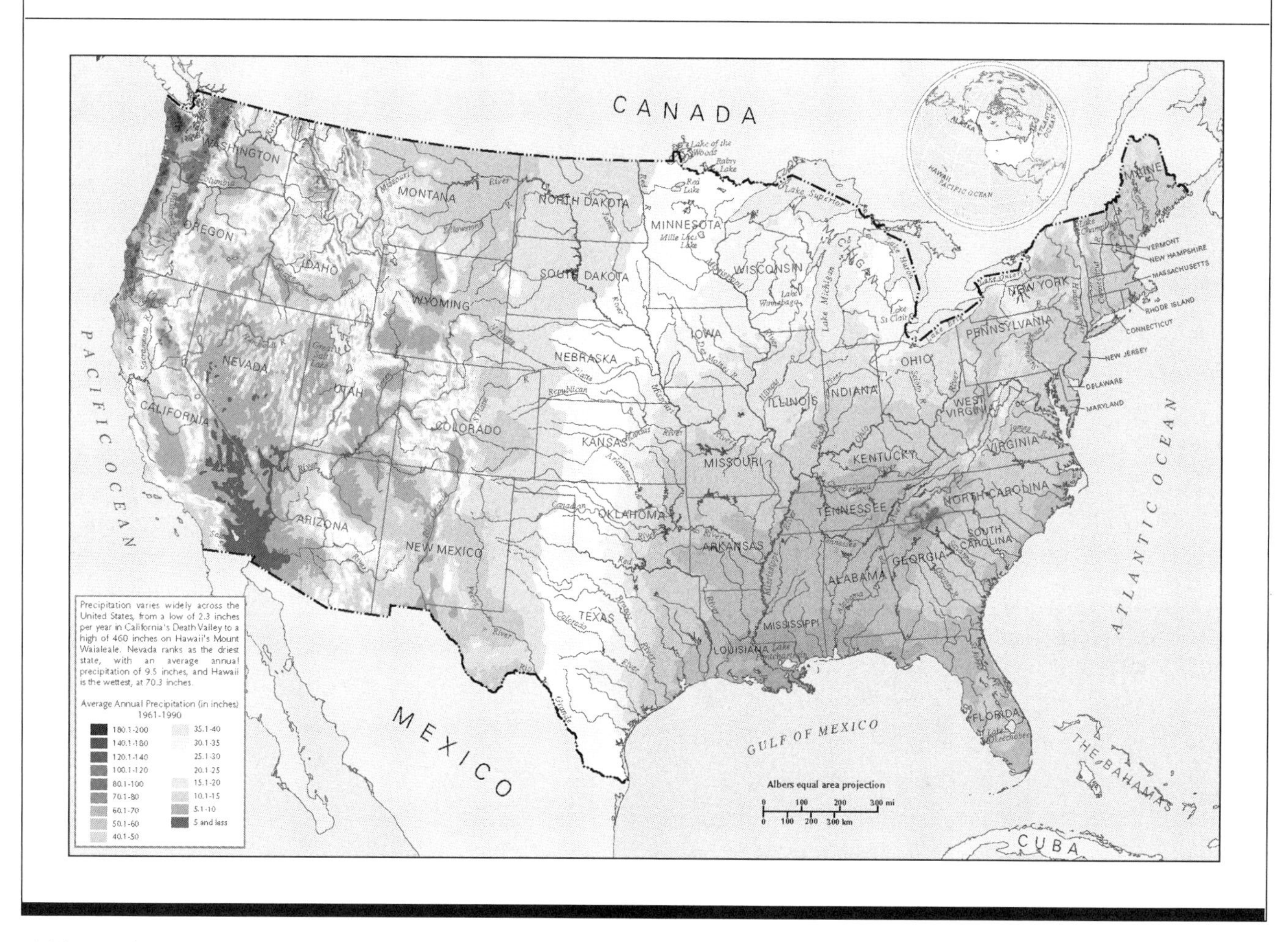

Additional precipitation maps available at www.wrcc.dri.edu/pcpn/us_precip.gif.

However, it's hard to deny the fact that cover crops use some moisture that might otherwise be employed by the cash crop. Many areas in the United States get plenty of rainfall to accommodate the needs of cover crops, but some areas may not. Cover crops in dryland systems may reduce the yields of subsequent cash crops if the need for additional irrigation is not accounted for. The results will depend on your yearly rainfall amount, the rainfall distribution across the seasons, the cover crop, and the cash crop that follows. However, a study done in Texas indicates that large amounts of surface residue (5 tons/acre of wheat straw) can increase soil moisture considerably – up to 73 percent. One way to manage water at planting time is to delay planting for two to three weeks after killing the cover crop, in order to allow the soil moisture to recharge. Some cover crops are more water efficient than others. For example, black medic, 'Indianhead' lentils and field peas are water efficient substitutes for alfalfa and sweet clover. If you are in doubt as to whether your area has enough annual rainfall to support overwintered cover crops, there are a couple of things you can do. First, experiment with different kinds of covers to see what works in your area. Second, build up the organic matter in the soil with cover crops before you try organic no-till.

The added organic matter will assist with moisture retention over the long term. In areas that have only marginally enough rainfall, this could help tip the balance. Lastly, if you don't have as many problems with weeds during the summer, you can choose to kill your cover crops earlier, but you may need to use herbicides.

No Sweat: Here's What You Won't Have to Worry About Any Longer

But when you incorporate cover crops and no-till practices into your operation you can remove these three from your list: biodiversity, soil erosion, and organic matter management. As you read this section, it should become clearer why organic no-till makes sense and works so well.

Biodiversity

Cover cropping helps tremendously with building a diversity of life forms, from small arthropods to earthworms to microbes like fungi and bacteria. With a diversity of life forms, there's a natural system of checks and balances that provides competition for pathogens and pest insects.

The small guys: fungi, bacteria, actinomycetes

Each microbe has a niche in the organic no-till system, and has an important role to play. Organic no-till benefits microorganisms in many ways.

Fungi are important for a couple of major reasons. First, they are good decomposers, working on tough plant residue that's high in carbon. Second, most plants form symbiotic associations with fungi called mycorrhizae. The fungus acts as extensions of the root system, enabling them to more readily absorb nutrients and water and also provides a measure of protection against diseases. In general, fungi are more prevalent in forest ecosystems, but they are extremely important in agricultural soils as well. A good soil structure benefits fungi, since the organisms are primarily aerobic. Waterlogged or compacted soils can promote anaerobic conditions that are known to kill mycorrhizal fungi. Frequent tillage, as well as broad-spectrum fungicides, can also reduce mycorrhizal fungi. For these reasons, it seems logical that organic no-till would benefit fungi. There is some information to indicate that using cover crops between cash crops can promote the establishment of mycorrhizae in the following crop. The cover crop provides living roots for the mycorrhizal fungi to colonize during periods when there would otherwise be just bare soil. This produces a more vigorous population of mycorrhizal fungi for the next spring – ready to colonize the next cash crop and promote plant growth. These fungi also are a key to successfully sequestering carbon in the soil through the production of glomalin, a glue-like protein substance that helps stabilize aggregates of soil particles.

Bacteria are numerous in agricultural soils and are by far the dominant microorganism. Although some kinds of bacteria can survive in anaerobic conditions, most require well-aerated soils. Bacteria are extremely important in nitrogen cycling. Rhizobia bacteria are mutualists that infect the roots of legumes and fix atmospheric nitrogen from the air in the soil. Other bacteria are responsible for breaking down the organic matter in the soil. Bacteria are important in three enzymatic transformations: nitrification, sulfur oxidation, and nitrogen fixation. Nitrifying bacteria help plants by converting ammonium to nitrite and then to nitrate, a form of nitrogen preferred by most row crops.

Actinomycetes are sometimes classified as bacteria, but they have hyphae, which also makes them similar to fungi. They form an important part of the soil food web, since they break down tough materials such as chitin and cellulose. Lignin, a tough substance found in plant stems, is another plant substance that actinomycetes readily decompose. These microbes are important for decomposing rye stalks as well as crop residue. Like other microorganisms, actinomycetes do

Rhizobia bacteria nodules on legumes.

best in moist, well-aerated soil. However, they do better in dry conditions than many other microorganisms.

The larger guys

These organisms are useful for pest management and larger-scale soil conditioning. They are also benefited by organic no-till.

Earthworms are one of the better-known soil invertebrates, and most organic farmers are aware that they can make a big difference in their crop production and are an important indicator of their soil's health. Earthworms are usually more plentiful in no-tillage or conservation agriculture. Soils high in organic matter will support a more diverse range of earthworms, including the surface feeders that prefer to browse on organic matter at the soil surface. Earthworms are physically harmed by tillage, their burrows are disrupted and destroyed, and the plant residue that makes up their food supply is buried. Earthworms have a number of beneficial effects on soil quality, including stimulating microbial activity, increasing water infiltration, and breaking down surface residues. In no-till agricultural systems, earthworms become a main agent for incorporating crop residues. They accomplish this by pulling materials into their burrows as well as burying residues underneath their castings at the soil surface.

Spiders are capable predators and keep pest populations in check. Like weasels in a chicken coop, spiders often kill many more insects than they actually need to eat, sometime up to 50 times more. It's well worth your time to keep spiders happy since they will prey on many kinds of pest insects that are problems in agricultural crops, such as Colorado potato beetles, cucumber beetles, aphids, and Mexican bean beetles. Spiders are not particularly active in conventionally tilled fields, since they are quite sensitive to disturbance (such as tillage, harvesting, etc.) and are generally more vulnerable to pesticides than insects. Conservation tillage, by contrast, supports higher numbers of spiders, as do systems that include large amounts of soil residue or mulch. The mulch helps the spiders by contributing habitat as well as a source of moisture. Winter annual cover crops are particularly helpful to spiders by providing a place for overwintering. Farmscaping can also provide a stable habitat and increase spider numbers.

Insects, too, are supported by a diversity of microorganisms and other organisms. Insects and other arthropods can either be in or near the soil, or above it in crops and cover crops. Most insects are either beneficial or neutral in their effect on crops. Only a few species are actually pests. Does organic no-till encourage beneficials? Reduced tillage systems usually support more beneficial insects, since tillage can kill or disturb overwintering beneficials. This can help your crops get off to a good start, and (for conventional farmers) reduce the need to spray insecticides. Beneficial insects are often killed or disabled when insecticides are sprayed, allowing a resurgence of pest insects. More complex and varied insect populations allow the pest insects to remain in balance. Healthy plants can sustain some damage before reaching an economic injury level. In fact, plant health is your best defense against insect damage, and organic no-till definitely does support healthy plants.

Erosion control

One of the primary reasons that farmers transition to no-till (of any kind) is for erosion control. An improvement in soil structure will reduce the possibility of erosion by lessening surface crusting and compaction while increasing pore space and aggregation of soil particles. Enhancing soil structure can decrease bulk density. Organic no-till has some additional benefits over traditional no-till. With the soil covered for almost all of the year it becomes much less vulnerable to erosion. The addition of large amounts of cover crop residues helps to quickly build organic matter. Let's explore further how organic no-till can reduce erosion.

Year-round cover

Organic no-till provides almost year-round cover for soils. The thick mat of vegetation helps to protect the soil during the spring and summer. In the fall and winter, the roots and aboveground growth of the cover crop protect the soil. In climates that have winter snow cover, overwintered cover crops collect snow, which protect the soil from scouring winter winds.

Role of organic matter

Soil organic matter acts to protect the soil from erosion in a couple of different ways. First, it helps soil particles to aggregate, or form small nuggets that are relatively stable. These are much less likely to be washed or blown away. Secondly, the organic matter at the surface of the soil prevents crusting and improves infiltration.

Soil structure

In the organic no-till system, the soil structure is improved, which makes it more stable and resistant to erosion. Again, soil organic matter is at the heart of soil structure. It enables the soil to effectively resist physical stresses from compaction due to foot traffic and equipment. Organic no-till means much less field traffic since the number of field operations is drastically reduced.

Tillage

Organic no-till limits tillage that can have detrimental effects on soil quality and soil health. On slopes, tillage implements can physically move soil downhill, leading to a loss of topsoil at the top of the grade. Over time, this can contribute significantly to erosion problems. If the subsoil becomes exposed at higher elevations, this can exacerbate runoff issues.

Organic Matter Management

While reducing tillage can help to conserve the soil, it does little on its own to build soil organic matter (SOM). It is only when no-till practices are used in conjunction with cover crops and the applications of compost or manure that SOM levels increase and the quality of the SOM improves. Increased organic matter has many benefits to the cash crops. One study in Michigan concluded that with every one percent increase in soil organic matter, farmers are likely to see a 12 percent increase in crop yields. There are clear benefits to an organic no-till system. The key to building organic matter is to provide a combination of techniques, including cover cropping, rotations, and reduced tillage.

Cover cropping

One of the principle reasons for cover cropping is to build organic matter. The organic no-till system necessitates the use of cover crops that are high biomass producers. In order for the system to work, the cover crop needs to completely cover the ground so that no weeds are able to grow through the killed cover crop mat. Generally, you should expect to have a minimum of 5,000 pounds/acre of dry matter or more to provide effective weed management. You may need to use a higher seeding rate for the cover crops in order to harvest a bumper crop of organic matter. For grain crops, use approximately three bushels of seed to the acre and for hairy vetch use 28 to 30 pounds of seed. Don't skimp on cover crop seeding rates since you will be depending on a solid stand for weed suppression as well as fertility. Added to the soil on an annual basis, cover crops add substantially to soil organic matter.

Another big difference between organic no-till and other systems is that cover crops are allowed to mature, rather than being tilled in at a young stage. This means that the carbon to nitrogen ratio is higher, allowing the killed cover crop to resist decomposition and provide effective weed management. The mat of cover crop persists through the growing season, only decomposing very slowly through the assistance of microbes and earthworms. Rye has the highest C:N ratio, about 40:1, making it very resistant to decomposition. The higher C:N ratio has great advantages when it comes to soil building, too. The carbon in the killed cover crop will persist much longer in the soil as organic matter.

Reduced tillage

It's easier to increase organic matter in soils with a reduced tillage system. With less soil disturbance, the organic matter does not degrade as rapidly and tends to persist in the soil over time. As soil structure improves and erosion rates are slowed, even more organic matter is retained. Surprisingly, rotational tillage sequesters more carbon than long-term no-till. In a rotational tillage system, carbon is generated by cover cropping, then buried at a lower soil level during tillage. This helps to keep the soil carbon stable.

Benefits

The benefits of soil organic matter are numerous, including an active microbial community, disease suppression, better nutrient cycling, reduced need for fertilizers, improved soil tilth, and limited erosion. Organic matter is what organic farming is all about!

Resources

Alford, Randy, F. Drummond and D. Maloney. *Spider Predation in Agroecosystems: Can spiders effectively control pest populations?* Orono, ME: University of Maine, 2003.

Baker, C.J. et al. *No Tillage Seeding in Conservation Agriculture,* 2nd Edition. Cambridge, U.K.: CAB International, 2007.

Brady, Nyle. *The Nature and Properties of Soils*, 8th edition. New York, NY: MacMillan Publishing Co, Inc, 1974.

Coleman, Eliot. *The New Organic Grower.* White River Junction, VT: Chelsea Green Publishing Company, 1989.

Dufour, Rex. "Farmscaping to enhance biological control" ATTRA, 2000.

Hepperly, Paul and M. Ryan. "Can organic crops tolerate more weeds?" New Farm, 2005. *www.newfarm.org/depts/NFfield_trials/0705/weeds_print.shtml.*

Hepperly, Paul and R. Seidel. "Identifying weed-tolerant corn and soybean varieties" New Farm, 2005. *www.newfarm.org/depts/weeds/features/0905/weeds_rs.*

Ingham, Elaine, A. Moldenke, and C. Edwards. *Soil Biology Primer.* Ankeny, IL: The Soil and Water Conservation Society, 2000.

Magdoff, Fred and H. van Es. *Building Soils for Better Crops,* 2nd Edition. Beltsville, MD: Sustainable Agriculture Network, 2000.

Mahr, Daniel and N. Ridgeway. *Biological control of Insects and Mites: An introduction to beneficial natural enemies and their use in pest management.* Madison, WI: University of Wisconsin, Extension, 1993.

Nuttonson, M.Y. 1957. *Rye-climate relationships and the use of phenology in ascertaining the thermal and photo-thermal requirements of rye.* American Institute of Crop Ecology, Washington, D.C.

Ross, Ron. *What I've learned from No-tilling: Cropping secrets from 58 highly successful no-tillers.* Brookfield, WI: Lessiter Publications, 2007.

Sarrantonio, Marianne. *Northeast Cover Crop Handbook.* Kutztown, PA: The Rodale Institute, 1996.

Sustainable Agriculture Network. *Managing Cover Crops Profitably*, 3rd edition. Beltsville, MD: 2007.

Wilson, David. "Earlier-flowering hairy vetch a great advantage, but northern farmers need more" The New Farm, 2007. *http://newfarm.rodaleinstitute.org/depts/NFfield_trials/2007/0412/purplebounty.shtml.*

CHAPTER 03

THE SEARCH FOR ORGANIC NO-TILL

▶ THE BEGINNINGS OF ORGANIC NO-TILL

Stories always have a beginning, middle and an end. The story of how the organic no-till system originated is no different. It's important to look at the system's history to understand the design of the roller/crimper and why organic no-till works.

No-till is a "perfect" farming system – as long as you can get the crop seed in the ground, fertilize the soil and control weeds (especially perennial weeds). Farmers have been working towards the goal of no-till for a long time.

And the idea of "organic no-till" has often been the "holy grail" of organic farming techniques. While no-till farming is fast becoming one of the most widely practiced conservation strategies of 21st century agriculture, its development has progressed along with the expanded use of herbicides, and thus has been elusive for organic farmers. According to the USDA Economic Research Service, 52.5 million acres – or 17.5 percent of all U.S. planted cropland – were in no-till management in 2000, including 17.9 percent of all corn, 32.8 percent of all soybeans, 8.0 percent of all cotton, and 9.8 percent of all small grains in the contiguous 48 states. Along with other conservation tillage methods such as ridge-till and mulch-till, no-till is justly applauded for its ability to reduce soil erosion, build soil organic matter, improve water dynamics and increase farm management efficiency. Because protecting soil organic matter is a key factor in soil carbon sequestration, moreover, no-till is gaining further recognition as a strategy for mitigating global climate change, albeit when chemical fertilizers impact is mixed. As generally practiced, no-till relies on synthetic herbicides for field preparation prior to planting and offers no advantages over intensive tillage in terms of synthetic fertilizer requirements, post-emergent herbicides or other pesticide applications. USDA Economic Research Service reports that no-till soybeans receive on average 3.4 pesticide treatments per acre, while plow-till soybeans receive 2.6 treatments per acre.

There is some evidence that the improved soil quality resulting from no-till methods actually *facilitates* percolation of these agricultural chemicals into groundwater. Concerns about water quality, escalating fuel prices, signs of herbicide resistance in weeds, and increased U.S. dependence on foreign fertilizer sources all point to the need for a new, improved system of no-till farming, one that relies less on synthetic inputs and more on smart management.

And that's where this story begins.

The early days at Rodale

It was almost 20 years ago that I spoke at a farmers meeting on the Eastern Shore of Maryland. There was a small group of farmers that sat near the back of the room politely listening to my presentation about transitioning to an organic system, the many environmental and economical benefits of implementing organic principles, and the growing demand for organic products. When I finished and had just about ended the question and answer period, I remember one of them, representing the group, made the following statements:

Well, you've captured our attention with the information you present however; together we (the folks he represented) farm thousands of acres and you organic farmers till too much! We could never plow all the ground we farm and even if we could we've been told by NRCS (Natural Resources Conservation Service) that we'll have erosion if we plow.

And you know in many ways they were right, typically we organic farmers do plow too much. In some vegetable operations, growers will use primary tillage as often as three times a year, plus all the secondary tillage, plus the cultivation for weed management, wow! That can be a lot of tillage.

It seems natural to try to eliminate tillage from an organic system, which attempts to improve the natural resources it utilizes. At the Rodale Institute, we recognize that tillage can be destructive to soil macro and micro flora and fauna, can lead to soil erosion and takes time and energy.

It also seemed logical to attempt to use naturally occurring biology that would allow us to replace the chemical components central to conventional no-till. With this in mind, we began to conduct research at Rodale. Advances in planter technology gave us a big advantage as we attempted to establish cash crops with minimal tillage.

So, we began our journey following the path laid out by conventional farming systems. We began by reducing tillage through the practices known as conservation tillage. Our earliest work was centered on employing conservation tillage practices in order to get away from using a moldboard plow. We began to use a chisel plow that left a good percentage crop residue on the surface of the field, did not invert soil layers and minimally disturbed the soil while improving drainage. Farmers often start with a chisel plow when they start to reduce tillage. It's a way to move from inversion tillage to non-inversion tillage, which is better for the soil since it causes less disturbance through the soil profile.

However, the chisel plow created problems that were not noticeable in the first few years. Over time, we began to observe an increase in weed pressure from annual weeds. Here is what happened. With inversion tillage (moldboard plow) we were able to bury small weeds and create a good seedbed. The chisel plow, which works with a "stirring" action, did not kill all of the small weeds. Many of these weeds then had a "head start" on our cash crops. As more and more of these weeds escaped the cultivation practices, our weed pressure increased.

Our experience at Rodale points to an essential dilemma. Conservation tillage (including no-till) developed out of a chemically-based weed suppression program. Reducing tillage grew up hand-in-glove with the herbicide industry. In other words, as a conventional farmer reduces tillage he or she also adjusts the chemical herbicides to make up for changes in tillage. This is chemical weed management at its best. Needless to say, this type of management has no place in an organic system. We learned that you couldn't get something for nothing. In order for an organic system to succeed, you need to adjust and change other parts of the system. Consequently, our system was doomed to fail in a very short time. We were reducing tillage but not increasing anything except our potential for weed pressure to build.

The middle development years

It started to sink in that we needed to increase something if we ever had any chance of success with reducing tillage in organic systems. We knew it wasn't going to be herbicide, so what was it going to be? It was cover crop management!

No-till is a system with its own rules that differ significantly from other kinds of conservation tillage. In some ways, no-till is just another logical step in a progression from complete moldboard plowing, through minimum till, to no-till. As tillage is reduced, herbicide use is typically either increased or at the very least altered to cater to the reduction in tillage. By contrast, organic no-till depends on plantings of cover crops to suppress weeds, *replacing chemistry with biology.* If we add cover crops to the weed control strategy, we are no longer asking for something for nothing. We are substituting increased management of cover crops (biology) for the elimination of tillage.

Our first experiments didn't work very well at all. We began to realize that cover crops were an essential part of no-till, but we didn't realize then that they are the most important piece of the puzzle, but we hadn't figured out how to manage them without tilling them into the soil. To reiterate an important point, cover crops are the *key* to the program and are the very core of an organic no-till system. Understanding this essential point was an important development. However, we still had to do a lot of experimenting to develop a sophisticated, yet simple, no-till system that would work for real farmers.

What did work in the beginning was our adoption and to some extent, the adaptation, of existing no-till planting equipment into an organic no-till system. There is no reason that organic farmers can't make use of the dramatic changes that have been made in planting equipment over the past few decades. Ag engineers from many companies have spent thousands of hours working on mechanical planting systems that will cut, slice and move through the toughest surface residues. Now it was our job to adapt this equipment to plant through cover crop residue without first tilling it into the soil.

Using this planting equipment, it was now possible and entirely practical to consider using dense cover crops, left on the surface, as a mulch, due to the marvelous improvements in the ability of no-till planters to handle large amounts of crop residue. These changes included sharp coulters that are able to easily cut through residue, stronger and heavier planters, heavier drive chains, and springs that exerted more downward pressure.

We have known for decades, from work in the Rodale gardens, that we could use mulch to smoother annual weeds and prevent them from germinating and growing. The challenge was, how to mulch large acreage in a cost effective and time efficient manner. We knew we could never afford to simply adopt garden mulching techniques into farm-scale production, especially for lower value grain crops.

The concept of using cover crops as a mulch was simple. But how would we do it? We needed to design a complete system that would be built around a sound crop rotation that allowed for the planting of annual cover crops. In our case we began working with cover crops for the production of field corn. For some time, we had planted hairy vetch in our crop rotation as a nitrogen source for corn. Typically we would moldboard plow the hairy vetch, prepare the field for planting through several secondary tillage operations, plant the corn and make several trips with various cultivators in an attempt to rip out, bury or otherwise kill as many germinating weeds as possible. Now we wanted to try and manage the hairy vetch without tillage.

The quest for a systems approach was on. Our research at Rodale focused on winter annuals. The reasons for this were purely pragmatic. Here in Pennsylvania late fall, winter, and early spring are times of the year when the soil is routinely left bare of living plants in conventional systems. But, in organic systems we can plant a living cover crop of winter annuals. We also can choose winter annuals like hairy vetch that are legumes and will fix nitrogen, a fertilizer source for succeeding crops. This is essential for heavy nitrogen feeders like corn.

For our early experiments we used vetch, rye, or vetch and rye together. There are several advantages to selecting winter annuals. Many cover crop growers have long noticed that few annual weeds germinate with the fall-planted cover crops and survive till spring. In addition, few weeds germinate in early spring due to the presence of an existing cover crop. Winter annuals also grow during the cool weather months. Their typical life cycle would be to flower in late spring, set seed and begin senescing, turn brown, die back and drop their seed to start the process over again. This compliments warm season crops like corn, soybeans, pumpkins or tomatoes. By growing winter annuals we "farm the back side of the calendar" to produce a cover crop when most agronomic crops can't be grown.

Using winter annual cover crops provides us with a couple of advantages, based on the innate life cycles of the plants. First, there is the advantage of weed suppression. Second, the cover crop is physiologically ready to senesce at about the time that agronomic crops need to be planted. What we needed was a tool that would mechanically kill the cover crop once it had flowered and also be a no-till planter able to get the seed into the soil under the dense residue of the cover crop.

Our first attempts with organic no-till were not completely successful but there were enough accomplishments to indicate the system's potential. We tried many pieces of existing equipment to cut or mow the cover crop, and all had limited success. A flail mower effectively knocked down cover crops. However, the loose material on the surface caused many headaches for the planting equipment. As the planter went through the field it would drag the residue into a pile. The coulters on the planter were unable to cut through the residue and the planter rode up and actually lifted out of the ground. Needless to say, this was extremely frustrating. Plus we never could find a mower that would uniformly cut the cover crop and redeposit it evenly across the entire field. There were always clumps of material in some places and unprotected areas in others. And finally we saw that the mown materials decomposed faster since they had more surface area for the decomposing organisms to work on. This led to a quicker break down of the mulching effect and therefore a greater chance for weeds to break through.

Next, we tried a strategy of planting into a standing cover crop, followed by mowing with either a flail mower or a brush hog. This was more successful since the planter could pass through the cover crop that was still attached to the ground. The various mowers we used, however, did not evenly distribute the cut cover crop and this rough uneven surface residue affected emergence of the cash crop. In some areas we got a good germination rate, and in others, the cover crop residue prevented crop emergence. Also, mowing takes a lot of time and lots of horsepower. These downsides led us to keep searching for a better way.

Achieving no-till success and what's next

It was about this time that an accident led us to a new method of killing cover crops. We had a number of different research plots set up for experimenting with no-till. At this point, I don't remember what results any of the experimental plots yielded. But, along the field edges outside of the research plots area, we had planted some vetch, which I drove over repeatedly with the tractor in the process of tilling and planting the experimental plots. The following day, I noticed that the "rolled" hairy vetch was dead where I had driven over it. When we planted the research plots we ran the planter into these field edges and stuck corn seed into the trampled cover. To my surprise 100 percent of the vetch died leaving behind a thick mat of dead mulch. It was perfect – the corn germinated right through the mat. It is ironic that the best results in the experimental plots came from the field edges where no experiment was planned. But that's exactly how working farmers come up with solutions and new ideas – by observing nature and noticing how it works.

This "accidental" experiment occurred in the mid 1980s, but we spent the next couple of decades figuring out the details and shaping the "accident" into an organic no-till system. We knew we couldn't control cover crops by just driving over them, or recommend this method to farmers. Yet, this type of rolling was immediately appealing since it would distribute the cover crops evenly and they would remain anchored to the ground and less likely to plug up the planter. We tried two kinds of implements – a rolling harrow and a Buffalo stalk chopper. Experiments were done with rolling before planting and after planting. Again, we had mixed results with just enough success to keep us interested. We could see the potential of the system – if we could only find the right combination of cover crops, equipment and timing.

Although there were several obstacles to developing an organic no-till system, one of the biggest stumbling blocks was the equipment for killing or terminating the cover crop. We couldn't find any tools that were specifically designed to accomplish the tasks we had in mind, and none of the "off the shelf" equipment seemed to do the job. First, all of the equipment was pulled behind the tractor. Whether it was a mower, a rolling harrow or a stalk chopper it was not the first thing to come into contact with the cover crops. The tractor tires had a tendency to push the cover crop down (but not kill it) allowing the pulled implement to pass over the plant material without affecting it.

We concentrated our efforts on the equipment needed to improve the predictability and success ratio in terms of percent kill of the cover crop and establishment of the cash crop. Gradually, we realized that we needed specialized equipment to roll and crimp the cover crop. The tool needed to have three characteristics: a) it should be front mounted to improve the contact between the tool and the ground, b) it should roll the cover laying it in one direction, and c) it should crimp but not cut the plant material. We had finally identified the design criteria we were looking for.

Now we had all the pieces in place. We had cover crops that could perform the functions we required, we had a specialized tool to roll and crimp the cover crop, and we had planting equipment that could get the seed in the ground. All that was left was to work on the system to address the dozens of nuances that make an intensively managed system work. There were many questions still to be answered: when do you roll, what species and variety of cover crop should be planted, how do you tool-up and adjust the planter, are there insect dynamics that need to be addressed? These were and are some of the challenges that still exist in the system.

The future may include the use of more high-residue cultivators to manage weeds in a no-till system.

The no-till work continues

We are continuing to explore ways to solve the problems, which may arise from time to time in an organic no-till system – as happens in any other farming system too. While the organic no-till system is very exciting and holds great promise for farmers to aid in reducing the need for cultivation and tillage, there may be times when the weed pressure is too great or perennial weeds get a toehold and begin to express themselves in a no-till crop when they break through the mulch supplied by the cover crop. If this situation occurs, farmers and crop managers may have the opportunity to intervene with additional field operations.

In this particular case, standard cultivation of the crop is almost impossible due to the tremendous amount of cover crop residue remaining on the field (our weed suppressing mat). Not to fear, new technology is available to remedy this situation. There are high-residue cultivators on the market that have the ability to move through the field sliding under the mulch and cutting off the weeds just below the surface of the soil. Let's look a little closer at this technology to see how it might be useful in our intensively managed cover crop no-till system.

Before we can discuss how the tools work we need to have a clear understanding of what it is we want to accomplish. Only then can we select or even design tools that will fit our needs and accomplish our objectives. To follow are photos that will help explain when and where cultivation makes the most sense and how the tools available might work to achieve the goal of killing the weeds. Weeds typically appear between the rows in an organic no-till system rather than in the row right with the crop as with standard tilled and cultivated fields. This fact gives us the opportunity to go into the field and attempt to cultivate them out when they are slightly larger than we would consider doing in a typical till and cultivate system when farmers work so hard at getting the weeds out at the smallest stage.

The goal with using a high-residue cultivator is to dislodge and cut the roots of the weeds without disturbing the mulch residue we are depending upon so much for our primary weed control. In order to do this the cultivating implement needs to have as few tools actually touching the soil as possible to avoid a raking action occurring and pulling up all the mulch. In the implement pictured below, there is a sharp coulter disc positioned between two large depth control wheels followed by a single standard with a large angled sweep tipped with a chisel point to pull it into the ground. The coulter disc cuts through the mulch creating a slit for the standard holding the sweep to pass through. The sweep tracks through this slit sliding into the soil at a depth of about two to three inches under the mulch, lifting it slightly but not raking it, burying it, or moving it.

The end result is a field that has its mulch layer intact, and weeds that have been severed from their roots. If you simply tug on the weeds you should be able to lift them from the ground without pulling up any of the root. These weeds will then dry out and die. The high-residue cultivator works best when the weeds are large enough to be cut but not so large that they might be maturing or setting seed. It is also important to have the cash crop large enough to withstand some bumping by the operation but small enough to allow the equipment to easily pass through the rows without driving down any of the crop. An appropriate time for this operation would be about the time of last or "lay by" cultivation on a standard till and cultivate system.

The primary goals and objectives of a true no-till system haven't changed and I haven't abandoned the idea of eliminating cultivation from the production of no-tilled row crops However, with minimal activity, research is indicating we have the ability to rescue a crop from weed infestations that threaten to reduce yields or overtake our no-tilled crop. Research using this equipment is still in the early stages and agricultural engineers may need to modify existing equipment to handle the tremendous amounts of mulch residue more efficiently. High-residue cultivators my have a role to play in the expansion of the adoption of no-till technology as it affords additional opportunities to meet the ever changing challenges to farming.

This high-residue cultivator has a sharp coulter disc positioned between two large depth control wheels followed by a single standard with a large angled sweep.

CHAPTER 04 THE ROLLER/CRIMPER

▶ THE RIGHT TOOL FOR THE JOB

As with any field operation on any farm, you need the right piece of equipment to accomplish the task effectively and efficiently. This is especially true in a cover crop system where every operation has an impact on the success of crop yield and quality. These ramifications are particularly evident in organic systems where every part of the system is closely interconnected to every other part. Organic farming needs to be considered as a holistic system.

Adopting organic no-till methods creates a dynamic change to this holistic system. It's hard to make one change without affecting the whole farm management plan. As we discuss organic no-till, we need to be especially mindful of how it will impact every other part of the system. The impacts can be seen from an agronomic perspective through changes in weed species and location, from a soils perspective as you'll see changes in the soil's ability to retain water and support greater microbial diversity, and from an energetic perspective since there will be tremendous reductions in the amount of embodied energy in the production process.

As discussed in chapter 3, through some experimentation with organic no-till, it became obvious that we needed a specialized tool to do the job. The roller/crimper is the tool that makes organic no-till possible because it does just that. Although there are other similar tools available, the roller/crimper is the one that is currently best suited for managing cover crops in organic no-till. Tools don't have to be that different to be revolutionary. Small modifications can make the tool perform much better. Any tool that will save you time and energy will be a good investment and pay for itself.

Essentially, the roller/crimper is a drum or cylinder with curved blades, which when operating, lays the cover crop over in one direction and crimps or crushes its stems. The combination of these two actions kills the cover and turns it into a thick, weed suppressing mulch in a single pass. You won't need herbicides to provide 90 to 100 percent knockdown. Farmers can use the roller/crimper as part of an organic operation, or as part of a conventional one to reduce the use of herbicides and improve the bottom line.

Design & Development of the Roller/Crimper

The design and development of the roller/crimper at Rodale began with an examination and analysis of many another tools including rolling stalk choppers, rolling harrows, and even flail mowers. These tools were already in use on our farm. Although they were designed for other functions, they appeared to adapt well to managing cover crops. However, none of these tools were designed specifically to roll cover crops and each had drawbacks. So we sought to develop a specialized tool for the job of rolling and crimping cover crops, instead of using a modified implement intended for another purpose.

Let's start with the example of the rolling stalk chopper. The rolling stalk chopper consists of eight rolling drums (in a 4 row unit) arranged in two parallel rows. The implement is rear mounted on a tractor. As with any farm tool, some things about the rolling stalk chopper worked well, and some things didn't. The rolling stalk chopper has two big drawbacks. First, the machine is rear mounted on the tractor, which leads to some problems in completely killing the cover crop. As the tractor tires pass over the cover crop, they knock down the cover crop and make an indentation in the ground. This is especially true if the soil is wet. This means that the implement can't do its job effectively – the cover does not receive the full impact of the rolling stalk chopper. The stems of the cover crop remain uncut and often have a tendency to stand back up. This defeats the purpose of the operation and eliminates the mulching effect of the cover crop.

Also, since the rolling stalk chopper is rear mounted, the planting must be done in a separate pass. This two-pass operation increases the time and energy invested in establishing the cash crop. With the thick mat of rolled cover crop covering the ground, it can be difficult to see where the planter has already been. Traditional row markers can't make a good line in the thick residue and foam markers would be a necessary option.

The Buffalo rolling stalk chopper has two sets of rollers with parallel blades. Photo courtesy of Steve Groff.

Another issue with rolling stalk choppers or mowers, as well as some other tools that have been used for organic no-till, is their tendency to cut the cover crop into small pieces. The cutting creates several problems. First, the cover crop breaks down faster and is less effective for weed control. Second, when the cover crop is cut, it is no longer anchored in place by its roots. Consequently, it ends up in all kinds of places it shouldn't. For example, it can get dragged by the planter and clog the machinery. In addition to the problems with the machinery, it creates bare patches that can become weedy later on in the season. The mulch is not distributed evenly across the field, with some thick areas and some thinner ones.

There are several other key design points that we considered important when reviewing existing equipment and the creation of our own roller/crimper. One of those was the number of moving parts – in other words, the number of points where the cover crop could get tangled in the machinery as the rolling operation takes place. By creating a roller with only two bearings we were able to minimize both wear points as well as reducing the areas where wrapping of the cover crop might take place. We also wanted to design the blades in a way that would prevent them from ripping or pulling at the cover crop. This pulling action would create bare patches in the cover thereby providing an opportunity for annual weeds to germinate. This was accomplished by mounting the blades onto the cylinder at an angle of 7 to 10 degrees off of perpendicular. We'll discuss this in more detail later in this chapter.

Design elements

The design flaws we saw in using existing equipment were the impetus for developing a completely new implement – the roller/crimper. As the roller/crimper developed, the following elements were incorporated into the design. These elements addressed some of the problems with other tools, which were never really meant to roll thick stands of cover crops. The end result is a specialized tool that provides a 90 percent to 100 percent knockdown for cover crops, even for tough combinations like rye and vetch.

ONE BIG ROLLER The Rodale roller/crimper design features one large drum with blades that cover the width of the planter (in our case 10 feet 6 inches for a 4 x 30 inch row planter), instead of the eight rollers in the rolling stalk chopper. These rollers can be built in gangs mounted separately on the planter frame to create larger roller/crimpers to accommodate wide planters. To date I know of several 30 foot rollers in use with great success. With fewer sets of bearings, the Rodale roller/crimper is easier to maintain, and has fewer moving parts which could get clogged with heavy residue. This is especially important for vining crops like vetches or peas. The roller/crimper's bearings on each end are inset by three inches and fronted with a smooth shield. Shielding the bearings is crucial to successfully rolling thick dense cover crops. The shields prevent the plant material from wrapping around the bearing and quickly tearing large patches of cover from the field.

The roller/crimper was designed to perform a specific function. As such, it can be scaled up or down to suit the particular needs of many growers. In its simplest form it doesn't need to even be a roller. A handheld version using human foot pressure on a crimping blade can work in tight spaces like a greenhouse floor. On a larger-scale a roller can be built to run in front of the very largest planters or grain drills.

BLADES IN A CURVING CHEVRON PATTERN A set of parallel blades is a design feature common to the rolling stalk chopper and knife rollers used in South America. The curving chevron blades of the Rodale roller/crimper have a couple of advantages over the straight parallel arrangement. First, the chevron prevents bouncing and neutralizes the side-to-side draft produced by a simple spiral. The bouncing effect of a straight blade design might work if the roller were pulled on the rear of the tractor but mounting it on the front makes the bouncing intolerable. With this pattern, a portion of a blade continuously touches the ground at any given time, which means that more pressure can be exerted per inch of blade to crimp the cover crop and the bouncing eliminated. The chevron pattern actually magnifies the weight of the roller several times as the weight travels along the length of the blade. This is an important feature, since with more weight you'll get a higher kill rate.

▶ THE RODALE ROLLER/CRIMPER AT A GLANCE

- Roller diameter: 16 inches.
- 10 Blades: 4 inches tall, spaced evenly around the roller.
- Width: 8 feet (3 row), 11 feet (4 row) or 16 feet (6 row), as needed. Custom-made rollers are available up to 40 feet wide.
- Weight (11 foot roller/crimper): 1,200 lbs. empty, 2,000 lbs. filled with water.
- Hitch: Made to fit category I or II 3-point hitch.
- For more information see the computer aided designs (CAD) drawings in the Appendix section of this book.

ANGLED BLADES Blades on the roller are angled or lean back (7-10 degrees) from the direction of motion. This important feature ensures that the roller will not kick up dirt or tear the cover crop, exposing bare soil. By creating this reduced angle the blade is already lifting off the surface as the tip of the blade travels around the central axis. As we have already mentioned, it's very important to have a minimum of bare soil exposed for the best weed control. These blades are blunt rather than sharp, which means that the cover crop is crimped, not cut. The blades crimp the cover crop stems approximately every seven inches, damaging the vascular system of the plant and causing it to wither and die.

ADJUSTABLE WEIGHT Weight of the right amount and in the right place are key factors for success. The Rodale roller/crimper is designed so that it can be filled with water to add or subtract weight as needed. This can be an advantage in managing thick stands of cover crops or working in fields that are either too wet or too dry. When full, a 10 foot 6 inch wide roller/crimper weighs approximately one ton, including 800 pounds of water.

FRONT MOUNTED Unlike other rollers, the Rodale roller/crimper is designed specifically to be front mounted on a tractor. While it can be pulled behind the tractor, there are some important reasons for keeping it on the front. When the tractor pulls the roller, the tractor often leaves tire depressions, especially if the soil is moist. The cover crop can get lodged in these depressions, which prevents the blades of the roller/crimper from making contact with the cover crop. As a result, there may not be an adequate kill rate. You may see strips of un-crimped and re-growing cover crops. Mounting the roller in front of the tractor also frees up the rear of the tractor to mount a planter, drill or transplanter. This effectively allows the equipment to work in tandem creating a one-pass system to manage the cover crop and plant the cash crop.

A modified roller/crimper can be used in small areas, such as inside a greenhouse (above).

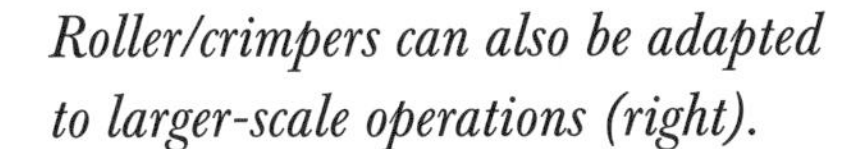

Roller/crimpers can also be adapted to larger-scale operations (right).

Why farmers like the roller/crimper

The roller/crimper is the best tool for organic no-till for these important reasons:

Ninety to 100 percent knockdown. When done at the correct time in the cover crop's life cycle, the roller/crimper is very effective in a single pass, even without additional herbicides or weeding. It's an effective tool for an organic system.

Easily handles tough combinations like rye and vetch. Vetch's vining growth habit is often challenging as it can get caught in machinery. The roller/crimper is a better tool for the job since it has fewer moving parts that result in less plugging. Plus the roller/crimper has enough weight to completely crush even thick stands of cover crops.

Creates an effective weed suppressive mulch. Instead of cutting up cover crops like some mowed systems, the rolled cover crops are left in place, which reduces plugging problems. It then creates a mulch mat that stays in place through the entire growing season. Cover crops left in place help fight erosion, hold moisture and keep the soil cooler as well.

Soil disturbance is minimal. The goal of the roller/crimper is not to cut the stems, but lay them flat, creating a dense, thick mulch. Fewer weed seeds have the opportunity to germinate and compete with crop plants, and soil health is improved.

Front mount enables a one-pass system. The front mounted roller/crimper enables a one-pass system with a no-till planter rear mounted on the tractor. This reduces the number of field operations and saves fuel and time.

Affordable. Currently, roller/crimpers range in price from $2,600 for an 8-foot roller to $4,500 for a 15-foot roller. Compared with other "tillage" equipment, this is cost effective and value priced technology. With the assistance of CAD drawings, you can either make a roller/crimper yourself, or have one made locally and save the cost of shipping.

Works well with soil types of all kinds. The roller/crimper has been tested on many soil types, and performs well on all of them. An exception is with extremely rocky soils. Large rocks can lift the roller, preventing it from making contact with the cover crop and creating problems with cover crop termination. This is one circumstance where the system may not work as well as it could.

Works in dry or wet soil conditions. One of the advantages of a cover crop based no-till is that it works with dry or wet soil. It's possible to roll and plant wet fields without creating problems with soil compaction and smearing since the tractor is really travelling across a carpet of cover crops. These rolled mulches spread the weight of the tractor over a larger surface area and prevent contact with the soil. With dry conditions, you can increase the weight of the roller/crimper and the planter to compensate for the harder soil.

Future design modifications

Here is where the next charter in the story starts to be written. Knowing full well that there is no perfect piece of equipment, it has to be assumed that the roller/crimper could be improved and then improved again. Since building the prototype model and seeing hundred of others in the field I have seen the possibilities for new design changes.

As an example, many vegetable growers have asked for a bell-shaped roller to work the shoulders of a raised bed. Some folks have suggested that a wavy blade would increase the surface area of the blade as it touches the surface of the soil, and still others have said that more blades on the cylinder (or blades closer together) might work better. I'm sure as you read this book and work with no-till in the field you may have some ideas for improvement as well. This is how we can all move towards a brighter future for this technology.

How the tool is used

Like any tool, owning it is only half the equation. Learning or developing the skills to use it is the other half. One practical application we have discovered is that a small grain cover crop like rye or barley leaves a better mulch pattern on the ground when it is rolled at an angle of 30 to 90 degrees from the direction in which it was planted.

▶ HELP FROM A NEIGHBOR

The cover crop roller was constructed with the help of John Brubaker, a farmer whose land adjoins the Rodale Institute research farm. John has been a collaborator with the Institute on other equipment development projects in the past, such as their compost windrow turner.

In 2002, Brubaker received a grant from the USDA's Sustainable Agriculture Research and Education (SARE) program to fund development of the roller/crimper.

Brubaker is a skilled metalworker and practical engineer, whose talents came in handy when designing and building the roller/crimper. He is also a member of the Groffdale Mennonite Church, which prohibits the use of rubber-tired tractors and motorized road vehicles. Consequently, he was familiar with working on steel-wheeled tractors.

It was Brubaker's familiarity with steel wheeled farm machinery that made him invaluable as part of the roller design team.

Roller/crimpers based on the Rodale design are currently being built by I & J Manufacturing in Southeastern Pennsylvania. View the rollers on their website at *www.croproller.com.* I & J Manufacturing can be reached by phone at 717-442-9451.

To further explain, if you seed the small grain with a grain drill the seeds will be in 7 or 8 inch rows neatly following the direction of the grain drill. If you come along when the grain has pollinated and roll it in that exact same direction, the plants will lay over neatly in those same 7 or 8 inch rows leaving "gaps" in the mulch between those rows where weeds will have an opportunity to exploit the bit of sunlight that reaches that area.

On the other hand, if you roll the small grain at a 30 to 90 degree angle from the direction the grain drill traveled, when the timing is right the stems of the small grain will lay flat across the grain leaving no bare areas or row spacing for weed seedlings to exploit. This may sound confusing but in practice it is quite simple. The technique requires no particular skill, just the knowledge to put it into practice.

Another thing to consider is the proper mounting of the roller/crimper on the tractor. What does this mean? Well, the roller can only crimp the cover crop if it has the ability to press it against the soil. The soil actually acts as an anvil when the blade of the roller crushes the cover crop. In order for that to happen on an uneven surface, like the ground, is to have the roller in a full "float" position. That means the hydraulic system must incorporate a valve with a "detent" or "float" position. Once the valve is pushed over center it will remain open allowing the hydraulic fluid to pass through in both directions without any restriction, permitting the roller to float over the surface of the soil no mater how rolling the terrain might be. Of course this isn't an issue if you are pulling the roller with a tractor or a horse in a two-pass system.

Rolling Tips for the Beginner

As with any system, there are skills a farmer learns along the way that make their operations run more efficiently and ultimately be more effective. A farming system based on cover crops and no-till is no different. I always say, "Just because I have a fine box of wood working tools – it doesn't make me a master cabinet maker." Well the same is true for managing a complex biological system like organic no-till. It will take several growing seasons before any practitioner will feel truly confident in his or her ability to implement the system. Changes in weather, soil conditions, or other matters outside of your control all may have an impact on the success or failure of the system to perform as expected.

Be persistent

My first tip for anyone beginning to incorporate rolling cover crops and no-tilling is – **don't give up!** Experience shows that the system works. We know we can kill annual or winter annual cover crops by breaking and crimping the stems once they have reached the stage of flowering. We know that thick mulches will smoother or prevent annual weeds from growing. And we know that since the system is based on sound biological principles that it will work for many crops, in many locations, and in many rotations.

Watch the details

My second tip would be to **be observant.** When learning new skills it is always beneficial to pay close attention to the details. Watch what is happening in the field, to the soil, and to the weeds and insects. Since the system changes the biology of the fields you need to be aware of where you are starting out and scout the fields for subtle changes. Watch for changes in the cover crops to time your rolling operations. You'll need to observe and analyze the percent ground cover or amount of mulching effect your cover crop has. And you'll need to pay close attention to your planting equipment to be sure it is getting the seed in the ground where you want it.

The all-important cover crop

My third tip for anyone staring out on this journey is to realize that **the cover crop is the most important.** This can be the hardest lesson to learn, but is also the most important. As you shift your operation away from annual tillage, or tillage to manage annual weeds, you need to shift your mindset as well. Your cover crops now become a critical link in your operational chain. So critical are they that the attention you pay to them will be equal to or greater than your cash crops. This is a very radical concept. Often when I see a system failure it's because the farmer didn't pay attention to getting the cover crop established properly. I'll hear comments like, "Well, I got the cover crops seeded about two months later than I had hoped." or "I only used half the recommended seeding rate because the seed is expensive." Most farmers wouldn't consider seeding their cash crops two months late or at half the seeding rate and expect success. You can't do that with your highly valued and critical cover crops either. The result more than likely will be thin stands, weed infestations, and the need to plow it under.

Have patience

My fourth tip is to **be patient.** In many cases the system fails because the farmer neglects some very important facts. Again the cover crop is the key. If you roll the cover crop before it has flowered it will more than likely try to stand back up and grow until it can flower and set seed. A plant's urge to reproduce is very strong. However, once the reproduction cycle is complete, after pollination, these annuals or winter annuals are relatively easy to terminate with the roller.

Be ready to experiment

The final tip is to **experiment on your own.** Every farmer should wear a researcher hat along with all the other hats (biologist, accountant, marketer, mechanic, electrician, etc.). Take a small portion of your farm and try some of these techniques on a scale appropriate for your operation before you risk a large percentage of your farm. Experiment to determine which cover crops fit your site and farm, how the timing of the cover crop maturity fits with your rotation or how your rotation can be modified to accept the cover crop. Never stop trying to improve on the system. These activities will always keep you on the cutting edge, learning more and more every year.

Tool Limitations and Possibilities

Rolling weeds

I sometimes get questions about using the roller/crimper as a tool for weed control. For example, a farmer might want to use it to roll a weed-infested field. Unfortunately, if it sounds too good to be true, it often is too good to be true. This is the case with the idea of rolling weeds; the weeds are merely knocked down by the roller/crimper, not killed. They will spring back into action and compete with crop plants. This is especially true for perennial weeds.

Our system is designed to work with annual and winter annual cover crops, such as rye, vetch, annual clovers, peas, barley or buckwheat. We roll these plants just as they are completing their life cycle – in effect killing them just a little bit early. In this way, organic no-till works in cooperation with nature. By contrast, if you try to kill a summer annual weed or a perennial weed with the roller/crimper, you are really working against nature. You are asking the plant to die in the middle of its life cycle, before it has had time to reproduce. No weed worth its salt is going to lie down and die before it has reproduced!

Use on other kinds of cover crops

Just as with weeds, the roller/crimper will only work on annual cover crops as they are completing their life cycle. We have found that annual cereal grains such as rye, barley and wheat roll well. The roller/crimper won't kill cover crops like red clover, which is a biennial, alfalfa, which is a perennial or 'Marshall' rye, a kind of annual ryegrass.

Rolling right along with cover crops

Here are some examples of cover crops that can be killed with the roller/crimper. For more information, see the chapter on cover cropping.

• Crimson clover • Winter rye • Winter barley
• Spring barley • Spring oats • Buckwheat
• Foxtail millet • Pearl millet

CHAPTER 05 THE ORGANIC NO-TILL PLANTER & OTHER NO-TILL TOOLS

If you are currently a no-till farmer, but haven't tried organic no-till, you'll want to prepare yourself for a new experience. If, on the other hand, you've never tried no-till methods to establish crops, then everything about it will be new, since there are many challenges to getting a good crop stand. The biggest difference, of course, is that you won't be tilling the soil to prepare the seedbed. Without pre-plant tillage the planting equipment will be expected to do all the work. The planter, drill or transplanter will need to cut through any plant residue remaining from previous crops as well as the thick cover crop mat.

Next, it must open a seed furrow in the soil, and then close the seed furrow tightly for good soil-to-seed contact. Plus, all this must happen in a uniform fashion while the tractor is moving at approximately three to four miles per hour. That's a lot to accomplish! It also means having your planting equipment in tiptop shape when you go to the field.

The main difference you'll notice between conventional no-till and organic no-till is the heavy residue on the surface of the fields. You may need to tool up so that you have a planter that is able to effectively cut through the residue, place the seeds in the furrow, and provide good seed-to-soil contact. Luckily, no-till planters have come a long way during the last 20 years and both organic and conventional farmers will be able to take advantage of these advances in technology.

You may experience a number of different problems with your planter during the transition. The heavy mat of vegetation produced by the cover crops can cause the planter's depth wheel to ride up. It can also be difficult to close the seed furrow to get good seed to soil contact. Soybeans, in particular, need excellent seed-to-soil contact to germinate well. Even with a first-rate planter, those experimenting with organic no-till should increase their seeding rate upwards of 10 to 15 percent to compensate for seed loss in the residue. We'll discuss the other potential pitfalls as we go along.

Components of the No-Till Planters

Currently, the Rodale Institute is using a Monosem no-till planter for organic no-till operations. However, any planter designed specifically for planting in no-till situations can be used to plant through a thick cover crop mat. When selecting the right planter for your operation, you'll want to keep in mind the crop you're planting, your soil type, and the tractor you'll be using. We chose the Monosem because it will plant many different seed sizes from grains to vegetables. Since we have diverse crops at Rodale, it made sense for us. A quick look at the planter's features will provide guidelines for selecting a planter suitable for organic no-till.

At Rodale, the purchase of a vacuum planter has made a big difference in the success of the organic no-till trials. The 4-row planter is a hybrid composed of a Monosem vacuum seed pickup attached to a Kinze toolbar planter. The planter is simple to calibrate, the vacuum system does a good job of singulating the seed, and it's easy to modify for our specific use.

The Monosem vacuum planter has several advantages. First, it creates a narrow planting strip and this minimizes in-row weeds. In each planting unit, a 15-inch fluted coulter in the front slices through the residue and pulls it away from the seeding area. Next, a 15-inch double disk opener creates a V-shaped planting furrow. Shoe-type openers, which create a furrow by dragging through the soil, don't work nearly as well. This type of opener drags the cover crop residue, resulting in poor seed placement. After the seed drops into the furrow, a Keeton seed firmer made of plastic or nylon ensures good seed to soil contact. Finally, the closing wheels pull the residue close to the seed furrow.

In order to plant into the high residue cover crop mat, there needed to be a couple of key modifications made. First, extra weight was added so that the planter would more effectively cut through the cover crops. With our planter, some downward pressure is created by the weight of the planter itself, as well as from the use of springs. However, this was not enough to cut through the cover crop mat. For this reason, we fastened 130-pound weights to each of the planter units.

In addition, 12-inch cast iron closing wheels replaced the standard plastic and rubber wheels. Again, the added weight of the wheels benefited the system. Two different kinds of wheels are used for different cover crops. Blunt and soft wheels are used for vetch, which snags easily on machine parts. Toothed cultivator type wheels are used for small grains. A word to the wise: we tried spiked closing wheels (such as Martin wheels) but found they tend to get tangled in the cover crop residue and needed constant attention.

As with all kinds of machinery, maintenance is essential. Older equipment that hasn't been well maintained may not be able to handle organic no-till, and can be frustrating to work with. Sharp coulters are especially important to cut through the killed cover crop. If the coulters are not sharp enough, or if they are out of adjustment, "hairpinning" can occur. In other words, the cover crop isn't cut but instead gets jammed into the planting furrow and creates significant germination problems and poor stands.

There are a number of other very useful planters, but it is not the goal of this book to endorse any one particular planter over another.

You'll want to select a planter that best suits your crops and production system. Don't expect the planter to function properly without setting and checking all the adjustments. You'll also need to check the adjustments in the field as you begin to plant. Verify that the seed placement is satisfactory in terms of depth, space between the seeds, and that there is good seed-to-soil contact. The seed furrow must also close satisfactorily for the best germination rate.

You may find that experimentation is your best ally. Combining parts from different planters often works better than using all of the original parts. For example, fellow Pennsylvania farmer Steve Groff of Cedar Meadow Farm has a planter made up of parts from about seven different companies.

There are other challenges to no-till systems that are not normally experienced in plow-till systems. For example, the simple task of lining up the tractor for each planter pass to ensure uniform spacing between rows becomes more difficult with a cover crop mat. In plow-till systems the operator simply follows the mark left on the soil surface by the planter's row marking unit. However, when the soil surface is covered with crop residue other devices may be needed. The roller itself may be a sufficient guide but a foam marking system can allow you to plant straighter rows.

Grain drills

Just as planters are critical for the establishment of crops grown on wide rows, such as 30 or 36 inches, proper grain drill selection can make all the difference in the world to the success of establishing grain crops, cover crops, or narrow row beans. I can't stress enough the importance of seeding and planting equipment to the whole system. You'll only be able to generate an acceptable stand of cover crops when the timing and the mechanics of the seeding operation are coordinated.

Like planters, grain drills come in all shapes, sizes and colors. Finding the one that best suits your operation will require some homework. Again, you'll want an implement that is designed for no-till planting and has the ability to slice through the dense cover crop mat to get the seed in the soil. Depositing the seed into the mulch, rather than properly placing it in the soil, will lead to poor stands and frustration. Many new grain drills on the market have incorporated features designed to do a better job of planting.

Things to consider when shopping for a drill include:

Total weight of the unit. This is important since it is partially the weight of the drill that actually pushes the coulters through the cover crop and into the soil.

Ease of adjustment. As with any piece of equipment the less time spent adjusting it, the more time you'll have to use it. Keep in mind with these systems you'll find the need to routinely fine-tune the adjustments for individual field conditions.

Ability to close off openings. Since you may want to plant on various row spacings, the option of blocking off individual openers or lifting whole gangs of drill units may be important considerations.

Location of the drive and transport wheels. Under conventional planting scenarios in which herbicides are used to control weeds this may not be a concern. But in a system where the cover crop mulch is expected to perform that task, anything you can do to minimize the disturbance of the mat and maximize the ground covered can help. The drive and transport wheels should be inside the width of the roller to enable the roller to crush the cover crop effectively.

Transplanters

If you can plant seeds directly into a rolled cover, why not transplant vegetable seedlings as well? That was the question asked several years ago by Professor Ron Morse of Virginia Tech. A number of different considerations are important when designing a transplanter as transplants have very special needs. They are more fragile and since they are already growing they need immediate access to water. Unlike seeds, which are in a dormant state, transplants are liable to break if handled roughly.

Ideally, the transplanter creates a root-friendly zone and provides water at the same time. No-till transplanting into newly rolled cover crops can create a hostile environment for these young plants unless careful attention is paid to every step of the process. Despite these challenges, many growers are having success in transplanting vegetables and tobacco using no-till practices.

The sub-surface tiller-transplanter (SSTT), developed by Professor Ron Morse of Virginia Tech, is intended for use with vegetable systems. It mechanically transplants vegetable plugs into killed cover crops. Morse developed the SSTT to cope with difficult soil conditions and high residues. One of the goals of the transplanter is to loosen the soil adequately for good soil-to-transplant contact, while providing a minimum of disturbance to the surface residues – which helps with weed control.

The SSTT has an upright, high clearance design with a double disk opener. It also has a special component – a sub-surface tiller that prepares a narrow strip of soil, as deep as eight inches, which enables the double disk opener to open a furrow for the transplants. This feature is especially helpful for planting into dry, hard soil or rocky soil, because it takes the brunt of the abuse that these soils have to offer. Press wheels at the back of the machine make sure that both soil and residue is drawn around the plant.

A deluxe version of the transplanter can also lay drip tape, apply fertilizer, and water in the transplant all at the same time. Morse is also working on a smaller, simplified version that will be affordable for smaller farmer operations. For information on how to build your own sub-surface tiller-transplanter, as well as small-scale equipment, contact:

Ronald D. Morse
Vegetable Crops Research
Virginia Polytechnic Institute
and State University
Blacksburg, VA 24061
(540) 231-6724

Front mounted 3-point hitch

In order to create a one-pass system, Rodale purchased a front mounted 3-point hitch from the Buckeye Tractor Company. Front mounted hitches offer good visibility and control, and combined front and rear tools improve traction and use of power in the field, particularly on front-wheel drive tractors. The hitches available from Buckeye and many other fabricators have standard 3-point connections to use with ordinary 3-point equipment. They can be installed on new tractors as well as on older tractors built since about 1960. The hitches are primarily sized by horsepower rating. Although it doesn't really take a lot of horsepower to operate a roller/crimper, you should make sure that your hitch has a lift rating that enables it to raise the roller/crimper when it is full of water. You will also need to purchase a hitch mounting frame. Several different models are available to fit each series of tractors. To learn more about the hitches and to check prices, go to *www.buctraco.com* or contact another manufacturer.

Row managers

For every situation there is probably a tool or attachment that can be mounted onto your planter, drill or transplanter to make it work better. Here is a brief, and I'm sure incomplete list, representing some of the attachments you might find useful. For

Regular equipment checks are very important.

more information see Appendix C, Manufacturers and Equipment Dealers.

Pequea planter residue slicer. This tool is a dual wheel coulter that is mounted in front of the planter unit. It replaces the standard coulter supplied with the planter. It is unique because it has two rubber wheels attached to the coulter blade that hold the residue in place, allowing the coulter to effectively slice through the cover crop. This attachment works well in conventional no-till or behind a roller/crimper to prevent hairpinning.

Yetter residue managers. These finger-type discs can be mounted on either side of the coulter to move the residue away from the seed zone. Under some circumstances this may be advantageous, particularly when planting small-seeded vegetables without tillage. However, once the cover crop mulch is pulled away from the seeding area, even just a few inches, the opportunity for weeds to exploit this area and grow is greatly increased.

Martin closing wheels. As mentioned previously, our work with corn and soybeans using rye or vetch at Rodale Institute has shown that these tools tend to wrap up and tear the cover crop. However, they may prove to work well under different situations or when mounted to a different planter. This may be especially true if you are going to try a zone-till system or actually move the mulch away from the planting area. Although in an organic system where no herbicides will be used to manage weed pressure it may not be recommended.

Disc residue managers. These tools are concave disc blades mounted on either side

▶ PLANTING ISSUES TO CONSIDER

DRILLING INTO WET/DRY SOILS:
- Adjusting the planter
- Use of spading wheels
- Applying fertilizer at planting

ZONE TILLAGE/STRIP TILLAGE:
- Gives a planting area for smaller seeded crops
- Doesn't disturb the soil very much
- Little loss of CO_2
- Tools for zone tillage

ORIENTATION OF RESIDUES TO PLANTER:
- Having an even layer of residues helps
- Roller/crimper serves to orient residues

NO-TILLAGE AND SEEDLING EMERGENCE:
- Benefits of high residue environment and effect on emergence zone
- Role of earthworms and microflora
- Possible problems with damping off and other fungal diseases
- Regional differences

CONSIDERATIONS FOR DIFFERENT KINDS OF COVER CROPS:
- Hairy vetch
- Rye

WEED CONTROL:
- Choose a slot opener with minimal disturbance

MARKER ARMS:
- Need for parallel rows
- Add weight to marker arms?

EVALUATING YOUR PLANTING:
- Pre-plant: check soil moisture and firmness
- Germination test if using bin run seed

▶ PLANTING ISSUES TO CONSIDER (CONT.)

- Check for proper seed placement, depth and coverage
- Check for insect predation/disease problems
- Monitor seedling emergence

DEPTH CONTROL CHALLENGES
- High residue
- Soil hardness
- Rough, uneven surfaces (more common in continuous no-till)
- Planting to moisture?

INTEGRATING THE ROLLER/CRIMPER WITH THE PLANTER

of a straight coulter that can move the surface residue away from the seed zone. Under organic situations where we are trying to "tuck" the residue tightly against the seed zone these attachments are counterproductive. However, under certain situations they may be just the right tool to get the job done.

Foam row markers

It can be a challenge to accurately line up each planter pass using standard mechanical row markers. The use of foam markers may prove to be a useful addition to any no-till planting implement. Be sure to check with the manufacturer of the foam product and with your certifier to be certain the material you apply is certified for your organic operation and complies with the USDA federal standard.

Evaluation and monitoring

Whatever equipment you choose, be sure to routinely evaluate the planting operation. This is especially important as you begin organic no-till, but it will continue to be important even after you gain some experience. Field conditions change from field to field and from year to year.

PRE-PLANTING

- Check soil moisture and firmness
- Check to be sure the cover crop is at the right stage for rolling
- Check the germination of the seed you will be using (especially if you are using saved seed or old seed)

DURING PLANTING

- Check the location of the seed to be sure it's properly placed in the seed furrow
- Check seed placement, population, depth and coverage

AFTER SEED PLANTING

- Continue to monitor the field for insect predation or disease problems
- Check and note seedling emergence

If you pay attention to the details, adjust your equipment properly, and have reasonably good weather you should be well on your way to becoming a successful no-till farmer. In fact once you get the seed in the ground and placed where you want it to be, the system is very forgiving of weather variations since your work is done. No cultivating or routine weeding!

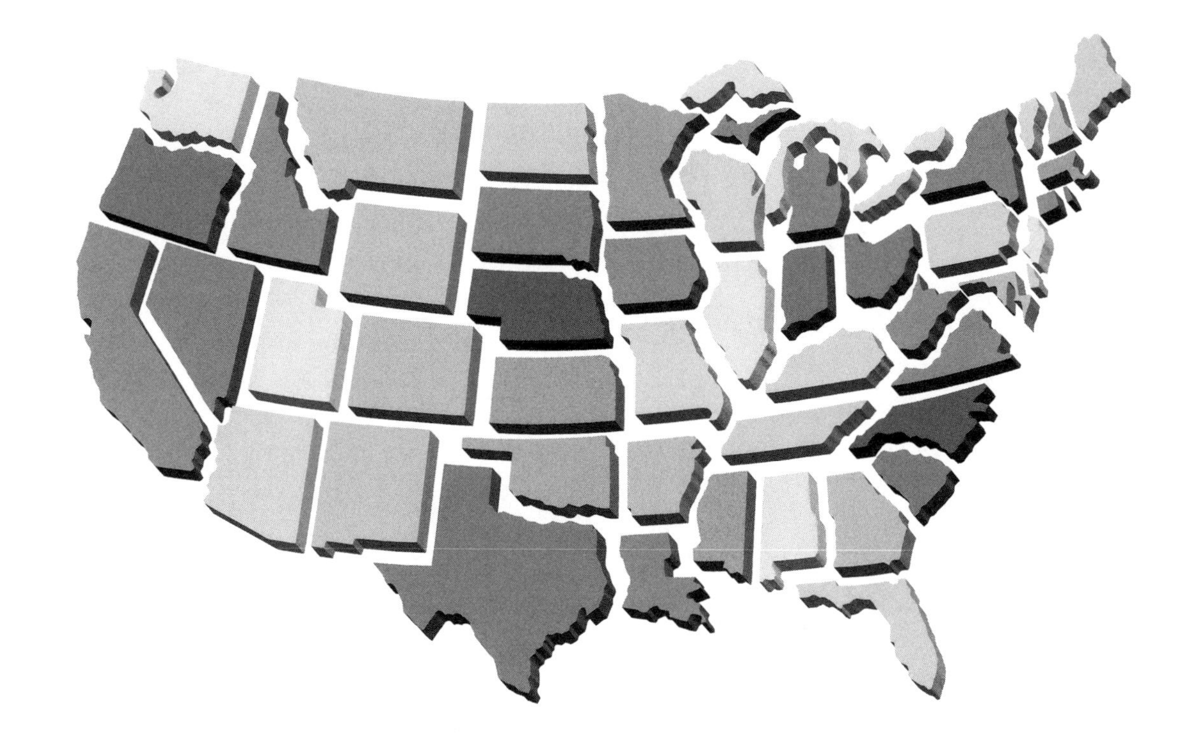

CHAPTER 06

MEET THE NO-TILL RESEARCH PARTNERS

▶ USING COVER CROPS & A ROLLER/CRIMPER

Much of the initial work represented in this book was funded by the United States Department of Agriculture's Natural Resources Conservation Service, (USDA-NRCS). We were fortunate that they recognized the tremendous impact that using cover crops can have on any no-till or conventionally tilled system. By adding cover crops into the rotation a whole new world opens up. A world of great possibilities; improved soil health; greater carbon sequestration; greater bio-diversity; reduced energy consumption – and the list goes on.

In 2005 Rodale Institute received a grant from the Natural Resources Conservation Service, (USDA-NRCS) to expand the use of no-till across the country using the roller/crimper and to allow farmers and researchers the opportunity to experience it first-hand. As part of this NRCS grant, eight different groups of farmers in various regions of the country received a roller/crimper and front mounted hitch for the tractor of their choice. Each farmer was paired with a research collaborator to help plan the project, collect data, and analyze results. The result was what we call the "No-Till Plus" project.

There's no substitute for on-farm research, which means learning, observing and tinkering with what needs to be adjusted. Rodale's direct interaction with the growers has enhanced their ability to adapt organic no-till to their unique situations. In fact I suggest that every one of you become a researcher as well. Whether it's this technology or some other, try it on your own farm in small test areas where you can use different cover crops, play with the timing of the operations, and gain hands-on experience with the tools.

In some cases during the project, the farmers and collaborators learned more about what doesn't work than what does work. Each farmer had to go through a trial and error period when they learned to adapt the machinery and techniques to their farm and their region. There were some challenges at the beginning of the project, such as when the shipments of front mounted hitches were delayed. This caused some farmers to roll/crimp and plant in two separate passes, while others delayed their planting until the hitches arrived. Some farmers used organic methods, while others used conventional herbicides, pesticides and chemical fertilizers as part of their management plan.

I hope that the information in this chapter concerning various uses of the roller/crimper technology will be helpful to conventional and organic farmers alike. As you read through this chapter you'll get a far better idea of the great diversity of approaches to similar problems which you'll likely encounter yourself – and the need to meet these challenges in creative ways.

For contact information on the farmers and collaborators, see appendix F No-Till Contacts at the end of this book.

Research from Across the Country

Now that you know a bit about the requirements for successful no-till, see if you can read through these experiments and find out why things happened as they did. It may help to look back at the points in chapters 1 and 2 as a review while you read through each section. We'll start our journey in Mississippi.

Mississippi

■ *Collaborator Seth Dabney, Ph.D. and farmer Perrin Grissom*

This area of the country has some unique considerations that are somewhat difficult to integrate with no-till. Dabney is based in the hills of Oxford, MS while Perrin Grissom farms in the delta area of northwest Mississippi with fine-textured soils that are silty clay to clay. The land is very flat and crops are often grown on hipped rows, which are similar to a raised bed. This is done primarily for drainage. The rows are 38-40 inches apart and raised, with a one-foot wide top where the crops are planted. Because this system doesn't lend itself well to rolling, the control for this trial was on hipped rows, while the experimental plots were on flat ground. Each section was 25 feet wide, consisting of eight rows. Because the roller was 15 feet wide, the sections had to be driven over twice with the roller/crimper and planted in a separate pass with a no-till planter. The land in standard hipped rows was planted in conventional no-till cotton.

2006 During the fall of 2005, researchers planted 'Paradana' balansa clover and 'Abruzzi' rye ahead of a cash crop of cotton. The weather was not particularly cooperative. Hurricane Rita came through the area on September 24 and left soils saturated. The cover crops were planted near the first of October after the soils had dried. No appreciable rain fell again until mid-November and the resulting cover crops (especially the balansa clover) were thin.

Because of problems with weeds in the balansa clover areas, the plots were sprayed with an herbicide in mid-April. In mid-May, the roller/crimper arrived and the cover crops were rolled down on May 15 in two passes. Cotton was planted the same day. Because the roller's front hitch was delayed, the rye had almost matured, using up almost all of the available water and temporarily tying up nitrogen.

The cotton did not establish well due to problems with the planter. The needed planter adjustments were not made to compensate for the depth of the mulch layer and the flat ground. Also, the rye area was considerably drier than the control.

The moderate stand of cover crops was not enough to shade out all of the weeds. Unfortunately, it also prevented the applied herbicides from reaching the soil surface, decreasing their effectiveness.

The areas cover cropped in rye did poorly, with sparse stands of cotton and small plants that grew slowly. Weed control was less than adequate. The yield was about 50 percent of the conventional no-till plots. The balansa clover plots did not have the same problems and yields were approximately comparable to the control areas.

2007 After the difficult 2006 season, Grissom and Dabney were looking forward to a better season for 2007. In the fall of 2006, a cover crop of balansa clover was planted and looked great through late December. Sometime over the winter, however, the plots were accidentally sprayed with herbicide, which made it impossible to conduct the rest of the experiment.

2008 The 2008 season experiments were conducted at Perrin Grissom's farm rather than at the Delta Demonstration Conservation Center in Metcalf, Mississippi. During the fall of 2007, Perrin Grissom planted his experimental plots with a cover crop of balansa clover with half of the plots also receiving rye. The cover crops were rolled and a crop of sunflowers was planted. Early in the season, the planting looked good. However, the farm received no rain and the sunflowers did not make a crop. Perrin is transitioning his farm into a bird sanctuary and will continue to experiment with the roller and cover crops. He hopes to develop a successful organic no-till system.

MISSISSIPPI SUMMARY Seth Dabney thinks that organic no-till farming will be very challenging in his area, citing problems with pests and diseases. He is particularly concerned with the plant diseases phytophthora and rhizoctonia and their impact when crops are seeded into green cover crops the same day they are rolled. Moving the cover crop residues away from the planting zone could solve some of the problems with these diseases. Waiting two weeks after rolling could also help matters, giving the cover crops a chance to die completely and mellow.

Dabney also has an interesting perspective on hairy vetch. Although this was not one of the cover crops trialed during the experiments, Dabney has had experience with vetch from other trials. The bloom date for vetch in Mississippi is in May, which means that it's too late to plant corn after this date if farmers wait for the plants to bloom. According to Dabney's research, the vetch can be killed when the vines are 3-4 feet long, after the leaves along the base of the stem have turned black and no longer have buds. After this point, the meristematic tissue is further along in the plant (at the growing tips) and the plant can be killed more easily when the stems are crimped.

North Dakota

■ *Collaborator Steve Zwinger and farmer Blaine Schmaltz*

2006 During 2005, rye was planted during the first week of October. Despite the late planting date, the rye established fairly well due to unseasonably warm fall weather. Two other cover crop treatments were planted in the spring of 2006, oats and barley. A control plot was left bare.

As the spring of 2006 progressed the winter rye did not perform well, due to very warm and dry weather. The conditions led to a reduction of plant tillers and a thinner stand. In fact, winter rye biomass was reduced by as much as 60 percent from previous years. Spring cover crops were sown May 10. The spring oats variety 'Ebeltoft' was sown at two bushels/acre, and 'Lacey' spring barley was sown at the rate of 2.25 bushels/acre. Soil moisture was below average, at about 50 percent of field capacity.

The rye, oats and barley were rolled on May 26 with the roller/crimper. Since the front mounted hitch was delayed and not available, Blaine Schmaltz rear mounted the implement and drove backwards through the field. There were some problems rolling the cover crops due to the low amounts of biomass. Estimated biomass yields were 2,000 pounds dry matter for the winter rye and less than 300 pounds dry matter for the oats and barley. Due to dry, hard soil conditions a number of trips were required to terminate the rye. The oats and barley terminated easily.

Using a rented John Deere no-till drill, the plots were sown to 'Maverick' pinto beans on June 5 at a rate of 90,000 pure live seeds/acre. Plant stands were best in the bare plots, and worst in the rye plots. The oats and barley plots had moderate establishment. The pinto beans grew very slowly due to drought conditions as well as record high temperatures. Precipitation for the area for April-July was only 40 percent of normal. The smaller than average plants did not compete well with the weeds. The rye plots had the lowest weed pressure, followed by the bare plots, while the oats and barley were the weediest sections.

A combination of drought and weed pressure left the pinto beans with essentially no yield. It was decided to abandon the trial on August 15.

2007 During 2007, Zwinger and Schmaltz experimented with a wide range of different cover crops, including fall-planted winter rye and triticale along with spring-planted barley and field peas. These were rolled on June 21 at varying stages of maturity. The weather was more cooperative, and they were able to get a good kill on the rye, which yielded 5,000 pounds/acre of biomass. The other cover crops had mixed results. The research results showed that the timing of the rolling was definitely a factor. The roller did not kill the triticale or barley because they were rolled too early – at early heading for the triticale and about 50 percent heading for the barley. The peas also did not die after being rolled even though they were rolled at various growth stages. Zwinger had chosen a semi-leafless variety that is upright in growth habit. After rolling, the peas sprung back up again. From what Zwinger has heard, he believes that he would have more luck with long vine/forage types, which have a growth habit similar to hairy vetch.

Several forage crops were sown directly into the rolled cover crops on the same date they were rolled. These included sorghum-sudangrass, sudangrass, pearl millet, German millet, Japanese millet, teff, a mix of forage milo and soybeans, forage oats, crimson clover, and berseem clover. Many of these did not establish well. Only four species established in the rye: sorghum-sudangrass, pearl millet, milo and sudangrass. The sorghum-sudangrass grew exceptionally well, and produced 6,000 lbs. of dry matter per acre by August 30. Of the different cover crops, rye gave excellent weed control that lasted all season and seems to have a lot of potential.

2008 During 2008 Zwinger and Schmaltz focused on rolling winter rye at two different biomass levels and rolling it at different times. They found that rye cover crops with high amounts of biomass were killed more effectively by the roller/crimper. Two plantings of rye produced different amounts of biomass – 7,290 lbs. dry matter/acre (at 63 inches tall) and 3,364 lbs. dry matter/acre (at 50 inches tall). The two timings were at early anthesis (two days after initiation) on June 19 and one week later on June 26. Generally when levels of biomass were high the rye terminated easily regardless of the timing, although it still appeared to kill better at early anthesis. The plantings with the lower levels of biomass were not killed at satisfactory amounts with either timing. The high levels of biomass again provided season-long cover and weed suppression. As a matter of fact, when a visiting organic inspector observed the rolled rye she thought an herbicide had been used to kill it.

NORTH DAKOTA SUMMARY There are a number of different challenges for farmers in North Dakota who would like to use the roller/crimper. A shorter growing season limits the options for seeding a cover crop and transitioning to a cash crop that will mature by frost. Buckwheat, dry beans and annual forages are the best choices for this short window. Because this area gets a lower annual precipitation rate (about 17-19 inches annually), farmers may have difficulty in establishing a cover crop that produces enough biomass, and then growing a cash crop during the remainder of the season. Aside from these issues, Zwinger and Schmaltz found that the roller/crimper was a good tool for killing cover crops. The technique makes sense from the standpoint of fuel savings, time savings, and moisture and soil conservation.

"The roller/crimper is an excellent tool – I think we're going to learn how to use it in different ways," said Zwinger. For example, he hopes to be able to experiment with using rolled sorghum-sudangrass as a winter cover to protect fall-seeded winter grains such as wheat. The sorghum would provide insulation against harsh winter temperatures and retain snow that would also provide protection as well as moisture. Although there is plenty of snow in North Dakota during the winter, snow cover is not dependable due to the constant scouring winds.

Zwinger also points out the need for earlier maturing cover crops, such as rye. Rye varieties bred to mature even a week earlier would make a big difference.

Future work

Zwinger is participating in an ongoing study with other researchers in Minnesota, Iowa, Wisconsin and at the Rodale Institute in Pennsylvania. The planned research will include plantings of vetch or rye, following a cash crop of wheat. Half of the replicated plots will be disked (as a control), and half will be rolled (for a no-till planting). Cash crops of sweet corn, dry beans (western locations) and soybeans (eastern locations) will be planted into the residue. Over the winter, the plots will be left fallow. During the spring a cash crop of oats will be planted with a no-till planter, and then the rotation will begin again with vetch and rye cover crops planted that fall. The trial rotation is designed to make the most of the Upper Midwest's short growing season.

Pennsylvania

■ *Collaborator Dave Wilson and farmers Kirby Reichert and Bill Mason*

RODALE INSTITUTE 2006 On September 8, 2005 replicated plots were planted to five different varieties of hairy vetch at the Rodale Institute. (For more details about how these vetch varieties performed, see chapter 7 on cover cropping.) When planting hairy vetch in the northeast, cultivar selection and timing is critical for the best winter survivability. The recommended planting date is at least 40 days (but preferably 50 or 60 days) before the first killing frost. Winter survivability is best when the plant has sufficient energy reserves to make it through the winter. The first killing frost was November 19.

Biomass cuts were taken in April and on June 9, immediately before rolling. The average dry matter weight was 6,146 lbs./acre. Vetch was in full bloom when it was killed with a front mounted roller/crimper and corn (Blue River Hybrids 68F32, Relative Maturity 113) was planted with a no-till planter mounted behind the tractor. The planter was a Monosem air seeder on a Kinze toolbar with a heavy residue coulter, double disk openers and cast iron closing wheels. To get an adequate planting depth of 1.5-2 inches into the soil, 130 pounds of weight was added per planting unit to aid the coulters in cutting through the thick rolled down hairy vetch mat.

Although the vetch was ready for rolling by May 19, Wilson chose to delay the rolling and planting until cutworms had matured and developed into moths. The mulch layer provides habitat for the worms, but delaying the planting takes care of much of the problem.

2006 was a wet year, with a total of 26.54 inches of rainfall. This was 10.44 inches over the 30-year average rainfall amount. The rolled mat of vetch provided good weed control for the corn early in the season when weed control is most important. Competitive in-row weed numbers were very low, from a combination of the mulch and the subsequent canopy of corn leaves. Eventually weeds do break through the mulch layer, but since these germinate later they are not as competitive with the corn crop. They also tend to be between-row weeds, which are less competitive with the crop.

Corn was harvested November 21 with the average yield for all the plots being 146 bu./acre. By comparison, the countywide average was 130 bu./acre and the average for southeastern Pennsylvania was 147 bu./acre. The success of the season was attributable to several factors: rolling vetch at full bloom, planter modifications, hairy vetch variety selection, and early establishment of hairy vetch.

2007 Several different trials were done during the 2007 season. A trial at the Rodale Institute research farm focused on determining the correlation between the date of rolling hairy vetch and the effectiveness of the roller/crimper to kill the cover crop. On several different dates in the spring, researchers took biomass samples from rolled test plots. Wilson kept track of the nitrogen content and the yields from the subsequent corn crop. Additionally, several different kinds of vetch were evaluated for winter hardiness. For the 2007 trial Wilson used a shorter season corn, Blue River Hybrids 40M21 (Relative Maturity 95). He decided that because of the late rolling and planting dates, a shorter season corn would perform better under these conditions.

Hairy vetch was rolled on May 30, June 7, June 14 and June 21. On the first two dates, when vetch was at 55 percent and 65 percent bloom, the roller/crimper did not effectively kill the vetch and there was considerable cover crop re-growth along with significant weed growth in these plots due to insufficient matting of the vetch. The later two rolling dates effectively killed the vetch and there was little re-growth. The research showed that the vetch should be in full bloom before rolling. This ensures that the roller will adequately kill the vetch, that there will be sufficient biomass to suppress weeds, and that there will be enough nitrogen to supply the corn's growing needs.

With the cash crop corn, the total weed biomass was much lower for the two later planting dates. Corn populations were also higher due to fewer problems with cutworm damage. As you might expect, the yields from the last two planting dates were over twice as much as the ones from earlier in the year.

BILL MASON FARM Bill Mason is an experienced no-till farmer who was 100 percent no-till before converting to organic. He grows corn, soybeans and barley, which he sells locally to Horizon Dairy. 2008 was his fourth year of farming organically. Currently he has 400 certified organic acres, with another 150 in transition to organic.

2006 In 2006, Mason did an informal trial with rye he had planted in the fall of 2005. He rolled the cover crop with a 15-foot roller he purchased from I & J Manufacturing, then planted 120 acres of soybeans into the rolled cover crop. The weed control was excellent and the soybeans yielded 55 bu./acre.

2007 During 2007, Mason grew four different treatments of crimson clover and wheat, then rolled and planted to corn. The main challenge in this research was in adjusting the planter appropriately so that it cut through the mat of rolled vegetation, and achieved good seed-to-soil contact. The planter's springs (which provide down pressure) were not functioning and Mason did not discover the problem immediately. This affected about 25 percent of the research plot.

In all of the treatments, corn stands were not adequate for good yields.

2008 For the 2008 season, Mason planted triticale and three different kinds of rye in the fall of 2007. These were rolled down in the spring and planted to soybeans. The beans did well, despite a later than desired planting date of June 1, and yielded 45 bu./acre. The corn planted for the season did not do as well, however. Cover crops of crimson clover, and barley and Austrian winter peas were rolled down and corn was planted into the plots. Mason upped the seeding rate to a 35,000 planting population, and set the planter as deep as possible. In the plots containing crimson clover, the corn did especially poorly, yielding 20 bu./acre and dying prematurely. In the plot with Austrian winter peas, the yield was better, with 60 or so bushels per acre. By contrast, the control plot yielded 130 bu./acre.

Mason reflects that the no-till beans have done much better in the trials on his farm. Although they have a few more weeds than he's used to, the beans seem to consistently produce approximately 45 bu./acre. The corn, however, has presented more of a challenge, and Mason has decided to keep tilling for now. He emphasized that the cover crop is as important as the cash crop. Most of his farm is irrigated, and he likes having water available for the cover crop. He is pleased with the performance of the roller/crimper, and hasn't had any problems killing cover crops.

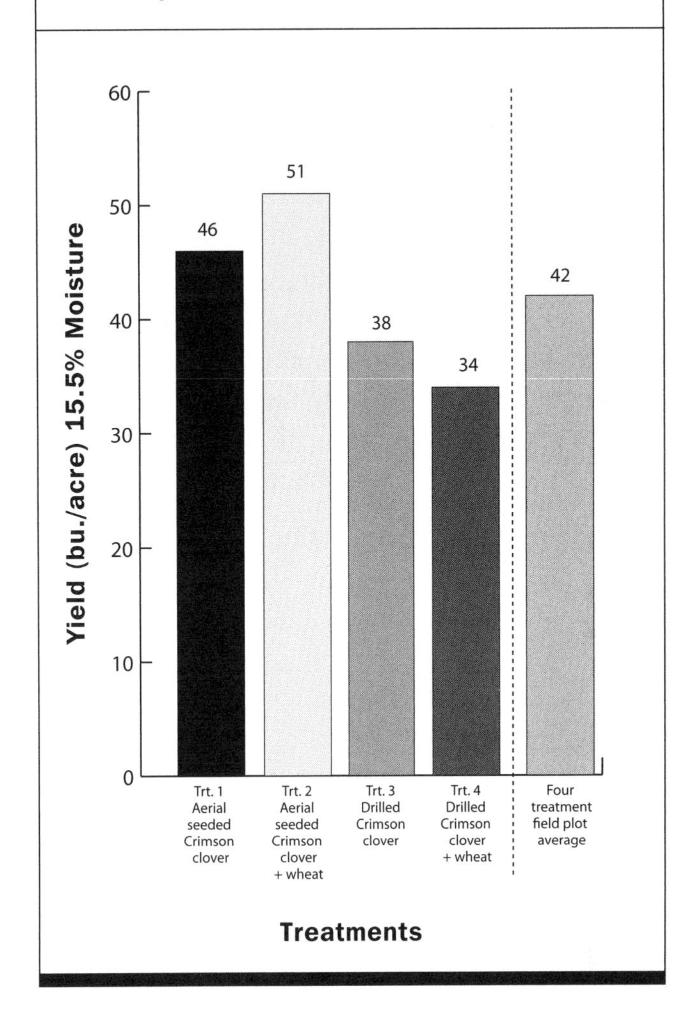

KIRBY REICHERT FARM Reichert farms about 750 acres, 300 acres organic and around 450 acres conventionally. The experiments had a number of difficulties during the first two years.

2006 In 2006, Reichert's older planter did not work very well, and the plots did not get proper seed placement. He later modified the planter by adding row cleaners to move the mulch away from the cutting edge of the planter. He also added heavier press wheels that would close in from each side, rather than over the top of the row.

2007 In 2007, trials were resumed but the area experienced a severe drought. "The ground was so hard we couldn't get the seed in the soil," commented Reichert. Continued dry conditions in the spring led to thin stands of cover crops with limited biomass. The cover crops planted were a mix of hairy vetch and crimson clover for a corn planting, and small grains for soybean cash crop. A few of the legume plots were adequate for rolling, but since these were scattered through the field it made more sense to till the plots under and plant the field for clean tillage.

2008 During 2008, the results were quite a bit better. The previous year, the plots were prepared with a cover crop of sorghum-sudangrass.

Several cuttings were taken during the summer. Afterwards, different plots were planted of either a mix of field peas and clover or hairy vetch. The following spring, the cover crops were rolled, and seven different kinds of high-moisture corn were planted. The weather was more cooperative and the area received plenty of rain. Weed control was excellent in the corn plots that followed the cover crop of peas and clover; red root pigweed was present but did not seem to affect yields.

Reichert said that the roller/crimper seemed to work well, although the ground needs to be quite smooth for the best level of control. Although he anticipated difficulties with rocky ground, it was not a significant problem. Overall, Reichert is pleased with the tool's performance.

PENNSYLVANIA STATE UNIVERSITY *(Advisor Bill Curran, Ph.D.)* Bill Curran started out as an adviser on the "No-Till Plus" project, but now does more research than advising. He first became interested in the technology as a result of a Rodale Institute field day in 2004. In 2005, Penn State built their own roller/crimper and started trials.

2005 The first set of trials, run by graduate student Steven Mirsky during 2005 and 2006, involved planting date and termination dates for cereal rye grown as a cover crop. The experiments involved measurements for biomass production for different planting dates, and an evaluation of kill rates for different termination dates. The research found that the roller/crimper could effectively kill rye either with or without the use of herbicides. They also determined that the optimal growth stage for rolling was early flowering (anthesis) or 61 on the Zadok's cereal development scale. Although this is a more conservative approach than rolling at an earlier time, it did yield effective and consistent results.

2006 Another trial in 2006 concentrated on winter rape. Rolling rape at the early or mid-flowering stages of growth was not effective. The stems tended to break. Subsequently the rape re-grew from the roots. A full rate of glyphosate (0.75 pounds/acre) was necessary to achieve greater than 85 percent control.

2007 In 2007 and 2008, another graduate student, Ruth Nick, coordinated a trial for hairy vetch at three different study sites – one at Rodale Institute and another two at different Penn State research farms in Lancaster County and at State College. They found that killing vetch was much less predictable than rye. Rolling alone provided about 75 percent control of the hairy vetch. A treatment of 2,4-D low-volatile ester (LVE) increased control to over 90 percent. Cereal rye has a determinate growth pattern, and the maturity is based both on heat units and day length. It's fairly easy to predict when rye will mature, but it's more difficult to predict the growth of vetch. Its maturity is much more likely to be influenced by environmental factors like soil moisture. Rye typically matures about three weeks earlier than hairy vetch, which makes it difficult to effectively kill a combination of the two. In addition, unlike cereal grains, for which scientists have developed an index of different growth stages, no scale has been developed for hairy vetch. Graduate student Ruth Nick has been working on developing such a scale for the purpose of pinpointing the best time to roll vetch.

Michigan

■ *Collaborator Dale Mutch, Ph.D. and farmers Matt Wiley, Erwin Felton and Matt Chalmers*

Dale Mutch is an extension specialist for cover crops and IPM at Michigan State University. Currently he manages eight acres of experimental plots. He has been experimenting with organic no-till since 2004. A write up of research results for 2004-2007 is available in the appendix at the end of this book or at *www.covercrops.msu.edu*. Over all, results have been variable, but Mutch is encouraged by his research findings.

2004 This was the first year that the experiment station worked with the roller/crimper, and everything worked very well. Rye and vetch were planted in separate plots, and rolled at flowering on June 4. Dark hilum feed-grade soybeans were drilled into the plots in a separate pass, and no supplemental weed control was used. From an October 7 harvest date, soybean yields of 58 bu./acre (hairy vetch) and 62 bu./acre (rye) were harvested. This was much better than the surrounding area, which yielded 40 bu./acre. Mutch is not sure how to explain the excellent results from the first year, since they have not had a comparable season since then.

2005 The results from this season were not nearly as favorable. Several treatments of rye and vetch and cover crop mixtures were planted August 25, 2004, but did not grow well due to a drought. The rye and vetch were short and the stand was thin. When Mutch tried to roll the cover crops early (May 23), in an effort to conserve moisture and get the soybeans planted sooner, the cover crops stood back up and continued to grow. That was an experiment that Mutch won't repeat. The highest yields came from the rye only treatment at an average of 20.3 bu./acre. A six-week drought was one of the reasons for the low yield.

2006 Several treatments of rye and vetch were planted August 24, 2005. On June 5, 2006, they were rolled and planted to food-grade soybeans. Due to a heavier than normal mulch layer, planting this year was difficult, with poor seed-to-soil contact. For this reason, about 2/3 of the soybeans were replanted, although the replanted plots did not yield much better than the ones that were not replanted. Rye plots had the highest yield, while vetch plots had the most weed pressure. Overall, this was a good year with adequate yields.

2007 Trials involved several plantings of rye (eight plots of 'Wheeler' rye and two of 'Hancock'). After a late planting (November 6) the cover crops germinated well and continued to grow through the fall. During spring the cover crops grew well, but the rest of the summer was a record drought. Since drought conditions set in before the soybeans could canopy, weeds began to dominate later in the season. Yields were very low. Interestingly, the traditionally cultivated organic treatments did considerably better.

MICHIGAN SUMMARY Mutch has learned a considerable amount during these four years. One thing he stressed was the importance of growing a thick, healthy stand of cover crops. He recommends fertilizing with chicken manure as a source of nitrogen.

"When you roll the rye, you can actually hear it cracking and popping. That's a good sign," he said. Putting a priority on the cover crop is a necessary adjustment to the traditional way of thinking, which puts more emphasis on the cash crop.

Rye has turned out to be a much better match for soybeans than vetch. The vetch seems to stimulate small-seeded broadleaf weeds like pigweed and lamb's quarters. The research farm uses a 2.5 bu./acre seeding rate. They have had the best luck with 'Wheeler' rye, a tall variety that does well in Michigan. It is also strongly allelopathic, which makes weed control easier.

A good no-till drill is also important. It must be able to get through the mulch and provide good seed-to-soil contact. Good coulters are important, and a redesign was necessary for their planter. Mutch mentioned that a good no-till drill would actually help to kill the cover crop.

For Mutch the roller/crimper works well and despite mixed results he is encouraged enough to continue field trials. He says that the system has great potential because it saves so much time over other methods. But he warns that rocky ground may cause problems. According to Mutch, you need a flat field with no large rocks or bumps; otherwise the roller/crimper can't do its job effectively. A final tip for new growers is to experiment on a small scale. "Don't do the whole farm," he said.

FUTURE WORK The roller/crimper system has a number of different applications that have not been fully explored yet. For example, Mutch has been working with farmers who have rolled and crimped rye and then planted blueberries into the mulch. The farmers till a 15-18 inch zone to plant the blueberries, and then leave the rest of the mulch undisturbed to provide weed control for the row middle. This year he'll be working with another farmer who is planting pumpkins. The farmer plans to plant a crop of pumpkins into a rye cover crop.

Georgia

■ *Collaborator Juan Carlos Diaz-Perez, Ph.D., assisting collaborators Frederick Reed and Sharad Phatak, with farmer Mark Vickers*

Georgia has a strong tradition of conservation tillage. The state is first in the nation with 40 percent of crop acres farmed no-till. The major no-till area of Georgia is located in the lower coastal plains, which has sandy loam soil. Overall, extremely dry conditions during the two-year trials have made it difficult to grow good stands of cover crops. Georgia had not received the usual winter rains, and the winters of 2005-2006 and 2006-2007 were very similar. As a result, the cover crops did not yield an adequate biomass.

Farmer Mark Vickers is quite experienced and has farmed no-till since 1991. Vickers has been experimenting with a rolling system of his own, using a 4-inch galvanized pipe suspended approximately 2 inches above the ground under the bell of the tractor. This effectively knocks down the cover crop, but Vickers relies on herbicides to actually kill the plants. Since he has been using this method for at least five years, he is very familiar with planting into heavy residues.

2006 In the test plot area as well as in the control area, rye ('Wrens Abruzzi') was planted at a rate of 1 bushel/acre during December. The rye had matured enough for rolling by May 19. The control plot was rolled down using the grower's standard practice, and the test plot was rolled using the roller/crimper. Because of dry winter conditions, the cover crop did not produce substantial biomass, estimated at 1200-1500 lbs. of dry matter per acre.

The cash crop of peanuts was planted on May 20 as soil moisture was becoming limited. In the roll-crimped plot, no pre-plant insecticide or herbicide was used at the time of planting, but Vickers used an herbicide spray of Storm with Select to control weeds such as morning glory, pigweed and grasses. In the control plot, Strongarm, Valor and Thimet pesticides were used at planting, and burndown was done on June 18 with Storm and 2,4-D. Both plots received applications of chlorothalonil, boron and Karate for velvetbean caterpillar control.

Drought was a serious problem during the 2006 growing season and affected yields considerably. The fields received 5.8 inches of rainfall and were irrigated eight times at 1 inch per application. However, the test plots received uneven watering, due to their location at the end of the irrigation pivot, as well as from high winds that caused irrigation water to fall unevenly.

The yields for the test plot were 3,003 lbs. per acre, while the yields for the standard plot were 4,311 lbs. per acre. Some of the differences in yield can be attributed to differences in production methods, since the test plots received no applications of Prowl, Valor or Thimet, as well as uneven watering. Weed control and early insect control were similar in the test and standard plots.

2007 Both plots, the conventional no-till and the experimental plot, were planted with 'Wrens Abruzzi' rye on December 6, 2006 at the rate of 2 bushels/acre. Due to a dry winter and spring, the biomass was sparse.

Luckily, the farm received 3 inches of rain on June 5, and rolling and planting were done as the soil dried out, on June 9-11. The conventional plot was rolled down using the farmer's traditional method described above. He also planted peanuts with a no-till planter and applied pesticides at the same time. The experimental plot was rolled down using the roller/crimper and in a separate pass Vickers planted peanuts. While the peanut seed for the conventional plot was treated with an inoculant, the experimental plot received no treatment.

During the first three weeks of July, the area received 2.7 inches of rain. From the end of July through September 1 there were numerous record-breaking temperatures and very dry conditions. During the season, the fields received a total of 10 inches of rainfall. The conventional and rolled down plots were treated differently in the trial. The conventional plots were irrigated seven times at one inch per irrigation, while the rolled down no-till received one inch of irrigation at the end of July.

The plots also received different kinds of inputs. In both the conventional and rolled down plots, the cover crops were burned down with herbicides. In the conventional plots, herbicides were used to control weeds for the rest of the season. By contrast, the rolled down plots were not treated with herbicides after burndown. Mowing twice controlled the weeds. In the conventional plots, several insecticides were used to control pests.

These differences meant that the input costs for the plots were quite different. As you'd expect, it made a difference in the bottom line for the farm. The yield difference for the plots was substantial – the conventional plots yielded 4,260 lbs./acre, while the rolled down plots yielded 3,260 lbs./acre. On the other hand, the costs for the conventional plots, including materials and labor, totaled around $465 per acre, while the cost for the rolled down plots were approximately $253 per acre. This meant that the net income for the rolled down plots was $315 per acre, while the net for the conventional plots was only $278 per acre. Although this research seems to be more about the costs of inputs than anything else, it does give a clear indication that a lower-input system, such as organic no-till, can be cost effective.

GEORGIA SUMMARY "Our biggest challenge is always weed control. Weeds, weeds and weeds," said Sharad Phatak of the University of Georgia. Rick Reed agrees with this statement. "You need to have your weed seed bank under control before you transition or you aren't going to be able to make it," Rick Reed said. Although they have worked with growers who produced cover crops with tremendous amounts of biomass, it didn't seem to stop the weeds completely. The mulch layer doesn't break down significantly during the long growing season required for crops like peanuts and cotton, but there are still more weeds present than some growers would like.

Like Dale Mutch, the researchers from the University of Georgia stressed the importance of adjusting your fertility and pH. A surface application of fertilizer may be necessary. The correct kind of equipment for planting and rolling is also a must. Small-scale growers may find it difficult to make the needed investments.

Phatak, who has done extensive work with beneficial insects, says that including habitat for beneficials should definitely be part of your farm plan. There are many different ways to include habitat for beneficials, including planting a border row along your fenceline. Crimson clover is one crop that Phatak recommends, since it creates a lot of diversity. It reseeds itself from year to year and makes a good cover crop for corn and tomatoes.

FUTURE WORK For the future, the researchers plan to work on weed control, as well as summer cover crops. Among those with good potential are sorghum-sudangrass, velvet beans and sunn hemp. Unfortunately, sorghum-sudangrass is the only cover crop for which there is a ready source of seeds. It is considerably more difficult to source seed for velvet beans and sunn hemp. (See appendix B in the back of the book for cover crop sources.)

Iowa

■ *Collaborator Kathleen Delate, Ph.D. and farmer Ron Rosmann*

2006 Trials were conducted at the Rosmann Family Farm in Westphalia, Iowa and at the Neely-Kinyon Research and Demonstration Farm in Greenfield, Iowa.

Two treatments were planted – a mix of winter wheat and peas, and a mix of winter rye and hairy vetch. The treatments were planted on September 12, 2005 at the research farm and on September 19 at the Rosmann Family Farm. Seeding rates at the Neely-Kinyon Farm were 75 lbs./acre for the wheat and pea mix, and 96 lbs./acre of rye and vetch mix (64 lbs./acre rye and 32 lbs./acre vetch). At the Rosmann farm, the seeding rates were higher with a similar composition: 94 lbs./acre for the wheat/pea mix and 100 lbs./acre for the rye/vetch mix (60 lbs./acre rye and 40 lbs./acre vetch). Both sites had a good stand of cover crops.

Rolling and drilling took place on May 29 at the Neely-Kinyon Farm and June 2-3 on the Rosmann Family Farm. The rolling was conducted at the dough stage (headed out but not fully developed). The roller/crimper appeared to work well, but the cover crops did not fully die and partially came back up. A lack of rain during June and July meant that the cover crop continued to grow, but the corn and soybeans did not.

In another set of plots, 'Roma' tomatoes were planted on June 15. Because of dry conditions, irrigation was purchased and the plants were irrigated when necessary.

The roller/crimper did a poor job of killing the cover crop, but there were few weeds after planting. Although the farmer did some hand weeding, this was primarily for cosmetic reasons. Yields were variable, with excellent results for tomatoes (400,000 fruit per acre); corn and beans were poor (90 bu./acre and 15 bu./acre, respectively). Low rainfall contributed to poor yields, but competition from cover crops was also a problem.

2007 Research continued at the Neely-Kinyon Research and Demonstration Farm. On October 31, 2006, cover crops were planted for the following crop year. The three treatments were a) control (no cover crops, followed regular cultivation for weed control), b) combination of winter wheat and Austrian winter peas, and c) combination of rye and hairy vetch. Germination of the cover crops was excellent.

Cover crops were rolled on May 23, 2007, when the small grains reached anthesis. Corn and soybeans were planted at the same time. A similar planting was done in the control plots. Unfortunately, the cover crops were not completely killed by the roller/crimper, so they were mowed on May 31.

'Roma' tomatoes transplants (seeded April 23) were transplanted into each treatment on June 27. Measurements of plant height, weed populations, number of leaves and flowers were taken for each plot at intervals during the summer.

The different crops that were trialed had quite different results. June and July had low rainfall conditions, which impacted the corn and soybeans. Corn, especially, was severely affected by the drought. The cover crop continued to grow and provided competition for the crop plants. The tomatoes were irrigated so the dry weather did not affect them.

The cover crop treatments provided different levels of weed control. The rye/hairy vetch treatment decomposed more slowly and provided better management of early season broadleaf weeds. Grass weeds were lowest in the hairy vetch/rye plots at the end of the season.

Tomatoes yielded well and were of high quality in all of the plots. The highest number of top-grade tomatoes came from the vetch/rye treatment. Soybean yields in the cover cropped areas were successful and averaged 45 bu./acre. Soybean grain quality was excellent, with an average of 34 percent protein. However, the corn plantings were not a success story. The corn in the no-till treatments suffered from the dry weather, and

▶ TOMATO PLANT DATA IN COVER CROP TREATMENT TRIAL
(Neely-Kinyon Research & Demonstration Farm, 2007)

Treatment	Plant height (cm)				Leaves (number/plant)			Flowers (number/plant)		Fruit (number/plant)
	JUNE 24-26	JULY 3	JULY 17	AUG 1	JUNE 24-26	JULY 3	JULY 17	JULY 3	JULY 17	JULY 17
No Cover	29.8b[z]	38.1b	55.9	76.4	8.3	13.3	37.1	0.17	18.3	1.8b
Rye & Hairy Vetch Cover	34.9a	45.3a	57.3	74.3	8.7	12.3	40.1	0.08	19.9	3.0ab
Wheat & Winter Pea Cover	35.6a	46.0a	58.0	72.1	9.3	12.9	39.6	0.29	22.4	5.5a
LSD[x] 0.05	2.8	4.1	NS	NS	NS	NS	NS	NS	NS	2.6

[z] Means followed by the same letter down the column are not significantly different at $P \leq 0.05$.

[X] Fisher's protected LSD (Least Signigicant Difference) test

▶ TOMATO WEED POPULATIONS IN COVER CROP TREATMENT TRIAL
(Neely-Kinyon Research & Demonstration Farm, 2007)

Treatment	Weed Populations (weeds/m²)									
	JUNE 20		JULY 3		JULY 17		AUG. 1		AUG. 13	
	Broadleaves	Grasses	Broadleaves	Grasses	Broadleaves	Grasses	Broadleaves	Grasses	Broadleaves	Grasses
No Cover	8.3a[z]	0.17	140.3	6.8	73.5	2.3	37.8	4.5	16.0	4.5a
Rye & Hairy Vetch Cover	1.9b	0.00	44.8	6.5	29.0	4.5	54.0	6.5	7.3	1.0b
Wheat & Winter Pea Cover	11.4a	0.17	69.0	13.5	44.3	2.8	59.3	8.0	11.5	3.3a
LSD[x] 0.05	6.3	NS	NS	NS	NS	NS	NS	NS	NS	1.3

[z] Means followed by the same letter down the column are not significantly different at $P \leq 0.05$.

[X] Fisher's protected LSD (Least Signigicant Difference) test

▶ YIELD & TOMATO QUALITY IN COVER CROP TREATMENT TRIAL
(Neely-Kinyon Research & Demonstration Farm, 2007)

Treatment	Yield (fruit/acre)	Tomato quality (%) No. 1	No. 2	No. 3
No Cover	645,269[z]	83.4b	6.8ab	9.8
Rye & Hairy Vetch Cover	583,123	90.8a	5.0b	4.2
Wheat & Winter Pea Cover	547,114	85.5b	7.4a	7.1
LSD[x] 0.05	NS	5.3	2.0	NS

[z] *Means followed by the same letter down the column are not significantly different at $P \leq 0.05$.*

[X] *Fisher's protected LSD (Least Signigicant Difference) test*

▶ SOYBEAN & CORN PARAMETERS IN COVER CROP TREATMENT TRIAL
(Neely-Kinyon Research & Demonstration Farm, 2007)

Crop	Treatment	Weed Populations (weeds/m²) June 7 Broadleaves	June 7 Grasses	June 21 Broadleaves	June 21 Grasses	Yield (bu./acre)	Corn borer evidence (%)	Corn borer presence (%)
Soybean	No Cover	2.75b[z]	2.17	0.25b	0.25	50.45a	N/A	N/A
	Rye & Hairy Vetch Cover	2.08b	2.83	2.08b	0.08	43.41b	N/A	N/A
	Wheat & Winter Pea Cover	6.50a	2.25	7.33a	0.33	45.55b	N/A	N/A
	LSD[x] 0.05	2.71	NS	2.18	NS	4.61	N/A	N/A
Corn	No Cover	2.17b	1.33b	1.00b	0.08b	123.87	8.3	0.0
	Rye & Hairy Vetch Cover	10.17ab	0.67b	6.83b	0.33b	10.00[y]	8.3	0.0
	Wheat & Winter Pea Cover	18.00a	13.33a	21.92a	12.42a	10.15	16.7	0.0
	LSD[x] 0.05	11.29	4.17	7.38	5.40	N/A	NS	NS

[z] *Means followed by the same letter down the column are not significantly different at $P \leq 0.05$.*

[y] *Yield estimate due to lack of harvestable ears*

[X] *Fisher's protected LSD (Least Signigicant Difference) test*

▶ **SOYBEAN GRAIN QUALITY IN COVER CROP TREATMENT TRIAL**
(Neely-Kinyon Research & Demonstration Farm, 2007)

			Grain Quality (%)		
		Moisture	Protein	Oil	Starch
Soybean	No Cover	11.79c[z]	34.38	18.74a	24.39
	Rye & Hairy Vetch Cover	12.20b	35.22	18.11b	24.16
	Wheat & Winter Pea Cover	14.61a	34.43	18.70a	24.37
	LSD[x] 0.05	0.16	NS	0.44	NS

[z] *Means followed by the same letter down the column are not significantly different at* $P \leq 0.05$.

[x] *Fisher's protected LSD (Least Signigicant Difference) test*

growth was depressed as the season progressed. Weeds were five to nine times higher than in the tilled treatment. Yields were very low, with 10 bu./acre in some of the no-till plots, versus 124 bushels in the tilled treatment.

The results from the soil analysis were also inconsistent. In the soybeans, the highest total nitrogen, carbon and organic matter were in the pea/wheat treatment. On the other hand, in the corn plots, the opposite was true. Total soil nitrogen, carbon and organic matter were higher in the tilled plots.

2008 From 2007 through 2008, a no-till organic soybean demonstration was established at John Lubke's farm in Ridgeway, Iowa. A cover crop of hairy vetch and rye was planted at 96 lb./acre on October 15, 2007, and rolled the following spring on June 25, 2008.

Soybeans were planted on the same day but not as a one-pass operation. The cover crop stand had appeared adequate the previous fall, but several gaps were observed at the time of rolling, suggesting either inadequate overwintering or poor germination. Due to a low level of mulch from the cover crop, there was excessive weed growth in both the non-planted areas and in between the soybean rows. This led to significant weed development and competition with the soybean seedlings. Poor weather (floods in early June and dry weather in July and August) led to minimal growth from the soybeans. Soybeans did not grow more than 1.5 feet in the no-till field compared to 2.5 feet in the neighboring tilled organic soybean field.

Because of the potential for a less than 10 bu./acre soybean crop, the no-till field was baled on September 20, in order to salvage some value from the plot. The bales contained soybean leaves and pods, which were fed to on-farm livestock.

Currently, a full no-till organic experiment is underway in concert with The Rodale Institute, the Universities of Wisconsin and Minnesota, Michigan State University, and North Dakota State University. The cover crops were planted on September 8, 2008, and germinated and grew well that fall.

Virginia

■ *Collaborator Ron Morse, Ph.D. and Farmer Paul Davis*

Professor Ron Morse of Virginia Tech has a long history of pioneering work with no-till for vegetable farmers. He has been working with no-till for 40 years. At the experimental station there are 15 acres of research plots, including 10 acres devoted to organic production. See chapter 5 for more information about the Ron Morse subsurface tiller-transplanter for vegetables.

▶ PAUL DAVIS FARM: COVER CROP BIOMASS (TONS PER ACRE)
(Late April, 2006)

Cover Crop Planted	Early Seeding (September 30)	Mid Seeding (October 20)	Late Seeding (November 10)
Crimson Clover	1.46	1.63	N/A
Barley	2.08	1.35	1.23
Oats	2.09	1.45	1.85
Rye	4.21	3.59	1.34
Hairy Vetch	2.84	2.04	1.64
Rye & Hairy Vetch	3.31	3.70	2.42
Average	**2.67 tons/acre**	**2.29 tons/acre**	**1.70 tons/acre**

Trials were conducted at the Paul Davis farm in Providence Forge (near Williamsburg) and the Virginia Tech Kentland Ag Research Farm near Blacksburg. Paul Davis is both a farmer and Extension Agent. In his region, which is close to the Chesapeake Bay, about 95 percent of farmers are using no-till systems. They've managed to reduce runoff by 76 percent, an important issue for their area that drains into the bay.

2006 A number of cover crops were seeded into plots on three separate planting dates in the fall of 2005. For most of the cover crops, the optimum planting date was from the earliest seeding, on September 30.

The cash crops planted were soybeans and pumpkins. On May 6, the soybeans were planted and the cover crops were rolled in one pass. The percentage kill rate varied considerably: barley (80 percent), rye (70 percent), oats (40 percent) and hairy vetch (20 percent). Vetch was rolled at early bloom and grains were rolled at the soft dough stage.

For the pumpkins, the cover crops were rolled on May 7, but the pumpkins were not planted until June 19, which is the traditional date for this area so that pumpkins are ready for Halloween sales. As a result, weed competition was high.

For both cash crops, weed pressure was moderate to high. The best weed suppression occurred in the plots with the rye and hairy vetch. Suppression was also highly correlated with cover crop biomass. The roller/crimper functioned much better with the thicker and taller cover crops.

2007 Cover crops were planted in the early fall of 2006 and grew well, due to abundant rainfall. By the following spring they had generated considerable biomass. Rye and rye/legume mixtures produced the highest biomass, ranging from 3.5-4.5 tons dry weight per acre.

At the Paul Davis farm, full season soybeans were seeded into six different cover crops: rye, barley, oats, crimson clover, hairy vetch and a rye/hairy vetch biculture. On May 8, seeding and rolling was accomplished in one pass, using a front mounted roller/crimper and a rear mounted seed drill. Paul Davis noted that the soil was in better condition and earthworms were more prevalent.

At the research farm, three different cover crop treatments were grown: rye, rye/hairy vetch and rye/Austrian winter peas. All cover crops were rolled on June 5 and seeded in a separate pass on June 12 with pumpkin 'Magic Lantern'.

Plots were evaluated for effectiveness of kill with roller/crimpers and weed suppression. Percentage kill was best in rye and rye/Austrian winter peas, averaging greater than 90 percent. In general, the cereal crop monoculture and cereal/legume bicultures killed more effectively than the legume monoculture. Although weed control was good in the rye and rye/pea mix, the other plots had moderate to high re-growth of the cover crops as well as weed pressure. An application of herbicides was required to achieve a complete kill in all plots.

VIRGINIA SUMMARY The roller/crimper appears to function well, but the thicker and taller the cover crops, the better percentage kill, and weed suppression is also more effective. For this reason, high seeding rates of 120-160 lb./acre of rye and rye/Austrian winter peas are advisable.

Ron Morse suggests using an additional means of killing the cover crop in order to reach complete kill. Flail mowing was rejected as a method of controlling cover crops, since it causes rapid breakdown of the cover crop and subsequent problems with weed control. In addition to the possibility of herbicide use, there are a couple of mechanical controls that show promise. These include roll/crimping the cover crop, and then flail mowing only the top layer of the cover crop to kill any re-growth. An alternate method is to roll/crimp twice, first with immature cover crops, approximately 7-14 days earlier than normal, and then rolling again at the normal growth stage (anthesis or full bloom) and planting in one pass.

Paul Davis mentioned that no-till with cover crops works well just about everywhere – as long as farmers can make time for it. In particular, organic no-till has good potential for vegetables (including pumpkins). For larger-scale operations, this cropping system may be difficult to manage, since timing is so important. He suggests the judicious use of herbicides would be a good way to make sure that crops get in the ground at the right time.

California

▪ *Collaborators Jeff Mitchell, Ph.D. and Anil Shrestha and farmers Paul Muller, Andrew Brait and Tom and Denesse Willey*

2006 During 2006, three cash crops were planted: eggplant, tomatoes and cotton. The eggplants were planted at the organic farm of Tom and Denesse Willey in Madera, California. Paul Muller and Andrew Brait planted the tomatoes at Full Belly Farm in Capay Valley. Anil Shrestha, weed ecologist at the University of California, conducted the cotton study at Five Points at the University of California West Side Research and Extension Center.

Cover crop mixes were 'Merced' rye, Trios triticale, 'Abruzzi' rye, Austrian winter peas, and Balansa clover. At all of the sites, the cover crops produced good stands and had good winter growth. All cover crops were rolled in March. The rolling went well, but the cover crops did not die, instead they sprung upright and continued to grow. An unexpected rain during April exacerbated the cover crop re-growth. The cover crops finally died about three weeks after rolling. The cover crops competed with all three cash crops during the growing season, taking up moisture that the cash crops might have used. During March in this part of California the soils are typically drying out and there is a severe risk of dry soils. Although the eggplant and the tomatoes were watered using drip irrigation, competition for water and nutrients was still significant.

On the Willey farm, eggplant transplants were kept on hold for an extra three weeks, and poor quality transplants contributed to lower yields. There was also a problem with gophers eating the eggplants in the experimental plot.

Yield results from the 2006 season were much lower than the control plots. The cotton stand was less than 10 percent of the control plot, which was raised using traditional till and cultivation. The eggplant and tomato plots yielded about 20 percent of the normal amounts. After the 2006 season, the farmer partners decided to discontinue the study.

2007 The following year on the research farm in Five Points, the researchers again tried a cover crop of rye and triticale followed by a cash crop of corn. Again, the cover crop did not die.

2008 For the 2008 season the researchers planted a cover crop mixture of wheat, oats and barley with a cash crop of cowpeas. The cover crop didn't die completely, and the researchers had problems with planting the cash crop. The cover crop became "hairpinned" in the planting furrows and prevented good seed-to-soil contact with the cowpeas. They ended up using a no-till John Deere 1530 planter to establish the crop after the drill-seeded cowpeas did not grow. No-till rolled cover crop cowpea yields were about 50 percent of those of the standard tillage, clean cultivation plots.

No-till research across the country

As you can see, every region and every crop presents its own set of challenges that need to be worked out in an individual way. I hope you can also see that the determination of the farmers and the researchers is prevailing and that solutions to the problems any new system presents are being found. Each of these key individuals and many more around the country are taking up the challenge of no-till into cover crops because they can see the power of these biological systems to save time and energy, help in managing weeds without tillage, and can lead the way to cost-effective crop production.

It was also clear from the beginning of this large project that there is no substitute for experience. Those growers and researchers that had additional years of experience using conventional no-till practices made the adjustment to no-tilling into cover crops much easier. This is an important fact to consider as you think about adopting this technology onto your own farm.

Do your own research!

Yes, experiment on your own farm with cover crops and no-till. Learn what your equipment can do and where the system weaknesses are. Organic no-till is a system that is based on biology and partnered with mechanical control tools, with the goal of killing the cover crop and getting the seeds through the mulch and into the soil. Getting this right may take time, practice and patience. But it does and will work.

CHAPTER 07

COVER CROPS

▶ THE FOUNDATION OF ORGANIC NO-TILL

As mentioned before, cover crops are extremely important to organic no-till. They are the foundation upon which you will base much of your operation from now onward. In fact, as you progress in organic no-till, you'll become accustomed to thinking of cover crops as your new cash crop. After you read this chapter, you'll have a clearer understanding of why it's important to invest just as much (if not more) time and energy in your cover crops as you might in your cash crops.

Fewer weeds, higher organic matter, soil stability, pest and disease management, increased microbial action, and more nutrients are some of the benefits of cover cropping. In a no-till system we use cover crops somewhat differently, since we do not incorporate them into the soil. Although they still supply many of the same benefits, the cover crops also serve as a mulch, providing a season of weed control.

Even if you use chemical herbicides in your no-till program, cover cropping can be beneficial for all of the same reasons. Cover crops can help boost your soil organic matter, and provide stability and structure while guarding against erosion for the entire growing season. If you take the time to get it right, cover crops will pay back your investment with interest by the end of the season, and for several seasons to come.

The Benefits of Using Cover Crops

Stabilizes soil

Cover crops stabilize soil in a couple of different ways – by increasing infiltration due to top growth of stems and leaves, and through the roots of the cover crop. Roots keep a low profile, but they are an essential part of the equation. The roots of cover crops, especially legumes, encourage beneficial fungi, which extend their hypae through the soil and exude glomalins, which bind the soil together.

Some cover crops have a deep root system and can help relieve compaction caused by tillage, heavy machinery, and working soil in wet weather. For example, forage radishes can be planted in the fall and grow quickly to a depth of 24-36 inches. After they winterkill, they leave holes in the ground that help to aerate the soil. Other subsoil looseners include sorghum-sudangrass and sweet clovers.

Organic matter

Both roots and top growth contribute organic matter to the soil, after rolling terminates them or when tilled into the soil to decompose. A combination of cover crops and compost or farm manure is an excellent choice for building long-term organic matter and providing sufficient seasonal nutrients to the soil. Dale Mutch, of the University of Michigan and Ron Morse of Virginia Tech, two of our partners in the No-Till Plus trials, recommend using fertilizer of some kind for your cover crops. That's because the stronger your cover crops, the better weed control you'll have the following season.

Cover crops help to repair a steady decline in organic matter that is very common in agricultural systems in this country and around the world. Nitrogen rich fertilizers and tillage encourage an extremely rapid rate of decay of soil organic matter. Cover crops may contribute to organic matter indirectly – by helping farmers raise a bumper cash crop each year. High yielding crops contribute more crop residue, in the form of roots and aboveground growth which does help to mitigate the damage caused by conventional farming systems.

Stimulates microorganisms

Microbial growth is stimulated by the addition of organic matter, as well as by the roots of the growing cover crops. Nature wants to have the soil covered with something green and growing year-round. By providing a cover for the soil in the form of cover crops, microorganisms have a continuous habitat and food source.

Microorganisms help keep the soil healthy by suppressing disease organisms, improving soil structure, and digesting organic matter so that nutrients can be used by plants. Simply put, microorganisms are the living part of the soil, and also the part that makes the soil work. Without the continuous breakdown of organic matter performed by soil microorganisms, soil nutrients would be tied up and unavailable to plants.

Stabilizes and adds nutrients

Cover crops cover the soil and can prevent excess nitrogen from leaching out of the soil during heavy rains. Cover crops act as a "catch crop" or "trap crop," holding on to available nutrients in the soil (especially nitrogen). When the cover crop is mature and begins to decompose, these nutrients are released slowly and gradually for use by the cash crop. Rye is particularly good as a catch crop.

In addition, legumes used as cover crops can fix nitrogen in special nodules on their roots, in collaboration with *Rhizobium* bacteria. The nitrogen can be passed on to the next crop you grow, for example sweet corn. Organic farmers depend on legumes in their rotations to provide much of the nitrogen for heavy feeders like corn, broccoli and garlic. In our rotations for organic no-till, we pair legumes with these heavy feeders, building a rotation that will work well long term. The air we breathe is over 70 percent nitrogen. These leguminous plants will pull this nitrogen out of the air and "fix" it in the soil for other plants – our cash crops to use. This will work for both tillage or no-till systems.

Some cover crops are useful in bringing up nutrients from deeper soil layers. Buckwheat, for example, is an excellent scavenger of phosphorus. It has a shallow, fine root system (active in the top 10 inches of soil), producing a weak acid solution that releases nutrients from the soil. Sweet clover, with its deep root system, is adept at accessing nutrients in the subsoil layer and making them available as stems and leaves decompose at the surface of the soil.

Pest and disease management

When cover crops are added to an agricultural system, pest and disease management becomes easier. Cover crops add organic matter, which feeds the microbes that can play an important role in disease suppression. Cover crops also encourage beneficial insects by providing a nectar source from their flowers, as well as habitat.

Cultivate a healthy population of micro-organisms and you'll also have less to worry about plant diseases. For example, compost, which has abundant microorganisms, has been proven to suppress populations of harmful microorganisms like *Pythium* and *Rhizoctonia,* which cause damping off disease.

Suppresses weeds

In the organic no-till system, the primary function of the cover crop is to serve as a mulch to suppress weeds. Besides acting as a mulch, there are other ways in which cover crops suppress weeds. Covers such as buckwheat are sometimes called "smother crops" because they grow so densely that they out-compete weeds. Others like rye, oats and sorghum-sudangrass have an alleopathic effect on weeds – they actually exude compounds from their roots that reduce the seedling growth of weeds.

Water conservation

In terms of soil moisture, cover crops are a double-edged sword. On the one hand, cover crops definitely need water to grow. In a climate with abundant soil moisture, this is not necessarily a disadvantage. In dry climates, however, cover crops may use moisture that would otherwise be used by your cash crop.

On the other hand, cover crops can increase and stabilize soil moisture by increasing infiltration, improving soil structure, and increasing soil organic matter. In other words, once killed and left on the surface as in our organic no-till system, any water from rain or dew is held by the mulch and released to the cash crop. Thus, even if you live in an area with low annual rainfall, there are some powerful arguments for cover cropping. Although improved infiltration can be seen during your first cover cropping year, it may be 2-3 years before there is a noticeable difference in soil structure and organic matter.

Characteristics of Successful No-Till Cover Crops

Many, many kinds of plants can be used for cover cropping, but only some are suitable for use in organic no-till systems. In order for the cover crop to be successful, it needs to have a couple of important characteristics.

Carbon-to-nitrogen ratio

The ratio of carbon to nitrogen (C:N) affects how fast the residue breaks down. Plants with a high C:N ratio will have more carbon and break down slowly, suppressing weeds for the entire growing season. Rye, for example, has a C:N ratio of 40:1 and works well for organic no-till.

With small grains (wheat, oats or rye) that are allowed to mature, nitrogen tie up issues can occur. Here's how it happens. Microorganisms, which are responsible for the breakdown of residues, use

▶ CARBON TO NITROGEN RATIO FOR SOME COVER CROPS

Cover Crop	C:N ratio
Rye	40:1
Barley	20:1
Wheat	35:1
Vetch	15:1

nitrogen as a food source. If they can't get it from the cover crop, they look for it in the soil. When this occurs, the nitrogen is no longer available to the cash crop. Since we let grains mature in organic no-till, thereby increasing their C:N ratio, there is a possibility that a nitrogen tie-up will occur. However, this is largely avoided by the fact that the cover crops are left on the surface of the soil, where they decompose slowly. In fact, one of the main goals of organic no-till is that the cover crop residues should decompose as slowly as possible, providing for consistent weed control during the season.

▶ BIOMASS PRODUCTION OF COVER CROPS

(Adapted from "Cover Crops for All Seasons" by Mark Schonbeck)

Crop Species	Seeding lbs./acre[1]	Biomass tons/acre[2]	Growth stage for rolling
Crimson clover	15-30	1-3	Flowering
Bell/fava bean	80-150	1-2.5	Flowering
Sunn hemp	30-50	2.5-4.5	Flowering
Winter rye	60-150	2-5	Anthesis
Winter barley	¾-2	1.5-5	Anthesis
Spring barley	50-125	1.5-4	Anthesis
Spring oats	80-140	1.5-4	Milk stage of seed
Black oats	15-50	1.5-3	Anthesis
Buckwheat	60-80	2-3	Flowering
Foxtail millet	20-35	1.5-3.5	Milk stage of seed
Hairy vetch	20-40	1-3	Full bloom
Field peas	80-100	2.5-4	Flowering
Winter wheat	120-160	N/A	Anthesis

[1] Lower rates for drilling, higher rates for broadcasting

[2] Estimated aboveground biomass for cover crops grown until full bloom, immature seed stage, or winterkill in Zones 6a-8b.

Biomass production

The cover crop also needs to produce a large amount of biomass in order for the no-till system to work. Ideally the cover crop should yield around 5000 pounds of dry matter, or 2.5 tons/acre. Cover crops like rye, oats, wheat, sorghum-sudangrass, berseem clover, field peas and hairy vetch can produce ample amounts of biomass and leave a high amount of residue which makes an effective weed control layer.

It's important to understand that biomass levels vary greatly, depending on many factors including germination rate, winter weather conditions, planting time, etc. For example, the seeding rate for these crops is crucial. It's well worth investing in extra seed to make sure that you have a good planting that will serve as fertilizer and weed control later on.

A successful no-till cover crop operation.

Winter annuals

Crops that can be fall planted and overwinter are especially useful. Winter hardiness varies considerably. Rye, winter wheat and vetch are some of the hardiest cover crops, while field peas can overwinter in warmer climates. Winter annuals work well for many cropping systems, because they complete their life cycle in the spring, just as planting time for crops like corn and soybeans approaches. Sorghum-sudangrass and buckwheat can be spring planted and used for late summer or fall-planted crops. Unfortunately, you can't expect winterkilled cover crops to provide enough biomass the following year to provide weed control. These cover crops begin to decompose early in the spring; by midsummer there won't be much left to suppress germinating weeds. I do not recommend using winterkilled cover crops for organic no-till unless used for early spring cash crop plantings like oats or spinach.

Cover Crop Selection

Cover crop selection is crucial to the success of your organic no-till operation. Beyond the basic considerations of biomass and C:N ratio, it's important to match the cover crop to the cash crop you'll be growing, as well as determine what grows well in your area. The "No-Till Plus" project interviews earlier in chapter 6 have more information about the best choices for your area.

Rye

Rye has a number of advantages for the organic no-till farmer, and it's an excellent choice for pairing with soybeans. The hardiest of all cereal crops, rye can be planted late in the fall. This means that it is easier to plant after a main season crop such as corn. During cool weather, it grows rapidly and puts on considerably biomass. It can also be overseeded into crops such as soybeans and cabbage. If you are broadcasting late in the fall, you can boost the seeding rate as high as 200-350 lbs. per acre.

Rye is also good at suppressing weeds, for a couple of different reasons. First, rye has an extensive root system and generates lots of biomass. 5,000-7,000 pounds of dry matter/acre are typical in the Northeast. It is very competitive with annual weeds, especially those with small seeds like pigweed and foxtail. Second, rye produces substantial amounts of allelopathic chemicals that suppress weed growth. The suppressive qualities will last several weeks after the rye is terminated.

In the spring, rye starts growing actively as soon as the weather begins to warm and matures earlier than some other cover crops. For this reason, it's good for shorter windows in your rotation. The maturity will vary depending on soil moisture and temperature and the variety you select.

There are a few concerns about rye, however. One of the primary concerns is regarding a tie-up of available nitrogen. As mentioned before, mature rye has a C:N ratio of 40:1, which is far too much carbon for rapid digestion by soil microbes. This means that it persists as a mulch layer for a long while, but the downside is that it may tie-up nitrogen. Killing rye early, while it's still succulent and green, isn't an option with organic no-till. One way around this is to grow a mix of rye and a legume, such as hairy vetch or Austrian winter peas. By adding in a legume, you make sure that abundant N is available for soil microbes to perform the work of decomposing the cover crop, without having to resort to using what is already banked in the soil.

The other primary concern about rye is in regards to its water use, which can be high. Rye seeded in early fall can put on substantial growth by mid-winter, and captures snow which might otherwise blow away. However, its quick growth in the spring will use up considerable amounts of water that might otherwise be used for the cash crop. In the "No-Till Plus" trials, farmers in drier regions like North Dakota had more difficulties with rye in drought years.

Hairy vetch

Hairy vetch is an annual legume with a vining growth habit. It grows well in combination with cereal grains such as rye or as single-seeded stands. The vining growth habit can be both a benefit and a challenge for no-till farmers working with cover crops.

GENERAL BENEFITS Hairy vetch has a number of different advantages, and adapts itself to a variety of different weather conditions and geographic locations. It fixes large quantities of nitrogen. It is a great soil conditioner, breaking down more quickly than rye and adding organic matter generated from its abundant biomass. It uses water more conservatively than other kinds of vetch, and needs little in the winter dormant period. It attracts many beneficial insects, including lady beetles, minute pirate bugs and big-eyed bugs. It does, however, also attract some pest insects as well.

NITROGEN BENEFITS Vetch, like other legumes, has the potential to make a significant nitrogen contribution. This is a particular advantage to organic farmers, but it ought to appeal to conventional farmers as well. Vetch can contribute over 200 pounds of nitrogen per acre, but it's important to wait until the plants are in bloom to reach maximum yield. For this reason, hairy vetch is a natural fit with corn, because it's a heavy nitrogen user.

WEED CONTROL BENEFITS Vetch works well as a quick growing smother crop, with substantial benefits in the fall and early spring. Its primary method of control is to shade out weeds. The roots have a mild allelopathic effect, though certainly not as significant as rye or some other cereal grains. As the following study conducted by Rodale Institute indicates, the variety of vetch used can have significant effects on the biomass yield as well as the timing of the termination.

▶ HAIRY VETCH EVALUATION FOR NO-TILL CORN FOR FIVE HAIRY VETCH POPULATIONS — FIELD 60 (CENTER PORTION)

(The Rodale Institute, Berks County, Pennsylvania)

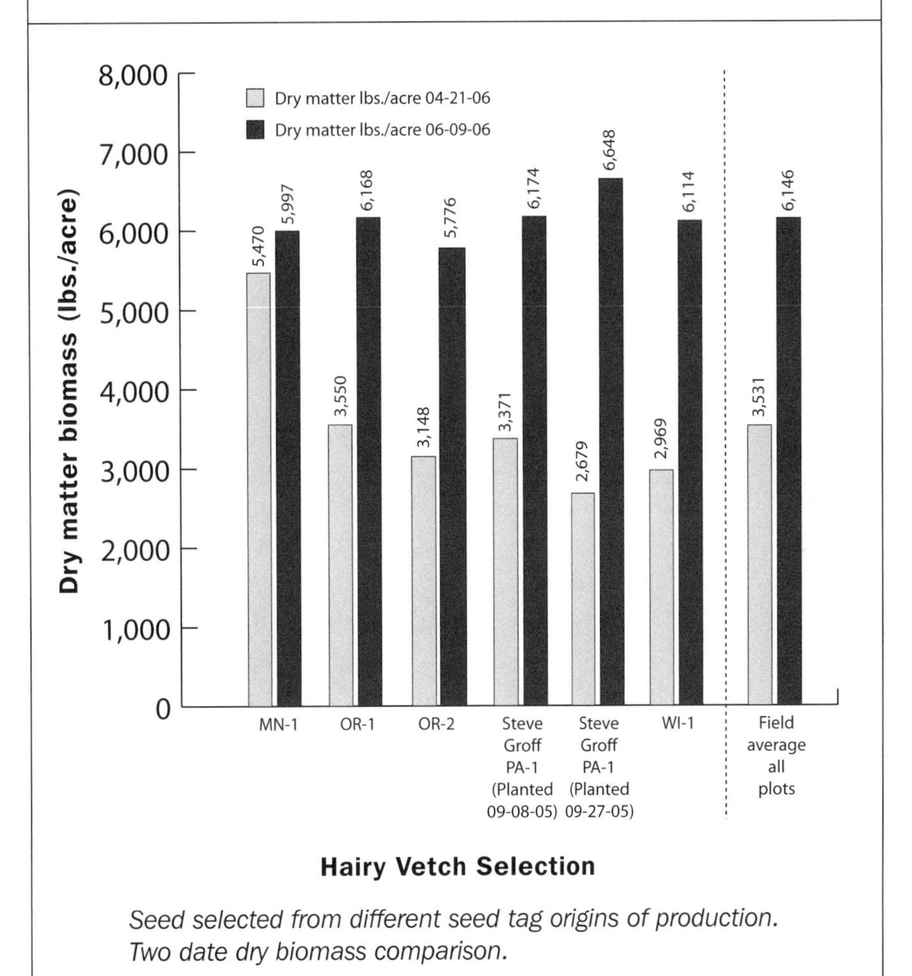

Seed selected from different seed tag origins of production. Two date dry biomass comparison.

After rolling, vetch will decompose readily due to its lower C:N ratio. After about three to four weeks, the vetch weed control tapers off, however the stems remain for many more weeks. It is important to pair vetch with a quick growing crop that rapidly establishes a canopy to shade out other weeds. That's another reason that corn is an ideal match for vetch.

REGIONAL CONSIDERATIONS Hairy vetch works best in the middle part of the United States that has cold winters and warm summers. It survives winters through USDA hardiness zone 4b. South of zone 7, crimson clover may be a better choice for cover cropping. Vetch does need significant moisture to germinate and grow, so it may not be the best choice for dryland farming with no irrigation.

JUDGING HAIRY VETCH MATURITY Vetch should be rolled at full bloom, but just what does that mean? As Dave Wilson of the Rodale Institute explains, the term "full bloom" has a specific meaning. When we say "full bloom" what we mean is there's at least one open flower on each stem. Take a look online or in book references so that you can see exactly what full bloom looks like, but you'll have to get out in the field and do some close observation when the time comes to really be sure. Judging the maturity this way is the easiest way for organic farmers to decide when to roll. For many crops, like corn, it's important to get as long a season as possible.

There are also some other researchers who have slightly different ways of judging maturity. For example, Bill Curran of Penn State likes to wait a little longer for vetch to mature, until he can see some pods with immature seed developing on the lower portions of the stem. Usually farmers don't let their cover crops go to seed because of problems with reseeding. Grain farmers need to be particularly cautious, because vetch can become a weed. Vetch has the same life cycle as wheat and if left to go to seed will express itself next time wheat shows up in the rotation. Ten to 20 percent of the seed is "hard seed" which will not germinate in the first year. If the vetch cover crop goes to seed, this creates even more of an issue. Of course, if you don't have grains in your rotation, a few vetch plants the next year may not cause much of a problem.

Seth Dabney (see chapter 6 for more about his research) uses a third way of judging vetch maturity. He looks mostly at stem length and plant condition. Dabney waits until the stems are 3-4 feet long, and the lower leaves have turned black and no longer have buds. This is an earlier stage of maturity than full bloom, but Dabney finds that he can still kill vetch with the roller/crimper at this point.

Whichever method you choose to use will depend on what crops you grow, your rotation, whether or not you use herbicides, and the length of your season.

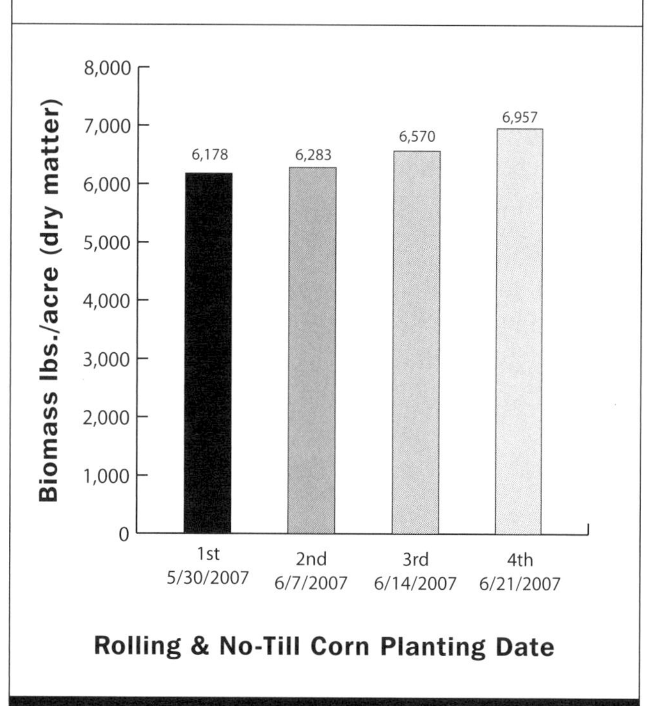

▶ COMPARISON OF HAIRY VETCH USING FOUR ROLLING DATES
(The Rodale Institute, Berks County, Pennsylvania)

DETERMINING "FULL-BLOOM STAGE" FOR HAIRY VETCH *(Dave Wilson, Research Agronomist, The Rodale Institute)* Hairy vetch (*Vicia villosa*) when planted in the fall in the Northeast, behaves as a winter annual legume. The optimum germination temperature range is from 59 to 73.4 F (15 to 23 C). The plant germinates, emerges and initiates growth in the fall. The plants generally forming a crown and then live dormant over the winter. The optimum temperature for early root growth is 68 to 77 F (20 to 25 C). As with most annual legumes it grows a shallow taproot to a depth of 1-3 feet. In the spring, as soil and air temperatures increase, growth is re-initiated, with 3 to 7 branching stems developing and each can grow from 3 to 12 feet long. The plants then bloom, set seed pods and die afterwards. The fall-planted hairy vetch will begin to flower from early May to early June. The time of bloom will depend upon the temperature in the spring and the cultivar.

Flowering is controlled primarily by temperature-dependent physiological processes. Spring temperature changes are the primary influence of these physiological processes. In the Northeast, from the end of April through the middle of June, the accumulated growing degree heat units can vary from year to year. This variance makes it difficult to predict exact time of bloom in any given year.

The terms 1/10 bloom, mid-bloom and full-bloom are typically used to describe the stage of maturity of legume forages such as alfalfa, medium red clover, etc. At 1/10 bloom, 10 percent of the stems have at least one flower; at mid-bloom 50 percent of the stems have at least one flower; and at full bloom 75 percent of the stems have at least one flower. This terminology is more familiar to farmers who grow forages and regularly estimate the bloom of the forage legume to know when to cut it for optimum quality.

Typically the same terminology is used when referring to a field of hairy vetch for rolling, since in an organic system, the hairy vetch must be at full-bloom stage for effective mechanical kill. If it is rolled before this stage, then typically the vetch will grow back and does not form an adequate mat and therefore is less suppressive on weed growth.

In the spring after prolific vegetative growth, the hairy vetch plant develops from the bud to the bloom stage. Most of its growth comes in late spring during the month of May. The buds will emerge along the stem and there can be 10 to 45 flowers or more along one stem at the height of bloom in June. Farmers not familiar with the plant may have difficulty determining the full-bloom stage.

SPRING TEMPERATURES AND BLOOMING TIME

Once again, the time of bloom is determined by both the environmental conditions in the spring and the cultivar selection. Spring seasons with prolonged cool, moist, cloudy weather can delay the appearance of the flowers on hairy vetch. In the early spring the optimum conditions for growth, water use efficiency, and nitrogen fixation are air temperatures of 68 F (20 C) and soil temperatures of 50 F (10 C).

The growth of hairy vetch can be correlated with growing degree days whose base temperature is 39.2 F (4 C) and which can be calculated using the formula (daily high temperature + daily low temperature)/2-39.2 F).

The above graph is the record of accumulated daily base 39.2 F (4 C.) temperature units at the Rodale Institute research farm over a ten-year period. The daily temperature units were determined using climate data collected at the site.

The accumulated temperature units from mid-May to mid-June as represented by the vertical lines vary from year to year. This temperature variance will either delay or hasten the bloom of hairy vetch. Rainy or cloudy periods in the spring will delay bloom.

During the spring of 2008, temperatures were above average for a few days during the end of April and beginning of May, but by mid-May the temperatures dropped below average and remained low for the remainder of May and June, which is the time when hairy vetch typically blooms. As a result of the below average temperatures the "full bloom" stage was delayed until the second week in June. This late bloom led to later than usual rolling dates.

The plots with Steve Groff's (Early Cover) hairy vetch were able to be rolled successfully by June 6. Subsequent rolling dates of other plots of this hairy vetch were accomplished on June 16, June 20 and June 25. On June 16 a more complete kill was achieved compared to June 6, which had some grow back. The rolling on June 20 and June 25 was the same.

In contrast the later blooming Nebraska seed source hairy vetch was not ready for rolling until June 16, with subsequent rolling events in other plots of this vetch on June 20, June 25 and June 27. The percent kill and matting of the vetch on these dates was similar.

Notice in the comparison for the last three years (March 1 to June 25) that in 2006 the temperatures were above the ten-year average and in 2008 they were below the ten-year average, in

2007 the temperatures started off below the ten-year average and then by the end of May they eventually reached and remained relatively the same as the ten-year average.

HAIRY VETCH CULTIVARS, WINTER HARDINESS AND BLOOM Hairy Vetch was also called sand, purple or winter vetch. In the past hairy vetch was classified into separate species, *Vicia villosa* and *Vicia dasycarpa.* But these two types have been merged into one species, *Vicia villosa.*

Five subspecies are recognized within *Vicia villosa,* two of these subspecies were known to be introduced to North America (*Vicia villosa* subspecies *varia* and *Vicia villosa* subspecies *villosa*) and used by farmers. These two subspecies differ in their relative degree of hairiness on the stems and leaves. *Vicia villosa* subspecies *varia* ranges from glabrous (smooth or bald) to less hairy than *Vicia villosa* subspecies *villosa.* In the past *Vicia villosa* subspecies *varia* has been referred to as "smooth vetch" due to this lack of hairiness. Glabrous is a botanical term meaning having a surface devoid of hair.

In the past there were over 30 USDA registered cultivars but they are currently not all available commercially. Except for a few cultivar releases, up until recently there have been no active seed certification programs for hairy vetch. As a result there are different types of hairy vetch that are labeled similarly and sold just as "hairy vetch." The parentage of the commercially available hairy vetch seed is often unknown. The different types grown commercially are varied in their degree of cold tolerance and also their time of bloom. Much of the hairy vetch available commercially is labeled as "VNS" (variety not stated), so the buyer does not know the variety.

The cultivars of the *Vicia dasycarpa* species, such as 'Auburn', 'Oregon' and 'Lana' and the *Vicia villosa* subspecies *varia* types of vetch tend to be heat tolerant and do better in warmer climates. In the past the majority of the hairy vetch seed produced in Oregon was the smooth type of hairy vetch. This type of vetch is usually less winter hardy, more heat tolerant and may winterkill in northern locations. The heat-tolerant cultivars were developed in California and Oregon, and usually bloom earlier than the winter-hardy types.

The Early Cover variety was released by the Jimmy Carter Plant Material Center and Auburn University; it is not as winter hardy and will bloom earlier than the cold tolerant and later-blooming types. As it is planted in more southern locations this earliness of bloom may be increased.

Steve Groff of Lancaster County, Pennsylvania commercially produces Early Cover hairy vetch. His selection appears to be more winter tolerant than the Early Cover produced in southern locations. Growing the vetch at his location for several years in Pennsylvania has allowed him to naturally select for plants that overwinter well at his northern location. His selection of Early Cover is not as hardy as the winter-hardy types of vetch but it is hardier than the Early Cover grown at southern locations. His Early Cover hairy vetch will indeed bloom earlier. At the Rodale Institute in Pennsylvania it will typically bloom 7 to 10 days earlier than the later blooming more winter-hardy cultivars.

The heat tolerant *Vicia dasycarpa* types of hairy vetch and the *Vicia villosa* subspecies *varia* types of vetch have smoother leaflets (they are less pubescent or hairy) and the leaflets have a deep green color with pink to violet flower petals.

The cold-tolerant cultivars of hairy vetch *Vicia villlosa* such as 'Madison' that was developed in Nebraska are more frost resistant, but tend to be later bloomers. The 'Madison' cultivar labeled as such is not commonly commercially available.

The cold-tolerant types often have noticeable hairy foliage that is characterized by pubescence on the stems and leaves as well as by the tufted growth at the ends of the stems. The pubescence gives it a grayish hue, the leaflets are bluish-green in color and the petals of the flowers are dark blue.

In Pennsylvania we have lost stands of hairy vetch over the winter due to winterkill. This is of great concern to farmers planting hairy vetch in

▶ COMPARISON OF TEN YEARS (1999 TO 2008) ACCUMULATED BASE 39.2 F (4 C) HEAT UNITS FOR HAIRY VETCH GROWTH & DEVELOPMENT

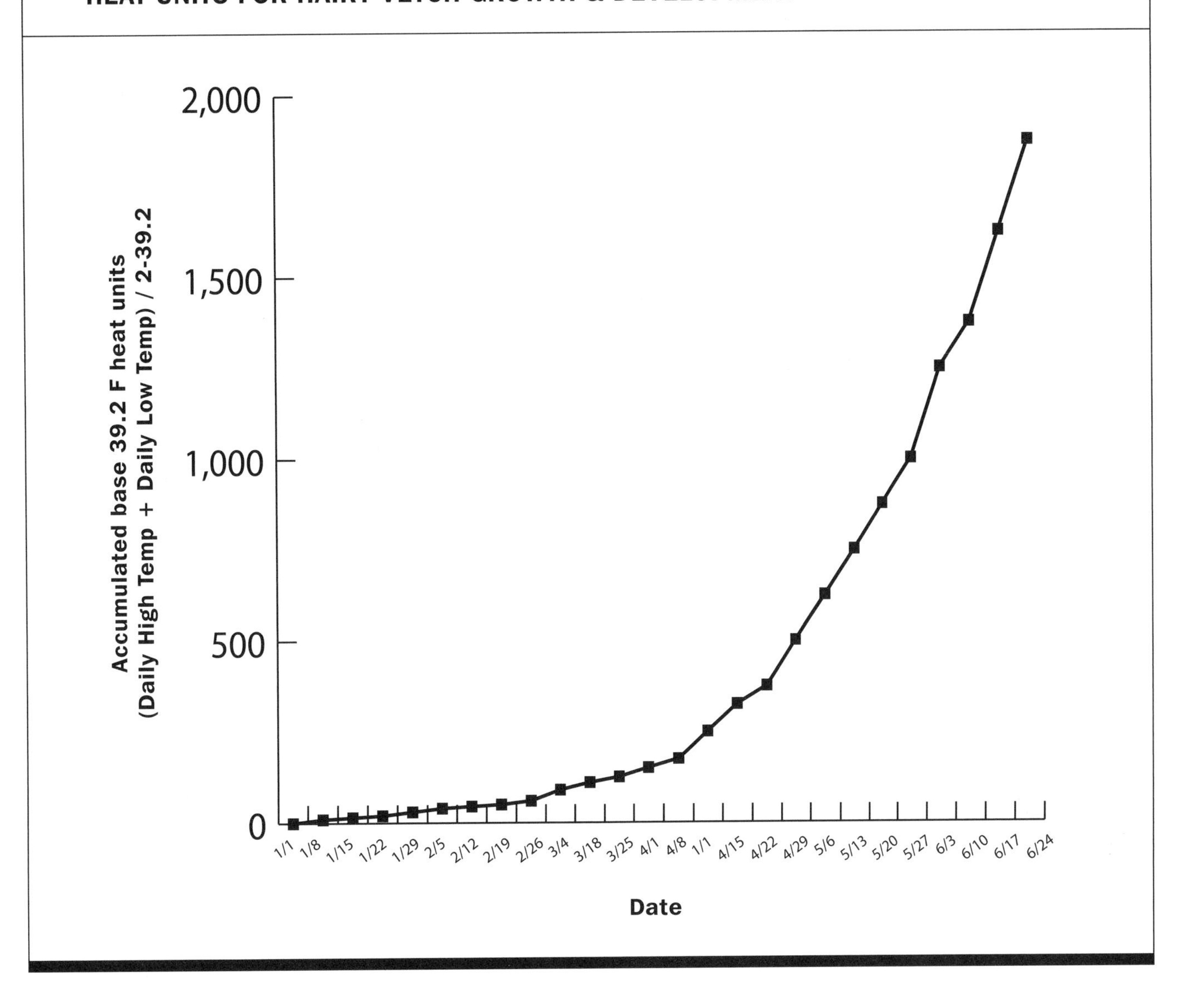

northern locations. As a result of the merging of the heat tolerant *Vicia dasycarpa* types of vetch and the winter tolerant *Vicia villlosa* types of vetch, both are currently labeled as *Vicia villosa* or commonly just "hairy vetch." Cultivar names are commonly not know and not listed so the VNS, (variety not stated), label is common.

Northern farmers need an indicator that the vetch seed they buy is bred for winter hardiness. As a result, it is recommended that farmers check the "origin" on the seed tag label. Listed after the origin will be the state or country where the seed was grown. Typically seed grown in Nebraska, Minnesota and Wisconsin are the winter hardy *Vicia villosa* subspecies *villosa* type of seed.

The 'Hungvillosa' cultivar is one of the most frost-resistant types. Seed of this cultivar is grown in Denmark and was available commercially through Seedway in 2007 and 2008. It is important to note that all of these winter-hardy cultivars are "late bloomers" and they typically don't reach full bloom until the first week of June.

NEW USDA HAIRY VETCH CULTIVAR RELEASES Working collaboratively with research geneticist Dr. Thomas Devine, of the Sustainable Agriculture Systems Laboratory USDA-BARC, Rodale Institute evaluated different selections of hairy vetch for winter hardiness and time of bloom. As a result USDA-ARS, The Pennsylvania Agricultural Experiment Station, The Rodale Institute and Cornell University Agricultural Experiment Station jointly released two new cultivars of hairy vetch.

The new cultivars are 'Purple Bounty' and 'Purple Prosperity.' Both of these cultivars were not developed using genetic engineering so they can be approved for certified organic production. Both of these are early-flowering cultivars that have sufficient winter hardiness to survive winters in the Northeastern United States. During research trials, 'Purple Prosperity' bloomed earlier than 'Purple Bounty' at the Rodale farm location in Berks County, Pennsylvania. Both 'Purple Bounty' and 'Purple Prosperity' bloomed earlier than Steve Groff's selection of Early Cover.

'Purple Bounty' will typically reach full bloom by the third week to end of May, 'Purple Prosperity' will be after that, reaching full bloom in the last week of May to the first week of June, and Steve Groff's Early Cover selection will be right behind the 'Purple Prosperity' by a day or two – also reaching full bloom during the last week of May to the first week of June.

In comparison, the winter-hardy cultivars of hairy vetch typically grown in Nebraska, Wisconsin and Minnesota will not be at full-bloom stage until the first to second week of June, so later rolling dates are necessary to get effective kill for these later bloomers. These later rolling dates also lead to later planting dates for corn, which means shorter season corn varieties with RM (relative maturity) values of 95 to 100 need to be used; depending on your location.

Year by year variances of this "full bloom" period occur due to differences in accumulated temperature units from one year to the next. All of these dates can be moved forward or back, depending on spring temperatures.

Breeders' seed for these two new cultivars ('Purple Bounty' and 'Purple Prosperity') were made available for commercial seed increase production programs and should become commercially available within three to five years.

Buckwheat

Maturing in just 70-90 days, buckwheat is ideal for a quick cover. It is very frost sensitive, so it can't be used as a winter annual. However, it does work well for short windows during the summertime. It could be planted in the spring after danger of frost is past and rolled by mid-summer for a fall-planted crop.

WEED MANAGEMENT BENEFITS Buckwheat is a wonderful weed suppressor – the main advantages come from shading and competition. Buckwheat grows quickly enough to shade out both perennial weeds like thistle and small-seeded annuals such as foxtail. Seeding rates at the upper end of the scale tend to yield better results for weed suppression. Broadcasting at a rate of 120 pounds per acre is quite effective for areas seriously infested with weeds.

RESEEDING ISSUES Buckwheat reliably reseeds itself and begins flowering early. The first seeds start to mature 7-10 days after flowering or about six weeks after planting. For this reason, buckwheat can become a weed fairly easily leading to the old saying, "once a buckwheat field, always a buckwheat field." Flowering may start as early as three weeks after planting, but is more likely to begin about six weeks after planting.

BENEFICIALS Buckwheat is quite attractive to beneficial insects. The shallow flowers make feeding easy for insects like hover flies and tachinid flies.

NO TILLING INTO BUCKWHEAT Buckwheat is best rolled at flowering. Its tender, succulent stems will break down quickly, due to its low C:N ratio. It has a fairly strong allelopathic effect, and this should prevent weeds from germinating for (length of time). No-tilling into buckwheat is easy, from a mechanical standpoint. The stems break easily and the resulting mat posses little problem for most no-till planting equipment.

Field peas & Austrian winter peas

Field peas are a useful cover crop from a number of different standpoints. They use water more efficiently than some other legumes, including hairy vetch. They also fix nitrogen rapidly and are top producers, usually contributing from 90 to 150 lbs./acre. Although they are not as hardy as hairy vetch, they can be planted as a winter annual in southern locations or in early spring in northern locations. For the purposes of organic no-till, field peas compare well with vetch. In trials in the southeast, Austrian winter peas outproduced vetch by about 18 percent in both biomass and nitrogen contributions.

WINTER HARDINESS Austrian winter peas will not reliably overwinter north of zone 6, but their hardiness is affected not only by temperatures but also by snow cover. Sustained cold below 18 F (-8 C). (without snow cover) will kill peas, which have only a shallow root system. However, they can withstand temperatures as low as 10 F (-12 C). for brief intervals. Interplanting with a grain can improve winter hardiness, because the grain serves as a nurse crop for the peas, protecting their roots from heaving out of the soil and accumulating snow.

WEED CONTROL Biomass amounts can be high – 5,000-8,000 lbs. dry matter/acre. However, peas tend to break down relatively quickly, and by themselves don't make good organic mulches. However, when combined with small grains, they can achieve C:N ratios of as high as 34. This should provide enough biomass to be a long lasting mulch.

TIMING Plant peas either very early in the spring, as soon as the soil can be worked, or early in the fall so that the plants generate 6-8 inches of top growth before cold weather sets in. Peas can be overseeded into other crops (like soybeans) at leaf yellowing or final cultivation, as long as the other crop does not provide too much shade cover.

For termination, roll at full bloom. This is also the stage of growth that will provide the optimal amount of nitrogen. Peas tend to be easier to terminate than some other cover crops and never seem to try and stand back up or re-grow.

Winter wheat

Winter wheat doesn't generate the biomass that rye offers, and it has a longer maturity date, but it does have certain advantages. It's widely adapted, the seed is inexpensive and it's easier to terminate. It is also a good scavenger of nitrogen if planted in the fall, and it works well in no-till or reduced tillage systems. Unlike with some other cover crops we've looked at so far, wheat cultivars don't seem to vary as much in terms of the biomass they produce. That means there's more flexibility in choosing varieties to work with, or you could just use bin run seed.

WEED SUPPRESSION Compared to rye, wheat is not quite as good at suppressing weeds. However, if planted at the correct time (a few weeks earlier than rye) it does generate considerable biomass. You might also consider using fertilizer to boost biomass. In a Maryland study, a heavy application of chicken manure followed by a winter wheat planting yielded 12,500 pounds of dry matter per acre.

TIMING OF PLANTING AND ROLLING Since wheat matures more slowly than rye, it may not be as suitable for long season cash crops. Plant wheat a few weeks earlier than rye for winter annual use – and slightly earlier than your cereal grain cash crop. Roll wheat at soft dough stage or later for the best kill rate. Generally, winter wheat is less aggressive than rye, and easier to terminate.

You might also experiment with spring planted wheat. If planted as soon as the soil can be worked in the spring, winter wheat should grow 6-10 inches tall, but will not head out or mature. As it starts to die back, or reach peak growth, roll and plant a late season crop into the residue. The limited biomass won't hold the weeds back for very long, but it might be long enough for a quick maturing crop, or one that canopies quickly.

Barley

Of the cereal grains used as cover crops, barley has the lowest C:N ratio, which means it's less permanent as a mulch. However, it does have its uses, particularly in far north areas and droughty conditions. It is also inexpensive and easy to grow. Barley can be grown further north than other spring planted cereal grains, due to its short growing window. It also uses soil moisture more efficiently than other cereal grains, making it an ideal choice for arid regions. In hardiness zone 8 or higher, it can be grown as a winter annual. Make sure to choose a regionally adapted barley variety.

WEED SUPPRESSION Barley grows quickly and outcompetes weeds by absorbing soil moisture and releasing allelopathic chemicals. Spring planted barley can produce abundant biomass, up to 4 tons per acre. That's not quite as good as rye, but not too far behind it, either. With a lower C:N ratio than rye or wheat, barley will break down quickly. You might consider looking into older varieties also. Many of these varieties are longer strawed, so they have the potential to create more biomass, but are also prone to lodging. This is a condition not suitable if you plan on harvesting the grain but could be a benefit in a rolling operation for no-till.

TIMING OF PLANTING AND ROLLING In zone 8 and warmer, plant winter barley in September for best results. It should grow all winter. Further north broadcast it at a rate of 125 lbs./acre or up to 140 lbs./acre for especially weedy fields. You can also drill at 100 lbs./acre.

Barley grows quickly. It can produce more biomass in a short window than any other grain. This will allow you to plant a later-season crop after rolling the barley. Roll at the mid to late bloom stage, before the barley has produced viable seeds.

Crimson clover

Crimson clover is an excellent choice for a no-till legume in the southeastern United States. East of the Mississippi (in roughly hardiness zone 5 and warmer) crimson clover can be grown as a winter annual. In some colder areas, including much of New England, crimson clover can be grown as a summer annual. Like other legumes, it can fix nitrogen – 70-150 lbs./acre. It's also an excellent choice for supporting beneficial insects, since it produces abundant nectar.

WEED MANAGEMENT Crimson clover provides ample biomass. About 3,500-5,500 pounds of dry matter per acre by mid-May in zone 8. For this reason, it's a good choice for organic no-till. For southern areas, it is a better weed suppressor than hairy vetch in the fall, and matures more quickly in the spring.

TIMING OF PLANTING AND ROLLING Crimson clover is a strong grower in cool, moist conditions. As a winter annual, seed the cover crop 6-8 weeks before the first frost date. When spring planted, seed after the risk of frost has passed. Roll crimson clover when it is in full bloom. Maximum nitrogen is available at late bloom or early seed set.

On Steve Groff's farm in Lancaster County, Pennsylvania, he no-tills vegetable transplants directly into killed crimson clover with no negative effects from residual allelopathic chemicals. Other studies have shown that strip tilling works for field crops. It's better to wait two to three weeks, however, if you are no-tilling directly into the mulch, until after the cover crop has started to break down. Otherwise, you may run the risk of damping-off pathogens attacking your direct-seeded crops.

Finding the Perfect Match: Pairing Cover Crops with Cash Crops

One of the key factors to successful organic no-till is matching a cover crop with a cash crop. Several issues confront the no-till farmer as he or she makes a choice. First, it's important to make sure that the timing works. Cover crops need to mature in time to plant cash crops that will produce adequate yields. Next, the cover crop should provide enough nitrogen as well as other nutrients to sustain the cash crop's needs for the growing season. Further, the cover crop needs to break pest cycles. Lastly, the weed control provided by the cash crop should match well with the needs of the cash crop.

Let's look at the following examples to see how they work. I know I've said it before but I'll say it again here, experiment on your own farm and with your own rotations to find the correct set of criteria you're looking for in a cover crop – then select the species and varieties that best suit your needs.

Corn with legumes such as vetch and Austrian winter peas

This pairing works well because vetch (or peas) provides the nitrogen that the corn needs. Vetch and peas are mature and ready for rolling down at the same time that corn needs to be planted. Vetch and peas both break down fairly quickly, but that's OK because corn grows quickly and competes well with weeds.

Soybeans with grains such as rye and winter wheat

Soybeans that provide much of their own nitrogen don't need the additional N produced by a legume. What it needs is effective weed control for a longer portion of the season. Soybeans are quite sensitive to weed pressure. Rye, with its high biomass and C:N ratio, suppresses weeds until late in the growing season.

Tomatoes with rye

Tomatoes also need good weed control, since they are a longer season crop. Many growers trellis their tomatoes, to provide better air circulation to help with disease control. During the harvest period, pathways need to stay free of weeds for the sake of efficient picking. Tomatoes do better with a consistent, even supply of soil moisture.

For more examples, see the sample rotations in chapter 2.

Cover crop mixes: do they work?

It's tempting to combine different kinds of covers into a mix, both because that's often how cover cropping has been traditionally accomplished, and because it does provide certain immediately obvious benefits. For example, legumes and grains are often combined; the grain provides lots of long lasting organic matter and the legume provides a nitrogen contribution.

However, there are some additional matters to think about when you are considering mixes for organic no-till. For example, in order to get a good kill rate for cover crops, the stage of maturity is critically important. It's quite possible that one species included in the mix will not be mature, while the other one is starting to set seed and needs to be rolled immediately. There's no doubt that mixes complicate matters considerably. If you're a beginner to organic no-till, it may be easier to stick to a single species of cover crop initially until you know more about the techniques involved. Then, experimenting with mixes may come more easily. At Rodale, we've had our best successes with single species cover cropping.

The Cover Crop Year

Fall planting

When you work with fall planted annuals, it's like farming the back side of the calendar. You start in fall by planting your cover crop as soon as your cash crop is harvested and the field can be prepared. Remember, the key to success in spring is closely linked to the work you do in the fall. Be sure to do everything possible to give your cover crops the best opportunity to grow.

TIMING Timing is extremely important. Remember, in order to do its job effectively, the cover crop needs to be able to generate significant amounts of biomass by planting time during the following year. You need to give the cover crop ample time to mature, so planting earlier in the fall is important.

VARIETY SELECTION Variety selection is important too. Select a seed variety that does well in your area by sourcing locally produced seed.

SPECIES SELECTION The cover crop you choose must be appropriate for your area. Hardiness, moisture needs, maturity date, and other considerations are important to think about. As we've discussed already, it's essential to match the cover crop with a cash crop that works well. Consider all the options before you make your choice.

SEEDING RATES Seeding rates vary depending on climate and soil conditions, but it doesn't hurt to sow the cover crop more heavily than you would normally. For example with rye, a normal seeding rate is 1-2 bushels per acre. With organic no-till a better stand will be achieved with a seeding rate of 2.5-3 bushels per acre. Don't skimp on seed. You'll want the higher plant populations to generate biomass and suppress weeds. Also, cover crops tend to have a higher kill rate after rolling with a thick stand.

FERTILIZER Just as you'd fertilize your cash crop, you may get better results by applying fertilizer to your cover crop. With additional nutrients in place, cover crops will grow faster, compete well with weeds, and generate more biomass. Fall is the best time to apply manure or fertilizer.

Winter into spring

BENEFITS OF WINTER COVER Depending on your climate, the winter annuals will either continue to grow during the winter or essentially remain dormant. Either way, your farm's soil benefits from the winter cover, which protects against erosion while keeping microbial populations alive.

EFFECTS ON SPRING WARM-UP AND SOIL MOISTURE Different species have different effects on the soil during early spring. Rye has a tendency to dry out soils (which can be beneficial for some farms) whereas vetch tends to hold moisture. Monitoring your soil moisture may be a key factor for decision making.

EVALUATING YOUR COVER CROPS Take a good look at your cover crops but don't judge them too early in the season. You may be surprised at how well they perk up once the soil warms. Check on their condition frequently, especially early in your adoption of the practice as there will be lots to learn. You might even roll an experimental strip to see how much coverage they provide for weed control. In order to have effective weed management for the rest of the season, the ground needs to be 100 percent covered. If the cover crop is too thin, you may want to consider tilling in the cover and planting with your regular equipment.

Ready to Roll

MATURATION As cover crops mature in spring, they typically get very tall. Rye, for example, can get as tall as 5-6 feet. This is necessary to generate enough biomass for organic no-till. Although green manure crops are sometimes plowed down at a smaller and less mature stage, cover crops for organic no-till are allowed to reach their full height.

PHYSICAL AND CHEMICAL CHANGES During the maturation process, the nutrients are pulled from the roots into the flowers and seeds so that the plant can reproduce. This means that the plant itself is vulnerable to disturbance.

TIMING OF ROLLER/CRIMPER USE Timing for the roller/crimper is extremely important. It's best to roll the cover crop down when it's at the peak of vegetative growth, when it is in full flower, but before it has produced viable seed. For example, rye and other grains are rolled at the flowering/green seed stage – basically during anthesis when you can see the pollen in the air if you bump the seed heads around. Vetch and other legumes are rolled/crimped at a stage at least 75 percent in bloom but full bloom is better.

RESEARCH RESULTS Planting times can make a big difference to the success of your cover crop and cash crops. Timing for cover crop killing is also very important. Crop results from the Rodale Research Farm illustrate how to experiment and make good decisions on your own farm.

Cash crop variety selection It's necessary to experiment with different varieties for your cash crops. Some perform much better when planted into heavy residues, while some of your favorite varieties may not do as well.

Summer monitoring post-rolling and planting

INCOMPLETE KILL ISSUES AT ROLLING If, after rolling, your cover crop did not kill effectively, how do you figure out what happened and why? Asking yourself the following set of questions may help. If you are a beginner or working with a new cover crop, you may decide to roll different sections on an experimental basis five to seven days apart.

- Was the cover crop really at the correct maturity stage? (see Zadok's Scale)
- Were some parts of the field at different stages?
- Did you check the entire field prior to rolling?
- If you used a mix of different cover crop species, did they all mature at once, or were some immature at rolling?
- What was the kill rate for each separate species?
- Was the cover crop too thin? The roller works better on thicker stands of cover crops.
- Was there a difference in different areas of the field and did the cover crop kill better in the thicker areas?
- Was the ground uneven in certain places?
- Were there rocky areas or divots in the field where the kill rate was lower because the roller/crimper could not do its job effectively?

As for remedies, you can re-roll the field if the cash crop has not emerged or you haven't set any transplants. Later in the season, you can drive between the rows with the tractor tires, or you can try to use a high residue cultivator to knock down any competing cover crop. The real trick is to be certain the cover crop as at the correct stage of maturity so that it doesn't become an issue.

MOISTURE ISSUES Another set of challenges surrounds moisture issues. If you think that soil moisture has not been sufficient to germinate and grow the cash crops to achieve an adequate yield, there are some ways to evaluate this problem. To figure out what happened, it's always useful to have a "control" area that is planted using regular no-till or standard tillage and cultivation methods if you are organic.

To evaluate moisture issues, consider the following questions.

- How much rainfall did the area receive during the winter and spring? Was this amount below average for your area?

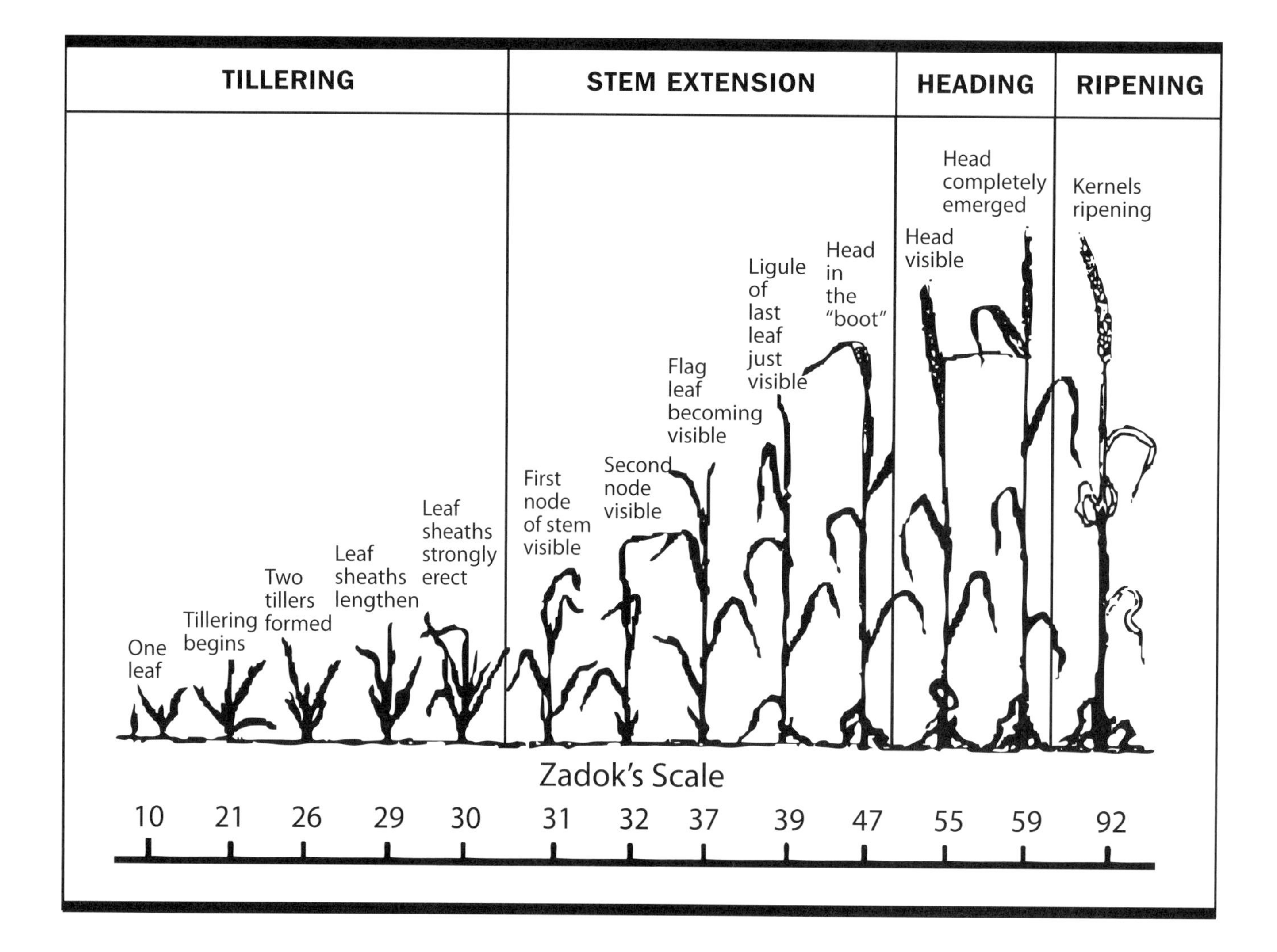

• What is the organic matter content in your soil? Do you think having additional organic matter would give you an edge in retaining moisture?

• Was the cover crop you used an efficient one in terms of water use? If not, is there a better choice for next time?

• What was the soil moisture level at planting?

• Does the typical timing of your winter/spring rains match up with the usual maturity date of the cover crop you are using?

Don't be afraid to ask other organic no-till farmers for advice. Since this is a relatively new set of production practices the more we all communicate the faster we can all achieve success. There are many people listed in this book that will be glad to work with you to help solve your problems.

Resources

Sarrantonio, Marianne. *Northeast Cover Crop Handbook.* Kutztown, PA: The Rodale Institute, 1996.

Schonbeck, Mark and Ron Morse. "Cover Crops for All Seasons: Expanding the cover crop tool box for organic vegetable producers." Virginia Association for Biological Farming, 2006. *www.vabf.org/infosheets/3-06.pdf.*

Schonbeck, Mark. "Cover cropping: On-Farm, Solar-powered Soil Building." Virginia Association for Biological Farming, 2006. *www.vabf.org/infosheets/1.06.pdf.*

Sullivan, Peston. "Overview of Cover Crops and Green Manures" ATTRA, 1997. *http://attra.ncat.org/attra-pub/PDF/covercrop.pdf.*

Sustainable Agriculture Network. *Managing Cover Crops Profitably*, 3rd edition. Beltsville, MD, 2007.

Wilson, Dave. "Choosing cover crops for organic no-till soybeans." The New Farm, 2005. *www.newfarm.org/depts/weeds/features/1005/weeds_dw_print.shtml.*

Wilson, David. "Earlier-flowering hairy vetch a great advantage, but northern farmers need more." The New Farm, 2007. *http://newfarm.rodaleinstitute.org/depts/NFfield_trials/2007/0412/purplebounty.shtml.*

Wilson, David. "Cold tolerant hairy vetch and late planting can be key factors for successful organic no-till corn in the Northeast." The New Farm, 2008. *www.newfarm.org/depts/NFfield_trials/2008/0117/notill.shtml.*

CHAPTER 08 BUILDING SOILS FOR YOUR ORGANIC NO-TILL CROPS

Organic farming is all about the soil. Under section 2114 of the Organic Foods Production Act of 1990 (7 U.S.C. § 6513), it states that "an organic plan shall contain provisions designed to foster soil fertility, primarily through the management of organic content of the soil through proper tillage, crop rotation, and manuring."

That means that building healthy soils should be the key goal of any organic system plan. But what constitutes a healthy soil? It is vitally important to have a firm understanding of basic soil science in order to manage any tillage or no-till system. This soil-building chapter will help you understand the qualities of healthy soil, and what is needed during the process of conversion to organic no-till. The chapter will also point out some of the benefits to be gained by such a transition.

Your soil is a living, breathing entity, and evaluating its biological health is extremely important to success with the no-till system. It wasn't all that many years ago when scientists argued that we couldn't use the term "healthy" to describe soils. Instead, we were supposed to use the word "quality." That meant we could discuss soil quality but not soil health. As organic farmers and researchers we know that the soil is very much alive – or at least it can be, and should be if we're doing our jobs as farmers. If something is alive, then it can have a dynamic state of being that can be described as "healthy." It also means we, as stewards of the soil, can impact its state of health through the practices (tillage), amendments, and the crops we use.

Assessing your soil is important before you experiment with no-till. It is also important after you have moved towards a no-till or rotational tillage system. Your evaluation should include a biological, physical and chemical assessment. You may also need to make some changes a year or so in advance of experimenting with no-till to increase your chances of success with this new system.

As you assess the problems on your farm, you can begin to get an idea of how no-till could help your operation. I suggest you transition a part of your farm to a no-till system based on cover crops rather than transitioning the whole farm at once. Rolf Derpsch recommends converting no more than 10 percent of your acreage when beginning your transition. This allows you to make some mistakes without unnecessary risk and loss. Start with a plan to convert those fields that have potential for success and which would benefit most from the practice. Most of all, be prepared to keep learning, and keep up with new developments in organic no-till and by seeking out information from the many researchers across the country that are now working with the system.

The Basics: Soil Type, Topography & Fertility

Soil type

There are three different types of soil textures: coarse textured such as sandy soils, silty soils and fine-textured clay soils. All soils are a blend of these three different soil particles. Although you probably already know your soil type, you should consider it again before trying organic no-till. This will become part of your planning process.

Organic no-till can help you address some of the challenges that you might typically experience with your soil type. In general, no-till is better suited to sandy or coarse-textured soils due to compaction that can occur in very fine-textured high clay soils. However, including selected cover crops in a cropping system can often mitigate the issue of soil compaction and hardpan development. Hardpan is a compacted layer that can develop through the misuse of tillage equipment and field traffic. It makes the soil impermeable to both air and water and limits crop success. While compaction is the bane of clay soils, the challenge with sandy soils is retention of water and crop nutrients.

In both these soil types organic matter improves the soil's resources. Organic matter opens compacted clay and makes sand more retentive to water and nutrients. Organic no-till offers a number of benefits for sandy soils. For example, over time sandy soils will benefit from the increased organic matter levels that cover crops will produce. And the dense root mat left by the cover crops will help retain moisture in the soil.

New organic matter adds carbon to the soil since about 50 percent of humus is composed of this element. For this reason, the terms "soil carbon" and "organic matter" are often used interchangeably. Organic matter refers to a complex mixture of biologically- based materials, which are reflected in a chemical sense by the measurement of elemental carbon. This carbon acts like a sponge, soaking up and holding water as it passes through the soil – then releasing it back into the system where your crops can make use of it. Organic matter also increases rooting activity, which will make sandy soils or shaley silt loams more drought resistant. Leaching of nitrogen is also reduced, due to an improved soil structure and constant nitrogen release from the soil organic matter. Finally, soil organic matter is the source of habitat and nutrition for the soil microorganisms that serve as the stomach of our soil system.

Fine textured or clay soils don't adapt themselves as well to no-till, especially when the springs are cold and wet. In this environment, it can be difficult to get soils to warm up and dry in the spring. If planted when too wet, the no-till planter can smear soil in the seed furrow, creating a difficult environment for germination and seedling emergence. For this reason, it's always better to wait until the soil surface has started to dry before planting. On the other hand, farms with clay soils also have a lot to gain from no-till – especially no-till systems that utilize cover crops. With the addition of organic matter, the tilth of clay soils will improve. As organic matter content increases many of the water issues commonly found in clay soils will also improve. These soils often tend to stay wet longer, but when they dry out they are subject to cracking and fissures. Plants are able to access moisture only during a relatively small window of time. The addition of organic matter modifies these soil properties, making it easier for plants to access soil moisture. If you are concerned about your clay soils staying wet and cold for too long in the spring, you might consider carefully the cover crop species you select to use with organic no-till to create a more beneficial environment for your crops.

Challenging topography issues

Organic no-till can help with a challenging topography, as well. Soil erosion is one of the main reasons that farmers adopt no-till practices. Cover cropping is yet another way of making sure that your soil remains stable. The thick mat of cover crop mulch helps in several ways: by reducing the impact of raindrops on the soil surface, by soaking up rainwater, by improving infiltration, and slowing water's progress across the surface of the field.

Grower Steve Groff, who began no-till farming because of serious erosion problems on his hilly farm in Pennsylvania, has an interesting video documenting the benefits of no-tilling with cover crops. During Hurricane Floyd in 1999, 11 inches of rain fell during a short time. He filmed the runoff water from his farm. It was clean compared to the muddy water coming from a neighboring field that had been farmed conventionally. Unfortunately we've all seen this occur on our own fields or those of someone in our neighborhood. Heavy rains can wash out fields, cause erosion, and move our valuable soil resource into streams and rivers.

If you have hilly ground, organic no-till will have some additional benefits for you. Organic no-till can also have positive impacts on ground or soil that is low and wet. Farmer Pat Sheridan of Fairgrove, Michigan, has had good luck growing a cover crop of cereal rye to dry out areas of his farm that typically stay wet in spring. Much of this ground is poorly drained, low-organic matter lakebed soils.

Rye can have benefits and liabilities connected with managing soil moisture. Since rye can draw water from the soil, drying it out, it allows for earlier planting is some cases but this same trait can be an issue in overly drought-prone soil. The mat of mulch provided by the Rodale organic no-till system increases the percolation and reduces runoff and evaporation. This can lead to gains of up to 50 percent in the efficiency of water use for summer crop production.

Fertility and nutrient-holding capacity

Soil fertility can be analyzed using a full soil test that includes the macronutrients: nitrogen, phosphorus, and potassium; the secondary macronutrients: calcium, magnesium and sulfur; as well as micronutrients: iron, manganese, zinc, copper and boron. However, the soil test is just a snapshot of how the soils function on one day of the year. Perhaps a better understanding of how your soil functions over time is to look at the biology, or living part of the soil. We also recommend pH adjustment as the starting point of any soil improvement strategy. The acidity reaction of the soil is extremely important and a good starting point for soil building.

Here are some indicators that your soil is functioning well (you can probably think of others):

• The soil is dark in color, which in many cases is an indication of richness in organic matter.

• The soil has a rich, earthy aroma. This so-called "good soil smell" indicates soils have active microbial populations and enough oxygen to prevent foul odors. Foul odors are generally an indication of poor soil health and quality.

• The texture is soft and crumbly, rather than hard and cloddy and shows good granulation.

• Several different stages of decomposing organic matter are evident.

• Earthworms, arthropods and other life forms are evident in the soil. A good soil is literally crawling with activity.

In order to make a successful transition to organic no-till, you'll need to build up the soil before transitioning. The soil must contain adequate levels of calcium, magnesium, potassium and phosphorus, as well as trace minerals. When these nutrients are in balance, soil life will be stimulated. As your soil health improves, the soil will feed the plants without the use of additional chemical fertilizers. A healthy soil sequesters or traps nutrients until plants need them, and has a well-developed soil structure that resists erosion and the rapid breakdown of organic matter. This results in "soil regeneration," a term made popular by Robert Rodale. However, the organic matter needs constant recharging in order to counteract depletion. When cover crops are grown they serve to feed the soil. When tillage is employed, the soil organic matter will likely become depleted. It is the balance of feeding and depleting actions that will lead to either a regeneration of the soil or soil degradation.

Organic no-till improves this process in a number of different ways. For example, no-till leaves cover crop residues at the surface of the soil, where they can readily decompose. Moldboard plowing, by contrast, may bury the residues at a deeper level where fungi and bacteria (which are mostly aerobic) are not able to function as well. The increase in crop residues and lack of disturbance fosters earthworms, which decompose organic matter and create infiltration pathways for rainwater. Earthworm castings are substantially higher in nutrients than the surrounding soil.

Water & Air

Compaction, erosion, water-holding capacity and drainage

A soil that is in good condition for agricultural production should be approximately 50 percent air, while the remainder is made up of the soil particles, soil organic matter and water. This ratio is quite important for good soil health.

COMPACTION Soil compaction is a serious concern for farmers, and can easily reduce yields by more than 10 percent depending on the crop and various environmental conditions. It can also lead to further soil and water degradation due to increased runoff and the break down of the soil structure. As soil becomes compacted, the larger pores are eliminated first. These larger pores are often home to earthworms and arthropods. Their presence in your soil is a good indicator of soil health. Ideally, you should be able to see lots of earthworm castings at the soil surface as well as holes in tilled clods of soil.

If your soil is compacted it's best to address the issue before conversion to no-till. With continuous no-till, it's difficult to remedy serious compaction issues once a commitment to the system has been made. Since organic no-till, as described here, is really a rotational tillage system that provides opportunities for tillage, compaction problems can be alleviated with the use of various tools including subsoilers, chisel plows, or even V-rippers. For this reason, organic no-till is considerably more flexible than conventional no-till.

Besides tillage, sub-surface compaction can be alleviated with the use of cover crops such as forage radishes, sorghum-sudangrass and sweet clover. These covers have a deep taproot that can penetrate hard soil layers and biologically break up compaction. In on-farm experiments, Dr. Ray Weil from the University of Maryland, has demonstrated that within 60 days the roots of forage radish can penetrate to about 35 inches (90 cm). Dr Weil, calls them the "biological drill" of the plant kingdom. Various cover crops, including rye, can be used to improve surface compaction. In general, using a good crop rotation using multiple cash crops and cover crops with different types of root systems can prevent compaction.

Once you've made the transition to organic no-till, it will be easier to maintain soil structure and prevent compaction. Higher amounts of organic matter and biological diversity, as well as reduced tillage, will protect and build the soil structure. Over time you will begin to notice cumulative benefits as your soil continuously improves.

Moving the window for spreading manure or compost into the fall can also help to avoid compaction. Manure spreaders are typically very heavy and go over the field during spring and winter when soils are often wet and vulnerable to compaction. Thus, by applying these materials at different points during your crop rotation, you can reduce your chances of creating compaction. At Rodale, we incorporate different green manure cover crops into our rotation that supply the bulk of our crop's nitrogen needs. As a result, we can apply compost at any time during the rotation. That's because the compost is now used to feed and stimulate microbial life in the soil – not as a sole source of nutrients to grow a cash crop. A combination of cover crops, compost and organic no-till allows the microbes to flourish, yielding healthy soil as well as healthy crops.

In the Rodale Institute Compost Utilization Trial, the use of synthetic fertilizer, raw manures and compost were compared in a corn, wheat and vegetable crop rotation. Over a decade of work in this ongoing experiment showed that all amendments had the ability to stimulate high yields. However, compost was shown to be superior to both raw manure and synthetic chemical fertilizer for its ability to build soil structure. We recommend using composted manure to optimize the structure of soil in no-till and tilled production systems.

EROSION Every farm has some erosion, and every farmer can do a better job of controlling it. Even if you have completely flat fields, you probably still have some type of erosion from either wind or water. If your farm fields are bare at any point during the cropping year, they are vulnerable to erosion. Erosion is also related to the loss of organic matter from soils and water quality. Although there are many ways of combating erosion, we'll focus here on solutions based on agronomic management practices. Steve Groff describes the chief advantages of no-till as its ability to prevent erosion by providing continuous soil coverage. For this reason, cover crops – not just tillage reduction – are the key to success with this approach. So often with no-till, farmers have concentrated on tillage reduction, but have not taken advantage of the benefits associated with covering the soil with active, growing plants.

No-tillage of any kind (traditional or organic) is better for highly erodible soils. Tillage contributes to erosion by allowing or even encouraging soil to physically move down the slope. It also tends to degrade the soil, speeding the process of decomposition and breaking up soil aggregates. Combined with heavy rainfall, leaving the soil bare can cause a considerable loss of topsoil. No-tillage, by contrast, leaves residue on the soil surface, minimally disturbs soils, and encourages good soil structure. Other practices employed successfully when tillage is necessary in the rotation are contour trips, terraces and the use of long-term hay crops.

You'll want to think about your farm, and analyze your erosion issues. Does your farm include some steep slopes? What time of the year are your soils most vulnerable to erosion from heavy rains or strong winds? Is the soil bare at these times under your current farming system, and are there opportunities to protect the soil by planting cover crops? What are the ways that organic no-till can help to ensure soil stability for your farm?

WATER-HOLDING CAPACITY All farms experience periodic drought, but soils differ in their ability to retain water for crop use. In general, soil in good condition should hold water for a long time without plants showing signs of stress. If plants run out of water a week or less after a good rain, it is time to build your soil with organic matter.

Organic crops tend to do better than their conventional counterparts during drought years. That's a conclusion supported by research we conducted over the past 28 years in the Rodale Institute Farming Systems Trials. That's not because it rains more on organic fields – it's because the rain is held in the upper layers of the soil profile where the crops can access it. The health and condition of your soil dramatically affects its water-holding capacity. Soil compaction creates problems because it reduces the pore spaces that store water after rainfall. A soil's water-holding capacity decreases sharply with a decrease in organic matter. In order for your soil to function adequately, you'll need some moisture in the soil for the soil life – fungi, bacteria, and small animals like earthworms. Most of these are in the top few inches of the soil – coincidentally the area that dries the fastest.

As you'll read in the "No-Till Plus" profiles, some cover crops need considerable amounts of water, and can take water away from cash crops. If your soils are degraded from years of overuse, you may want to take several seasons to build up the soil before you try organic no-till. This will ensure that the water-holding capacity of the soils is increased before you take on the challenges of adopting a new farming system.

DRAINAGE If your soil is poorly drained, you probably already know you have a problem – it's fairly obvious when you have water standing on the surface of the soil for extended periods of time. With good soil structure you should have little or no ponding or runoff, with the soil evenly moist throughout the growing season.

How fast your soil drains depends partly on soil texture. Sandy or shaley soils, with their larger pore spaces, will drain more quickly, while the smaller pores of clay soils will take longer. Soil texture will remain relatively stable over time, but there are things you can do to improve drainage rates.

There may be certain areas on your farm that are poorly drained because they are physically lower and receive runoff from other areas. All areas of your farm can benefit from improved soil structure. Higher fields can be improved to retain more soil moisture without runoff, while lower lying areas can be improved to have less compaction and larger pore spaces.

Compaction and poor drainage often go hand in hand. Areas that are poorly drained often become compacted because there may be times when it is necessary to run machinery on the land while it is still wet. Clay soils are often the most difficult to work because they remain wet for a long time. Cover cropping may help dry out these soils in the spring, and allow for earlier planting. In addition, tillage in organic no-till often takes place in the fall, which is generally a drier time of the year.

ORGANIC MATTER If your soil is in a healthy condition, organic residues should be visible at all times of the year, and at various stages in decomposition. Soil life should be visibly at work during warm weather, breaking down these residues into humus. With organic no-till, much of the residue will be at or near the soil surface. The color of the soil should be fairly dark, with the topsoil well defined and darker than the subsoil.

The living part of organic matter (colonized by bacteria and fungi) is relatively quick to develop with no-till or reduced tillage techniques. This component is important because it fuels a consistent release of soil nutrients that are used by actively growing crops. Humus, which forms the stable and less active portion of the soil organic matter, takes longer to build up – several years instead of several months.

Organic matter can be added to the soil not only through cover cropping and green manures, but also through the addition of animal manures and/or compost. Applied in the late summer or early fall, these can produce an extra fertility boost, as well as more carbon for the system. Different kinds of manure have different compositions of nutrients and organic matter. Compost is a relatively stable source of both carbon and nutrients that does not degrade easily or leach out of soils.

At the Rodale Institute we add compost after a winter wheat or spring oat harvest in August when the soil is dry to prevent issues with compaction of wet soil. Because the compost is stable and the nutrient base is not highly soluble, we avoid the issues with water quality that are sometimes experienced with applying fertilizer and raw manures.

AGGREGATE STABILITY Aggregates are the small nuggets of soil that make up good soil structure. They are byproducts of microbial breakdown of organic matter. As you examine your soil quality, you'll know if you have good aggregation by observing a crumbly, granulated texture, rather than cloddy soil.

In general, residues that contain a lot of cellulose and easy-to-digest materials have more of an effect on soil aggregates than compost. Compost has already gone through the process of decomposition and is in a relatively stable form. Just like humans, soil microorganisms benefit by having a diverse menu of different kinds of organic matter – some materials that are higher in lignin (the woody material in plant stems) and some that are greener and more succulent. You can achieve balanced nutrition for your microbes by working on a diverse crop rotation. Besides organic matter, applications of other amendments may also help. Soils with very poor aggregate stability may benefit from applications of gypsum. The calcium in gypsum is known to link humic organic materials with clay. This interaction is part and parcel of the aggregation and stabilization process needed for healthy soil.

Aggregation is aided by the ability of the gooey and gluey substances produced by fungi and bacteria and their ability to stick soil particles together. This conserves organic matter that otherwise would decay. When soil particles are glued together they not only serve to allow more water and air to penetrate but their size makes them much more immobile in terms of wind and water erosion. Improved aggregate stability really pays off with better soil structure, as well as soils that are resistant to compaction and erosion. And healthy soil will promote bumper crops on your farm.

TILTH Good tilth is immediately recognizable to experienced farmers. The soil should be soft and easily pulled apart without damage to its structure. The soil crumbles without forming into clods and is spongy when you walk on it. Tilth is a general concept that encompasses many of the qualities we have already discussed. In order to have good tilth (and the healthiest possible plants), soils need to have the following qualities:

Good porosity: Large pores absorb and store rainwater that plants can use effectively.

Be well aerated: Soil that is not compacted and has plenty of air space for good soil life and water.

Be highly aggregated: Soil that has a well developed structure that resists erosion and nourishes plants.

Have plenty of organic matter: Plus residues from microbes, earthworms and other soil organisms.

Soil with good tilth promotes plants with healthy root systems that are resistant to pests and disease.

A good example of the problems of poor soils is damping off, a disease in which seed and seedlings of corn, soybean, and most other crops can rot in overly wet and cold soil. By increasing the soil oxygen available through improved soil structure, damping off is greatly reduced. A recent test showed our organically managed soils from research plots in our long-term experiment, the Rodale Farming System Trial using the Iowa Cold Germination Test, and found that sweet corn emergence was improved 100 percent when compared to soil from conventional plots.

Crop & Environment

Root health

Are roots reaching their full potential to provide nutrients, stability and water to your crop? Dig down and evaluate your crop's roots during their rapid growth period. Look for major problems, such as stunted roots, or roots that change direction abruptly. They should extend down into the subsoil and have good development. Observe any diseased roots, or off-color roots that look rotten. Applications of compost can help suppress root (as well as leaf) diseases.

Many beneficial microorganisms live in the rhizosphere, or the zone of soil that is directly adjacent to the plant's roots. Others invade and inhabit plant roots, and co-exist in a symbiotic relationship. Most plants establish beneficial relationships with fungi called mycorrhizae. These fungi help plants to absorb nutrients and water from the soil, especially phosphorus. Most of these are too small to see without the aid of a microscope. However, you can check the roots of legumes (clovers, vetches, peas, beans) to make sure they are well-nodulated. The round structures on the roots are filled with bacteria that can feed the plant and soil with nitrogen from the soil air. If this process is active, the nodules will be abundant and in the young stages dark red in color when you cut them apart. You'll know when you've got a good population of microorganisms – the crop roots will be extensive and the plants will look big for their age and have good color.

Soil temperatures

With a heavy mat of cover crops on the surface of the soil, you can expect the soil to warm up more slowly in the spring. The mulch layer will also prevent extremes in temperatures during the summer months, which may benefit plants. This mulch layer will also prevent your soil from "baking" in the sun. The soil may also stay warmer during the fall, extending the period of time when plants are actively growing.

Depending on where you live, the temperature moderation afforded by the mulch layer can be either positive or negative. You might keep track of this by monitoring the soil temperature on a weekly basis throughout the growing season, comparing it to a clean cultivated area. How do soil temperatures differ through the spring? Do the plants in the mulched area catch up at some point? What are the end effects in terms of plant vigor and yield?

Soil temperature is a critical concern as we begin to address using these heavy cover crop mulches to replace black plastic in no-till vegetable production. While black plastic will warm soils early in spring they also bake them in the heat of summer. This increases the need for irrigation and kills off many of the soil microbial populations we've all been working so hard to build up. Soil roasting under a sheet of black plastic in 100 F heat isn't going to be conducive to building soil health.

Crop condition

Of course the most important indicator of the success of your soil management can be seen in the crops you produce. Your crops should be healthy and happy, with no visible signs of nutrient deficiencies or stress. Your yields should be good, and the crops should be of high quality, highly nutritious, with good post-harvest holding capacity.

There are a number of things you can do to monitor how your crops are performing. Keep track of yields. Over a period of years, how do they compare to an average yield for your area? Monitor and document any problems with pests. Did an increased number of beneficials have a positive effect on pests and disease? How did weed populations compare to other systems? Were there any shifts in weed species and did they affect your crop performance?

Organic farmers often notice that crops store better and are more nutritious than non-organic crops. Crops hold longer due to lower nitrate levels and higher levels of nutrients like calcium. In addition, organic crops are highly palatable to livestock. This kind of qualitative difference is often hard to measure without side-by-side trials.

Besides utilizing soil analysis to prevent problems, analysis of crop tissue is very important to understand how your crops can be managed and adjusted to optimize your results. This can be used as a supplement to soil analysis. Tissue sampling can help you understand how well your plants are able to access nutrients. Almost all testing labs can provide these services.

Some of these benefits might be noticeable immediately, while others may take several years to become apparent. Good recordkeeping is the key to tracking long-term changes and prevent you from making "snap" judgments based on limited information. If you are already farming organically, much of the recordkeeping will already be part of your requirements for certification.

Soil environment

The soil environment consists of organisms like fungi, many bacteria and actinomycetes as well as small and large animals. Your crop is part of this environment and directly and subtly influencing it as it pulls energy from the sun into the life of the soil. In order for your crops to yield well, the soil environment needs to also function well.

Larger soil organisms such as beetles, spiders, earthworms, springtails, etc. should be visible on a walk through the field. You should hope to see crop residues breaking down more quickly than before your conversion to organic no-till. You should also have fewer problems with pests and diseases because of the diversity of soil life.

Soil biology

Here are some simple, inexpensive tests that you can perform to ensure that your soil biology is thriving. Gather some topsoil from your field. Place it in a small dish, similar to a petri dish. Take a small piece of newspaper or paper towel and place it on top of the soil. Cover the dish with a plastic cover or kitchen cling wrap; set it in a warm place and then watch. If the soil is biologically active the microbes in the soil will actively break down the carbon in the paper and it will dissolve over a period of a few days. Run this test periodically and time the decomposition. As your soil improves, the rate of decomposition will speed up.

Tracking changes during a conversion to no-till

Noticing qualitative changes in your soil is crucially important to understand how your soil functions and evaluate changes needed to improve soil quality. These assessments can be made with a combination of tools and field observations.

Tools

SOIL TEST KITS A professional quality soil test kit will help you assess a number of different properties, including soil respiration, aggregate stability, soil nitrate levels, and infiltration. These test results when coupled with basic chemistry analysis as supplied by any university or private soils lab, will begin to paint a complete picture of your soil's state of health.

SOIL PENETROMETER A penetrometer can help you discover compaction layers in your soil. It can measure both the depth of sub-surface compaction (as with a hardpan) and the hardness of the compaction layer. Readings should be taken when the soil is at field capacity (about 24 hours after a soaking rain). Usually, the best time of the year for this is during the spring. It's usually recommended to take three to four readings per acre. Compare these readings to an area that is undisturbed, like a fencerow. Generally, readings over 75 indicate severe compaction, which needs to be remedied with subsoiling, or by planting a cover crop like forage radishes that help relieve the compaction.

You can also use a stiff piece of wire (like those that come with irrigation marking flags) for a less formal test. Generally, your soil is compacted if the wire is hard to push in or if it bends or breaks when pushed in.

Observations at Key Times

It is always important to make your observations at the proper time of the year when the data you collect will be most relevant.

Observation examples:

SPRING AND FALL This is the time to notice earthworm populations, which surge with abundant soil moisture and warm temperatures. Ideally, you should be able to notice 10 worms per square foot of soil.

SUMMER Keep analyzing crop health during the growing season, looking for nutrient deficiencies and stunting in times of stress. Collect leaves for tissue analysis.

AFTER A HEAVY RAINFALL This may not be your favorite time to be out in the field, but it is a good time to notice problems with erosion, infiltration, drainage, and by extension compaction and soil structure issues.

FALL This is a good time to take soil samples for analysis.

▶ CUTTING HEIGHT FOR CORN & RESIDUE BREAKDOWN

University of Nebraska ag engineer Paul Jasa recently offered his opinion on an ideal cutting height for corn, as well as his recommendation for trying to speed residue breakdown, in a recent issue of *CropWatch.*

QUESTION: With this year's above average corn height and ear placements 6 feet or higher on the plant, do we still want to pick the corn leaving an average stubble height or should stubble height be higher?

Also, we no-till our soybeans alongside our standing corn stalks. This generally works well until damp conditions during harvest cause problems. Today's hybrids don't break down and rot like they used to. Is there something, besides nitrogen, that you can apply on these corn stalks to help break them down?

ANSWER: The corn is very tall and some producers may be tempted to run the corn heads a little higher this year (as long as the corn keeps standing). However, with a systems approach to no-till in mind, I still like to run the corn head about 18 inches off the ground. That leaves the stubble about toolbar height on the planters and drills. Running higher than that may cause problems with hoses, wires, cables and chains being snagged on the residue next planting season.

Running this height leaves enough stubble to keep the wind off the soil surface, reducing the amount of residue that's blown around, and allows for some snow capture. Also, running this height processes most of the stalk through the snapping rolls so that the residue is broken open and exposed to the soil microbes. Running higher will result in much more residue lasting longer into the next season.

If you run higher, a lean bar on the front of the planter or drill will lean the stalks over to reduce catching on the planting equipment. But again, the stalks won't be broken open to allow faster cycling back into the soil system. If you need more residue, this is an option.

Regarding harvesting soybeans no-tilled into corn residue: I prefer the 3-inch sickle and guards to allow room for the stalks to get cut off. The 1.5-inch, quick-cut systems tend to plug up with corn stalks.

Tillage

Benefits of tillage

Although yearly tillage does have many drawbacks, rotational tillage also has some advantages, including preparation of a good seedbed, weed control, increasing the aerobic zone and incorporating organic matter. Rotational tillage does not create long-lasting problems with soil structure. In most organic systems complete tillage used in a solid crop rotation will be a valuable tool for managing perennial weeds, something mulches have difficulty doing.

"Bio-tilling" with forage radishes

Researcher Ray Weil at the University of Maryland has been experimenting with planting forage radishes, which send down a 1-2 inch diameter taproot, 12-18 inches deep. The fall-planted cover crop can loosen soils and sequester nitrogen (170 lbs./acre) before winterkilling in late December. They are also good growers, contributing an aboveground dry biomass of 8,000 lbs./acre and a belowground biomass as high as 3,700 lbs./acre. The winterkilled remains of the forage radish decompose relatively quickly, however, so it wouldn't contribute enough residue for a season-long mulch in a no-till system.

▶ CUTTING HEIGHT FOR CORN & RESIDUE BREAKDOWN (CONTINUED)

Also, I like planting directly down the old corn row so that the planter runs over the corn stalks. Set the planter deeper to get the seeds into the soil. Then the stalks decompose faster and aren't as much of a problem at harvest.

If it's dry, we can harvest either direction; however, if the stalks are damp, we tend to harvest in the direction the stalks are leaning (the direction of planting).

I haven't worked with any of the products to hasten residue breakdown and usually am more concerned with how to keep the residue longer. Nitrogen does feed the soil microbes to help balance the carbon-to-nitrogen ratio of the corn stalks to get faster breakdown. However, that only works if the residue is in contact with the soil and the microbes.

Tall, dry stalks after harvest won't break down much as there isn't much biological activity. If you're considering spraying on some nitrogen, do it in the early spring as a herbicide carrier for your early pre-plant and winter annual weed-control application. Applying it in fall isn't real effective, as many of the microbes become less active as the weather cools and potential nitrogen losses are much higher.

I have discovered that drilling a cover crop into standing corn stalks really speeds the residue breakdown. The drill does cut up the residue some and puts more of it in contact with the soil. The growing cover crop helps feed the microbes and the humidity under the growing cover crop speeds breakdown.

Using a brassica cover crop will break down almost all the residue, resulting in too little cover remaining if the cover crop is seeded early enough to get some good growth.

A legume cover crop will help balance the carbon-to-nitrogen ratio and make some nitrogen for the next crop. There are several options and we need more work and experience on which ones to select and how to manage them.

Reprinted from No-Till Farmer, *Post Office Box 624, Brookfield, WI 53008-0624. Website:* www.no-tillfarmer.com.

The taproots of forage radishes can alleviate compacted soil. In an experiment with several kinds of cover crops, including canola, oilseed radish, forage radish and cereal rye, forage radish was shown to have the most beneficial effect on soil compaction. In a later evaluation with a minirhizotron camera, researchers monitored the subsequent root growth of soybeans. Soybean roots were documented growing along the channels left by the decomposed roots of the cover crop. At Wye Research and Education Center (WREC) in Maryland, where the drought conditions and compaction were the worst of any of the test sites, the rye/radish combination had a significant effect on the soybean yield.

Another interesting characteristic of forage radishes is their allelopathic qualities. These radishes (like other members of the mustard family) produce glycosinolate compounds. The breakdown products of this chemical are volatile and function like a commercial fumigant. The toxic biological byproduct is cyanide. Forage radishes show potential for control of nematodes, diseases and weeds. A cover crop of fall-planted radishes is excellent for late-season weed management in an organic system.

Carbon Sequestration: Build the Soil While You Grow your Crops

Carbon cycle dynamics

Global warming is an issue under discussion worldwide. Organic farming systems can have a tremendous impact on the reduction of greenhouse gases. Although more than one gas is responsible for global warming, we'll focus on carbon dioxide for the purposes of this discussion. Carbon is released into the atmosphere when carbon in the soil, in the form of soil organic matter or humus, breaks down and volatilizes.

Carbon can be sequestered in more than one form. Plants are a major sink for carbon dioxide, but soil organic matter has the potential to sequester even more carbon than plants. Carbon is also released from burning fossil fuels and the creation of chemical fertilizers. Systems that use more petrochemicals also use more carbon resources. Dr. David Pimentel, a scientist at Cornell University, estimates that U.S. agriculture currently emits about 925 billion pounds of carbon dioxide yearly from crop and livestock production. If you adopt organic no-till practices on your farm you'll be reducing your carbon footprint and store or sequester significant amounts of carbon in the soil.

In collaboration with Dr. David Pimentel, Rodale Institute has demonstrated that farmers can achieve a 33 percent reduction of energy costs by using legumes in their annual crop rotations. The biological fixation of nitrogen replaces the generation of synthetic forms of nitrogen that require fossil fuels to create. When no-till is included in the farming system, farmers can reduce their energy requirements by 50 to 70 percent.

Comparison of Several Cropping Systems and their Impact on Carbon

CONVENTIONAL (CHEMICAL-BASED) SYSTEMS WITH TILLAGE AND CARBON Conventional tillage agriculture releases the most carbon into the atmosphere. As plowing and tillage occur, air is added to the soil and the decomposition process speeds up. If soils are not taken care of properly, erosion can remove large amounts of organic matter from the soil. In addition, chemical fertilizers and fossil fuels lead to a net loss of sequestered carbon. In this system the chemical fertilizers act as a fuel source that burns the carbon, releasing it back into the atmosphere. On some farms, soil structure breaks down due to a suppression of naturally occurring soil microorganisms. These microbes are imperiled when chemical fertilizers, fungicides and herbicides are used.

ORGANIC FARMING SYSTEMS WITH TILLAGE AND CARBON Even though traditional organic farming often requires a substantial amount of tillage and cultivation, organic farming has several things going for it. Because no chemical fertilizers are used, organic farmers add organic matter to soils through the use of cover cropping, manure-based fertilizers, and compost. As the microbial soil life is nurtured through a consistent addition of these materials, additional benefits are realized. For example, mycorrhizae in partnership with plant roots produce glomalins, a kind of glue that holds the soil particles together. They form aggregates that are quite resistant to soil erosion. At the Rodale Institute research farm, our Farming Systems Trial during the past 23 years has shown that organic farming can build soil organic matter by 15 to 28 percent.

CONVENTIONAL FARMING SYSTEMS USING NO-TILL AND CARBON No-till farming systems also have the potential to build soil carbon, but at a much lower capacity, a maximum of about 300 lbs./acre per year have been documented. The rate that carbon accumulates in the soil can depend on such factors as soil type, farming methods and climate. The increase may not occur at a steady rate, with a smaller increase during the first few years, then a rapid increase, and finally plateau after 20 or more years. The increase in the rate of soil carbon is due to the surface residues that are left on the soil from the previous year's crops, as well as the lack of tillage and soil disturbance. Plus, no-till uses less fuel to produce a crop. However, there is a downside to no-till – the use of herbicides to control weeds and the use of chemical fertilizers to supply crop nutrients leads to a reduction of the net amount of carbon sequestered.

Organic no-till: the best of all worlds

In many ways, organic no-till combines some of the best aspects of organic agriculture and no-till. First, it sequesters large amounts of carbon through cover cropping. It uses cover crops, grown at maturity, that provide large amounts of carbon as a means of weed management. These residues break down slowly over time. Although no-till alone can sequester up to 300 lbs. of carbon per acre per year, using compost and cover crops have been shown to sequester 2,000 and 1,000 lbs. per acre per year respectively.

Secondly, the killed cover crop mat protects the soil from erosion and builds soil structure, while providing a continuous food supply for microorganisms. Although accelerated breakdown of soil organic matter occurs during yearly tillage, this is not enough to outweigh the benefits of the system. In addition, organic no-till uses few petrochemicals – no herbicides, fungicides or insecticides, and less fuel than either organic tilled or traditional no-till systems. The combination of both no-till and organic agriculture is the best option for addressing global warming concerns while conserving the world's resources at the same time.

Carbon credits for organic farmers

Could organic no-till farmers reap the rewards of a cap and trade system for carbon credits? It's a possibility for the future. Currently, benefits are being offered only to farmers who either practice no-till, pasture, agriforestry, rangeland in the western states, or methane capture systems. Organic no-till, because it uses rotational tillage, does not currently quality for carbon trading. But rewards may be in the foreseeable future as we collect and document more information about organic and organic no-till methods. Carbon units could be traded by businesses who are given reduction goals and who would like to purchase excessive reductions (or credits).

Rodale's long-term goal is to help all farmers (organic and conventional) to move towards a holistic assessment of their farms, with credits for the net positive effect on carbon emissions. A sample program might include credits for increasing organic matter in the soil, and deductions for the amount of petrochemical fuel used on the farm. Organic no-till would likely come out quite well in such an analysis. According to the Farming Systems

Trial, organic farmers use about one third less fossil fuel than that used in the conventional corn/soybean cropping systems. Not only that, but data from the trial indicated that soils under organic farm management can accumulate about 1,000 pounds of carbon per acre of soil each year.

Farmers who are currently practicing conventional no-till may want to contact an organization such as the National Farmers Union or Farm Bureau to learn more about their carbon credit programs. These organizations serve as agents and can sign up farmers as offset producers. For more information see the sources at the end of this chapter.

Resources

Baker, C.J. et al. *No Tillage Seeding in Conservation Agriculture,* 2nd Edition. Cambridge, U.K.: CAB International, 2007.

Hepperly, Paul. "Organic farming sequesters atmospheric carbon and nutrients in soils." *The New Farm,* 2003. *http://www.rodaleinstitute.org/ob_2.*

Hepperly, Paul and Christine Ziegler Ulsh. "Good compost made better: Rodale Institute takes "black gold" one step further." *The New Farm,* 2006. *www.rodaleinstitute.org/20060413/ulshhepperly.*

Magdoff, Fred and Harold van Es. *Building Soils for Better Crops.* Beltsville: Sustainable Agriculture Network, 2000.

National Farmers Union Carbon Credit Program *http://nfu.org/issues/environment/carbon-credits.*

Ngouajio, Mathieu and Dale Mutch. "Oilseed Radish: A New Cover Crop for Michigan." *Michigan State University Extension Bulletin* E 2907, 2004.

Purakaystha, T.J., D.R. Huggins and J.L. Smith. "Carbon Sequestration in Native Prairie, Perennial Grass, No-Till and Cultivated Palouse Silt Loam." *Soil Science Society of America Journal:* Volume 72: Number 2 March-April 2008.

Sullivan, Preston. "Sustainable Soil Management." ATTRA, 2004. *http://attra.ncat.org/attra-pub/PDF/soilmgmt.pdf.*

Soil Quality Test Kit Guide. USDA-ARS 1999. *http://soils.usda.gov/sqi/assessment/files/test_kit_complete.pdf.*

Williams, Stacy and Ray Weil. "Crop Cover Root Channels May Alleviate Soil Compaction Effects on Soybean Crop." *Soil Society of America Journal.* 68:1403-1409. 2004. *http://soil.scijournals.org/cgi/content/full/68/4/1403.*

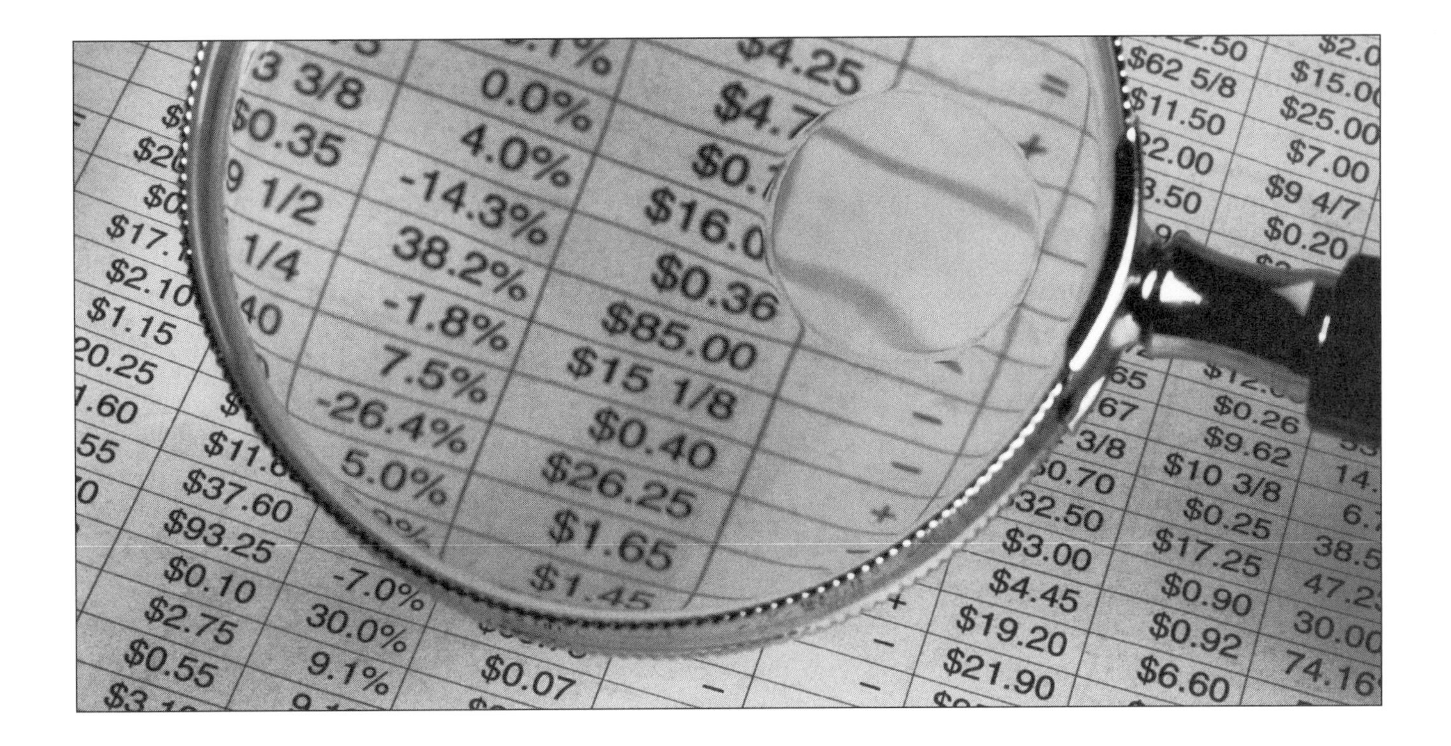

CHAPTER 09

NO-TILL FINANCIAL PLANNING

An organic no-till operation involves considerable planning, as we've already discussed. If you are currently farming no-till, the financial investment in converting to organic no-till is fairly minimal. If you currently use conventional tillage but want to experiment with no-till, the investment is more extensive. Of course, the amount of money needed will depend on the size of your farm operation. By giving you as much information as possible about costs, we hope to help you get started with your financial planning. Although you can't expect to become a millionaire farmer overnight, you should be able to save some money and improve your bottom line with organic no-till.

The Costs . . . and the Savings

Equipment costs

Equipment will be your biggest start up cost – especially if you are using conventional tillage. The following is an outline of the equipment needed and the approximate costs:

• Roller/crimper: $3,000-$15,000 (depending on width)

• Front 3-point hitch: $3,000 (approx.) at the Buckeye Tractor Company *(www.buctraco.com)*

• No-till planter: cost will vary depending on size, but it is worth looking to pay more for a quality planter in good condition as you'll be expecting a lot from it.

▶ SAMPLE EQUIPMENT BUDGET

Equipment	Cost
Roller/Crimper	$3,200
Front End Hitch	$2,500
No-Till Planter	$20,000
Planter Modifications	$460
Total cost:	$30,600

• Planter modifications: The costs will depend on the number of planter units and the modifications required. Allow anywhere from $100 per row and up.

• Tractor: The tractor size will be governed by the planter size. The tractor must be of suitable size to pick the roller off the ground for turning. Actual operation of the roller (pushing or pulling) takes very little energy since it simply rolls over the surface of the ground.

SAMPLE EQUIPMENT BUDGET:

Here's how much Rodale spent on our start up costs for the roller/crimper system. This might be what someone might spend for a medium-sized operation.

▶ COVER CROP SEED COSTS

	Rye	Vetch
Normal seeding rate	60 (drilled) -160 (broadcast) lbs./acre	15-20 (drilled) lbs./acre
Organic no-till seeding rate	120 (drilled) -240 (broadcast) lbs./acre (Rodale uses 150 lbs./acre)	15 (drilled)-40 (broadcast) lbs./acre
Organic seed cost	$14.50/ 50 lbs.	$92.50/ 50 lbs.
Conventional seed cost	$7.50/ 50 lbs.	$75.00/ 50 lbs.

Seed costs

You will probably pay more money for seed with the organic no-till system. With organic no-till, the cover crop is extremely important, and it pays to invest money in good seed. Locally sourced organic seed may be more expensive, but it's worth the cost. Seeding rates are higher in this system, so make sure to allow enough in your budget to cover these costs. The cash crop will have a higher seeding rate, as well to compensate for seedling loss due to the heavy mulch.

▶ COVER CROP SEED COSTS

	Corn	Soybeans
Conventional seed cost	$107-$196/50 lbs.	$24-$40/50 lbs.
Organic seed cost	$118-$137/50 lbs.	$21-$29/50 lbs.
Conventional seed rate	20,000-40,000 plant population	120,000-190,000 plant population
Organic seed rate	30,000 plant population	200,000 (30 inch rows)
No-till organic seed rate	32,000/ acre	220,000/ acre

▶ ENERGY USED IN DIFFERENT CORN PRODUCTION SYSTEMS

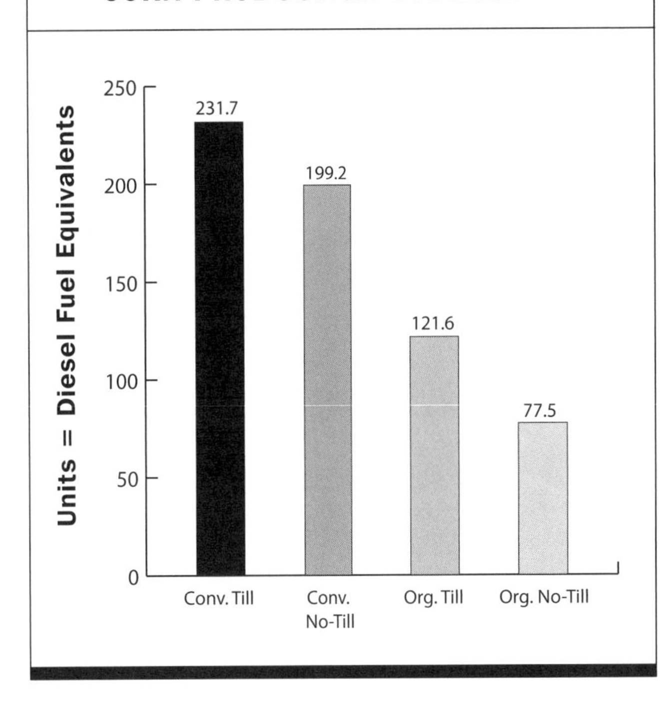

The Savings

FUEL

After a conversion to no-till, you can expect to cut your fuel costs by 50 percent or more. The number of field operations will decrease considerably.

The table above shows the energy used in different kinds of corn production systems. It represents all costs converted to diesel fuel equivalents and includes fuel costs.

HERBICIDE SAVINGS

Since herbicides are not needed in this system, you can count that as a savings. Conventional farmers may still want to budget some money for an herbicide application to take care of the few weeds that may break through the mulch.

INSECTICIDE SAVINGS

You should save money on insecticide costs, but you may have new pests to deal with. Conventional farmers will want to spray, and organic farmers may want to think through other strategies such as delayed planting, or field border plantings that encourage beneficial insects.

FERTILIZERS SAVINGS

You save here too, because in most cases you are growing your own fertilizer (nitrogen) with the cover crops. If you are transitioning to organic, you may still need to budget some money for fertilizer since it takes a while for nutrients to start cycling. In other words, most of the nutrients from the cover crops won't be available for crop use the first year. As microorganisms break down the cover crops and your organic matter goes up, you can cut back on fertilizer and achieve the same crop yields.

▶ FUEL COSTS ESTIMATES

Field Operations	Traditional Organic (per acre)	Organic No-Till (per acre)
Cover crop: Planting	$3.30	$3.30
Cover crop: Disking & incorporating	$2.40	N/A
Seedbed preparation	$2.30	N/A
Planting (and rolling)	$3.30	$3.30
Rotary hoeing	$2.30	N/A
Cultivation	$2.30	N/A
Combining	$11.00	$11.00
Disk crop residue	$2.40	$2.40
Total costs:	**$29.30**	**$20.00**

Your fuel costs will vary, but they'll always be less for organic no-till, because there are fewer operations per acre each season.

SAVING WITH ROW SPACING

You might experiment with narrower rows as a way to boost yields. Since organic no-till is a one-pass system for planting with no cultivation needed, you can narrow those rows from 30 inches to 20 inches or 15 inches and even consider using a grain drill for crops like soybeans and plant on 7 inch or eight inch rows.

USING THE CROP CONVERSION CALCULATOR

The Crop Conversion Calculator is a free tool that you can use online at the New Farm website, *www.newfarm.org*. You can use it to compare costs for your current farm operation and an organic no-till system. To get you started, we have included two sample budgets for different farms.

Iowa State has also developed a web page for Organic Crop Production Enterprise Budgets. The worksheets can also be helpful in figuring out your budget. The website can be found at *www.extension.iastate.edu/agdm/crops/html/a1-18.html.*

SAVING MONEY WITH LOW COST TOOLS OR SHARING TOOLS

- Rent a no-till planter
- Share a roller/crimper and a front end hitch with a neighbor
- Build a roller/crimper yourself

SHORTCUT THE LEARNING CURVE AND SAVE MONEY

With any new system, there is always a learning curve, and that learning curve can cost you money. With accurate recordkeeping you can learn more the first year and prepare yourself to make important changes in successive years. This can save money, time and resources. Some of the costs you may want to keep track of are:

- Seed costs (cover crop, cash crop) and seeding rates
- Cost of manufacturing compost (if this is new for you)
- Custom operations (if you choose to outsource)
- Machinery costs (repairs and maintenance)
- Farmer labor costs
- New equipment and modifications costs
- Herbicide and insecticide costs

ON-FARM RESEARCH

Trying a new technique in a small area is one of the easiest ways to minimize your risk. In order to have a representative trial, it's important that the plot is similar to other areas on your farm and to have the same growing conditions. You'll need to have a control plot with the same conditions. For information on how to conduct on-farm research you can visit the Organic Farming Research Foundation (OFRF) website at *www.ofrf.org* or request the publication "On-Farm Research Guide." Rodale also publishes a similar guide called "A Farmers Guide to On-Farm Research."

Here are a few tips for on-farm research:

- Consult with someone experienced in designing experiments, such as your extension agent.
- Conditions within your experiment should be as uniform as possible.
- Design plots that are easy to maintain.
- Keep a notebook dedicated to the research project. Document as much as possible as you go along.
- At harvest, measure yields from each plot, and document which plot each sample comes from.
- Design your experiment so that it has between four and six replications. This will eliminate much of the natural variation.
- Randomize your plots to eliminate any other sources of bias.
- Use a control that receives your normal practice or variety. This will give you a comparison to measure your experiment against.

▶ SAMPLE OF A MASTER LIST OF EXPENSES WORKSHEET

Expenses	Year 1	Year 2
Cover crop seed		
Cash crop seed		
Compost		
Custom operations		
Machinery: repairs		
Machinery: maintenance		
Labor		
Field preparation		
Spread fertilizer & amendments		
Cultivation		
Combining		
Disking		
Fertilizer		
Soil conditioners		
Fuel		
Total Expenses:		

RECORDKEEPING

Even if you don't do an official on-farm experiment, nothing is more important than good recordkeeping. Recording field operations and yield is important, but you'll also need to return to the field often to check the planting for crop quality. Digital photos are an excellent way of recording visual observations that don't translate well to written information.

Sharing Information With Others

Form a local group of farmers who are interested in pooling information. Although everyone will have different opinions about what will work on their farms, you may come up with some useful tips. Also check out the wealth of information online, including the New Farm forums.

NEW FARM FORUMS

The New Farm website *http://newfarm.rodaleinstitute.org/talk* has many informative forums to ask questions and share experiences. Under

> ▶ **RECORDKEEPING WORKSHEET**
>
> Fill out one per field
>
> Name of cover crop ________________
>
> Name of cash crop ________________
>
> Field location/ID code ________________

Recordkeeping Item	Numbers	Notes: field conditions & other info
Cover crops:		
Seeding rate		
Germination rate		
Planting date		
Precipitation		
Cover crop biomass estimate		
Date of anthesis/ blooming		
Date of rolling		
Rate of kill		
Cash crop:		
Date of planting		
Seeding rate		
Plant population estimate		
Insect/disease problems		
Weed issues		
Rainfall amounts		
Harvest date		
Yield		

the No-Till Plus section, forums include the following:

General – For questions and comments about no-till in general, the goals of The Rodale Institute's No-Till Plus Project, and the setup of this forum.

No-Till Equipment – Covers building, buying and modifying no-till planters, cover crop rollers and other implements.

Cover Crops and Rotations – For discussion about choosing and testing cover crops and designing crop rotation sequences for no-till systems.

All Organic – A place for organic growers to discuss the additional challenges and benefits of organic no-till.

Grant programs

A grant can provide start up capital, while providing a low-risk way to explore organic no-till. For the best results, collaborate with a researcher. Non-profit organizations and universities can apply for many more kinds of grants than can individuals. The following are grant programs that accept applications from farmers.

The Sustainable Agriculture Research and Education (SARE) program helps advance farming systems that are profitable, environmentally sound, and good for communities through a nationwide research and education grants program. SARE provides funding opportunities annually through four regions in a competitive process.

Contact:
USDA-CSREES
Stop 2223
1400 Independence Ave. SW
Washington, DC 20250-2223
Phone (202) 720-5384
Fax (202) 720-6071
www.sare.org

The Organic Farming Research Foundation's (OFRF) purpose is to foster the improvement and widespread adoption of organic farming systems. They sponsor research related to organic farming and help disseminate research results to organic farmers and growers.

Contact:
Organic Farming Research Foundation
P.O. Box 440
Santa Cruz, CA 95061
Phone (831) 426-6606
Fax (831) 426-6670
www.ofrf.org

The Environmental Quality Incentives Program (EQIP) provides a voluntary conservation program for farmers and ranchers who promote agricultural production and environmental quality as compatible national goals. EQIP may cost-share up to 75 percent of the costs of certain conservation practices. Some limited resource producers and beginning farmers may be eligible for cost-shares of up to 90 percent.

Contact:
Environmental Improvements
Programs Branch Chief
1400 Independence Ave. SW Room 5239
Washington, DC 20250
Phone (202) 720-1845
Fax (202) 720-4265
www.nrcs.usda.gov/programs/eqip/

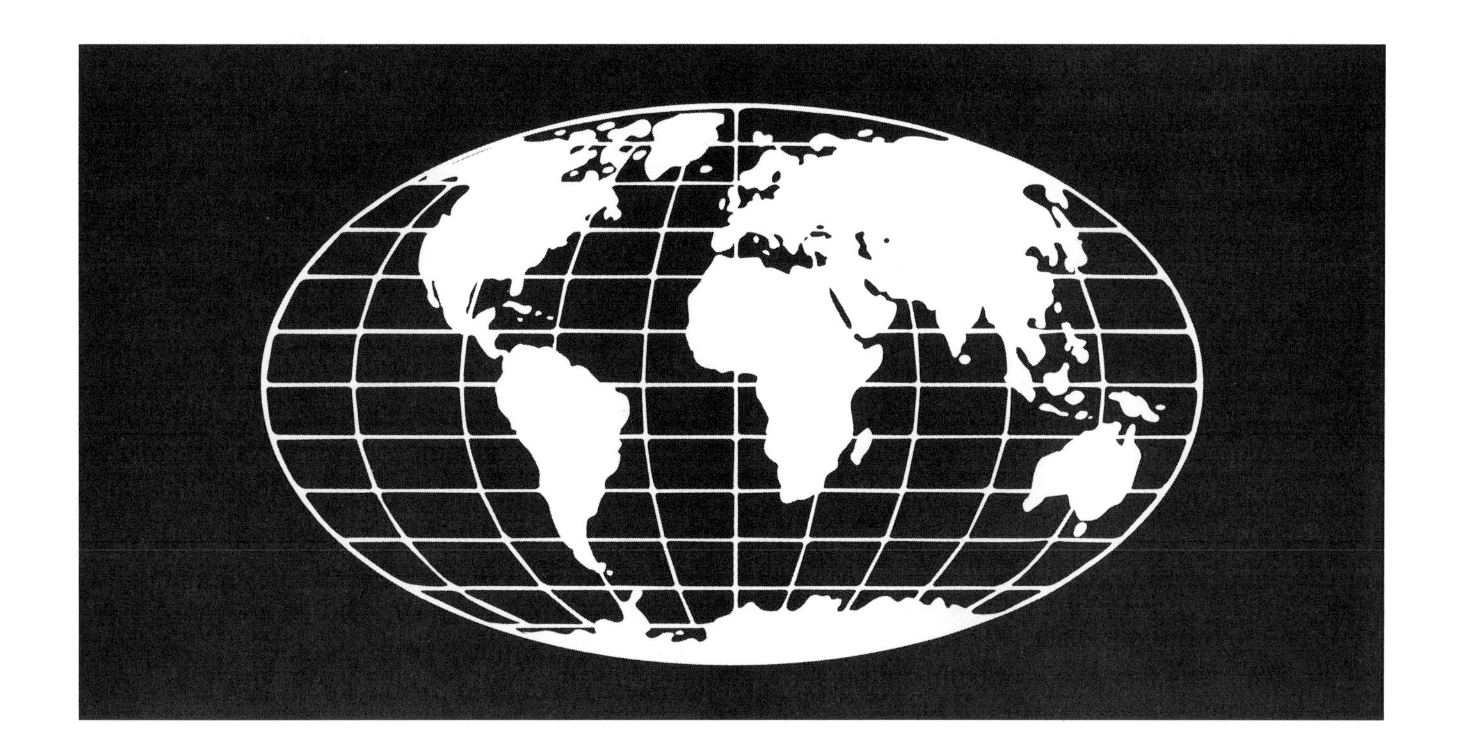

CHAPTER 10 ROLLER/CRIMPERS AROUND THE WORLD

One good thing about networking with other farmers is that most of the time you find out you're not alone. Others have the same challenges and worries that you do. That's why it's so important to get off the farm occasionally for a workshop, a conference, or a field day. We're hoping to get you off the farm with this chapter (if only in your imagination!).

Cover crop rollers are an idea whose time has come – we know this because many people are coming up with similar ideas at the same time. Here's a brief rundown on farmers from other countries who are presently using some of the technologies described in other sections of this book.

First we'll journey to South America, the home of the knife roller, which is the progenitor of all other rollers. We'll see the unique conditions that make rollers such a good tool for farmers. In Brazil and Paraguay no-till farming combined with cover cropping and rollers are widely accepted as a farming method.

Paraguay & Brazil

In Brazil, approximately 10 percent of no-till farmers use cover crops that they control with rollers or some other tool. This means approximately 25 million hectares, or about 62 million acres. A number of these are organic farmers. For Latin American farmers, no-tillage has been the most sustainable production system ever developed for agriculture. In countries like Brazil and Argentina, the introduction of no-till has helped to reverse declining crop yields. Farmers have adopted the system because it provides a way to make more money while protecting the environment all with less overall effort. Using the knife roller on cover crops has made organic farming possible for some, while reducing herbicide costs for others.

To learn more about the Paraguayan perspective, I talked with Rolf Derpsch, an agricultural consultant who lives in Asuncion, Paraguay. He has been working with no-till agriculture since the 1970s. Farmers in tropical regions have adopted no-till primarily to conserve soil, which can easily wash away during high rainfall episodes. Without vegetation covering the soil, it quickly degrades and becomes much less productive. Some areas receive much more annual rainfall than others. North of San Paolo (including Paraguay), the annual rainfall is much greater – about 1,800 mm (about 70 inches). South of San Paolo in a region called the Cerrado, the soil is much drier and receives about 100 mm of rain annually, or about 39 inches. Much of the rain falls seasonally, with a lengthy dry spell.

From my discussions with Rolf, it became very clear that cover cropping is intrinsic to the no-till system. Living roots and covering the soil at all times with living plants is extremely important. Cover crops are planted whenever the soil is fallow for more than six weeks. Areas that are merely fallow, without some sort of cover crop, are places where weeds may grow and contribute to the weed seed bank. Using cover crops cuts back on the cost of herbicides used to control those weeds. According to Derpsch, no-till needs soil cover for the best crops yields.

"Experiments carried out in Bolivia and Mexico have shown that the highest yields have been obtained with no-tillage and full residue retention," he stated. These residues fuel the soil system and add organic matter. The reduction of organic matter means less productive soil and more inputs.

Farmers in Brazil and Paraguay mostly use a knife roller, which is a cover crop roller with parallel crimping bars. Some are made with several steel drums, which alternate to reduce vibration and increase effectiveness. (See chapter 12, Gallery of Roller/Crimpers, for more examples.) Others, like the model below, have crimping bars of alternating lengths for the same purpose. Just as in the United States, the farm size varies considerably. Small farms often have draft animals that pull knife rollers, while larger farms have tractor-drawn models.

The type of cover crop used also differs depending on many factors, including climatic region and level of mechanical sophistication.

"One of the most successful green manure cover crops for small farmers in many regions has been *Mucuna pruriens* seeded with the hand jab planter into a standing corn crop at flowering. Also pigeon peas (*Cajanus cajan*) and sword bean (*Canavalia gladiata*) have been successful in these systems," commented Derpsch.

He added that in mechanized farming systems using tractors, black oat (*Avena strigosa*) seeded before soybeans is very popular in southern Brazil and Paraguay. Oilseed radish used as a cover crop with corn is also very popular. A combination of black oat, oilseed radish, lupins and common vetch has also been quite successful. Millet (*Pennisetum americanum*) and different varieties of Brachiaria are also used. In order to find cover crop varieties adaptable to the drier regions of the Cerrados, researchers have done considerable work with breeding. For example, The Agricultural Institute of Parana (IAPAR) has released a variety of black oat that matures in 150 days instead of the commonly available variety that matures in 120 days.

Indeed, one of the keys to success with organic no-till is working with cover crops well adapted to your region. Derpsch recommends experimenting with different kinds of cover crops to find a good match for your region and cropping system. This is a challenge to researchers, extension agents, and to farmers, who should all be involved in the process. Many creative solutions can be developed. For example, in regions like the Cerrado, there was considerable skepticism that no-till would work

> **▶ NO-TILL TIPS FROM ROLF DERPSCH**
>
> These ideas will help you get off to a good start with organic no-till, or no-till using cover crops.
>
> • Farmers should master the fundamentals of no-tillage farming before entering into the system. The critical steps to no-till adoption have to be taken into account for a successful adoption process.
>
> • No-tillage is more than simply not tilling the soil and doing everything else the same as in traditional farming. Crop rotation and green manures have to be part of the system.
>
> • Managing cover crops properly, such as with a knife roller (like the Rodale roller/crimper), will result in savings on herbicides and be more environmentally friendly.
>
> • Fallow periods of more than six weeks should be replaced whenever possible with cover crops to suffocate weeds, fix nitrogen, and add biomass.
>
> • Spend some time developing a crop rotation. Of great importance is choosing a cover crop well suited to your region. It's also important to study the positive residual effects of the cover crop on the succeeding cash crop. The residual fertilizer effect and weed suppression effect must be studied.

in such a dry climate. However, EMBRAPA (the National Research Institute of Brazil) and other organizations performed the research that was required to make sure that cover cropping was successful. They even imported cover crops from other countries in order to find the ones that were best suited to their region. The hard work paid off – no-till has caught on and been quite successful in the Cerrado.

Cover Cropping with No-Till in Switzerland, Swaziland, Central America & Germany

A number of farmers from other countries are actively working with cover crops and no-till agriculture. They use a combination of methods to kill the cover crops, such as rollers, herbicides and making use of natural seasonal events, such as dry seasons. It's one step on the way to conserving natural resources and combating global warming. If cover crops and no-till are used, can roller/crimpers be far behind?

Switzerland — Experimentation with cover crop rollers

In Switzerland, only about 3 percent of the cropland is no-till. Pasture is an essential part of crop rotations, as well as some cover crops such as mustards, oil radish, Phacelia, and annual grass-clover mixtures. Only a few (less than a dozen) organic farmers use no-till in part of their crop rotation. Nevertheless, researchers Andreas Chervet and Wolfgang Sturny are excited about the possibilities of no-till with cover cropping. In the direct payment system that was introduced in Switzerland in 1993, integrated crop protection is required. Protection of the soil is very important. If there is no cash crop planted by August 31, farmers are required to plant a cash crop. This sets the stage for future work with cover crops and no-till.

Swaziland — Intercropping

According to Theodor Friedrich, Senior Agricultural Engineer in the Agricultural and Food Engineering Technologies Service of the Food and Agriculture Organization (FAO) of the United Nations in Rome, herbicide use can be lowered with the use of cover crops in no-till systems. For example, in Swaziland, spectacular results were achieved by intercropping corn and cowpeas. The system used no chemical inputs and increased yields while decreasing labor.

Central America — "Frijol tapado"

"Frijol tapado" means "covered beans" in English and is a traditional method of planting beans. The farming method involves broadcasting beans into a standing cover crop and then cutting the cover crop with a machete. The beans grow through the cover crop and eventually cover it. Benefits of the system include prevention of weed growth, moisture conservation and disease prevention. The method also allows farmers to plant in very steep areas without much soil erosion. Sometimes the cover crop grown is *Tithonia diversifolia*, regarded as a weed in Central America and is called the garden flower Mexican sunflower in the United States.

Germany — The few, the proud . . .

Thomas Sander, a German farmer, reports that no-till farmers in his country are few and far between. "I am sure there are at most two handfuls of farmers who have experience with a no-till farming system," he said. Sander estimated that 3,000 to 4,000 ha. (about 9,880 acres) are under permanent no-till. He only knows of two farmers (including himself) who use cover crop rollers. One of these is an organic minimum-till farmer.

Although there has been little acceptance of no-till, Sander believes in the system. His farm is 450 hectares (1,111 acres) and includes such crops as wheat, winter barley, oil seed rape, fava/faba beans, yellow oats, corn, and sugar beets. When Sander first started no-tilling, he did not use covers, but quickly found they were essential to make no-till work. Now he grows a cover crop of black oat before beans and peas. He also grows a cover crop of peas and oats paired with a cash crop of corn or sugar beets. With the high price of nitrogen, the use of legume cover crops is very economical. Currently, his equipment includes a cross-slot drill from New Zealand, a Cambridge roller, and a Tyler-Benson Patriot Narrow Trax sprayer.

The biggest challenges with the no-till system in his climate are slugs and grassy weeds. Slugs can be a problem, especially in cold, wet conditions in autumn. Building up the humus layer in soils that have been plowed for over a hundred years can also be a challenge. It may take several years of no-till and intense cover cropping to return the organic matter to acceptable levels. According to Sander, no-till farming holds promise for the future because it is energy efficient, nutrient efficient, limits soil erosion, and is environmentally friendly. Images of the Sander farm can be seen at *www.infofarm.de/sn/BetriebSander/index.html.*

Direct-Seeded, Mulch-Based Cropping Systems in Cameroon, Laos & Madagascar

Direct-seeded, mulch-based cropping systems (DMC) are being actively promoted and trialed in a number of different countries by the French organization called the Agricultural Research Center for International Development (CIRAD). DMC systems combine many of the same practices as organic no-till: permanent cover for the ground, diverse rotations with cover crops, and no-tillage. Methods of killing the cover crops vary. Lucien Seguy, pioneer of French DMC research, believes that DMC can be implemented in all kinds of climates, from tropical rainforests to areas with very low rainfall. He also believes that Roundup Ready technology has little place in DMC systems, since resistant plants develop quickly.

"They could be useful for 2-3 years, *i.e.* the time required for the plants to 'turn around' because nature quickly turns around in this respect. Nature is richer and more intelligent and has incredible defense resources," comments Lucien Seguy.

Here's a short sampling of current direct-seeded mulch-based cropping projects.

Cameroon

Northern Cameroon, the location of the DMC trials, is an area with low rainfall (23 inches or 600 mm) and population growth has led to increased cropping, deforestation and overgrazing. DMC systems are being tested on farms and in experimental research plots. Common cash crops are corn, sorghum and millet. One sample rotation includes growing corn during the rainy season of the first year in association with a cover crop. During the dry season, the residue from the cover crop covers and protects the soil. Cover crops are mowed or knocked down with herbicides. In the rainy season of the following year, cotton is direct seeded into the dead cover crop, which provides weed control and a source of fertility. Positive impacts include higher levels of soil moisture, less runoff (reduced from 25 to 2 percent), increase in yields (varying between 12 to 22 percent increase for cotton), fewer weeds and pests, and more diverse soil life.

Laos

Laos has a very different climate, yet DMC systems have been successful here too. The region is hilly and the vegetation includes humid tropical areas and savannas. Annual rainfall is 1,100-1,600 mm (up to 63 inches) per year. Some of the problems that need remedying are soil erosion and degradation, decreased crop yields, population pressure, and the need for an alternative to slash-and-burn agriculture. Cash crops include rice, corn, ground nut, sesame and perennial crops such as coffee, tea and rubber.

Research projects began in 2005 and were aimed at disseminating information in Xayabury and Xieng Khouang provinces. Educators in these areas have been working with local villagers to plant legumes instead of using slash-and-burn methods of farming. Cover crops are seeded and grown to maturity, and food crops are subsequently no-tilled into them. Fallow periods are reduced as much as possible with cover crops that produce seeds and fodder.

Madagascar

Research in DMC systems started in 1990 and Madagascar is now the most advanced country in regards to diversified technologies for small family farms. There are four different ecological regions in the country that include very different weather patterns – everything from semi-arid to tropical, with lowland and highland regions. Some of the crops include rice, food crops like cassava and beans, and export crops like coffee and vanilla. Natural resources are fragile and soils are sometimes poor and highly erodible, due to a harsh climate with cyclonic storms.

In several different areas of the country, a local organization in cooperation with CIRAD has set up research plots where DMC systems are trialed using traditional farming methods as a control. At the same time, farmers are introduced to the technology and make adaptations as needed. A range of different technologies makes DMC available to even the poorest farmers, with some individuals using a stick or a hoe to plant crops. The research farms have identified cover crop plants that are appropriate for each agro-ecological area, and researchers are increasing and disseminating seed. These include legumes like *Stylosanthes guianensis* and perennial forage grasses such as *Brachiaria ruziziensis.*

Hopefully you'll benefit from seeing how other countries have developed and adapted no-till systems with cover crops to meet the needs of their local farmers. As you can see, farmers and researchers can work together and come up with extremely diverse and creative ways to engage in agriculture while preserving natural resources. No-till is extremely flexible and can work on your farm too – with enough hard work and experimentation. Although the techniques sometimes take years to develop and implement, these folks have made it happen!

Resources

Corbier-Barthaux, Constance and Jean Francois Richard, eds. "Direct Seeding Mulch-Based Cropping Systems: An Alternative to Conventional Cropping Systems in Developing Countries." Fonds Francais pour l' Environment Mondial and Agence Francais de Developpement. Paris, France: 1997. *http://www.afd.fr/jahia/webdav/site/ffem/users/admiffem/public/Rapports_biodiversite/DMC_Sept07.pdf.*

Friedrich, Theodor. "Does No-Till Farming Require More Herbicides?" Outlooks in Pest Management. August, 2005.

Frijol Tapado System *http://www.tropag-fieldtrip.cornell.edu/thurston_TA/ptapado.html*

No-Tillage *http://www.rolf-derpsch.com/notill.htm*. Website for Rolf Derpsch, no-till consultant in Paraguay.

CHAPTER 11 ROLLER/CRIMPER GALLERY

Cover crop rollers have many different designs with different capabilities. Some, such as the rolling stalk choppers, are actually implements modified from their original use. Others are modeled on the knife rollers currently in use in South America. Still others are created from original, experimental designs like our own Rodale roller/crimper.

In other sections of this book we looked specifically at the roller/crimper that was designed at Rodale Institute. We took a look at the history of our own design trail and we looked at some work that was been done around the world. In this chapter we'll visit with other farmer-designers and farmer-fabricators to see how they chose to tackle the task of building an implement that would enable them to kill cover crops without tillage.

It's helpful to take a look at these different rollers as you consider transitioning to organic no-till. We'll point the way to more information, more research, and more interesting on-farm experiments so you can learn all about the process of selecting or designing equipment that will suit your own particular needs.

The Rodale roller/crimper.

Harvest Gold

Let's start with the Rodale Institute's cover crop roller/crimper, designed and built in late 2002 by myself as the Institute's farm manager and neighboring farmer John Brubaker, with the assistance of a Northeast Sustainable Ag Research and Education (SARE) grant. Although this roller/crimper is described fully in other chapters, I've provided a summary here so you can compare it with other models.

This roller/crimper works exceptionally well and does what it is designed to do. The front mounted design works well to make sure that the cover crop is rolled evenly and the kill is complete. Adding water to the steel drum can modify the downward weight. The chevron pattern of the blades allows the tractor to steer the equipment across the field evenly.

I have used the Harvest Gold with a combination of hairy vetch followed by corn, and then rye planted into soybeans. Both combinations work well.

No modifications are planned for the future – we're pretty much happy with what we've got. Although I'm open to suggestions and interested in hearing from folks about design changes they did that would make it even better.

The Crimp-O-Matic

John Hayden of The Farm Between in Jeffersonville, Vermont, built this simple, hand-and-foot powered crimper tool by attaching a piece of manure scraper bar (he also suggests an angle iron would work) to a board and then threading lengths of rope to each end. By taking a length of rope in each hand and stepping on the board every eight inches or so, Hayden says, you can flatten the cover crop in the same way that people make crop circles. Hayden and his farm team have used the tool in their greenhouse and then planted tomatoes into the mulch.

Currently, they use the tool outdoors in the field for flattening rye and then planting brassicas into the killed cover crop. Since the farm is located in northern Vermont, the soil stays cool and moist under the cover crop, which can be a drawback for heat-loving vegetables like peppers. Fortunately, the system works well for brassicas, which appreciate cool soil during the heat of summer. John has found that the tool does not adequately kill vetch when it is planted in combination with rye. "This would be a great tool for home gardeners," mentioned Hayden. "But you wouldn't want to do more than a quarter acre with it."

A simple hand and foot powered crimping tool for smaller areas.

Alabama roller built by Dr. Wayne Reeves of USDA-ARS. Photo courtesy of Steve Groff.

The Alabama Slammer

Dr. Wayne Reeves and Randy Raper have experimented with several different designs with varying degrees of success. The Alabama slammer is their second design, which consists of a steel cylinder with bars of angle iron welded to the outside. It is modeled on knife rollers used in South America. Other designs are featured later in this chapter.

Another design consisted of rebar welded to a steel drum. This model was designed to pull behind a subsoiler called a paraplow. Because of hardpan on the coastal plain of Georgia, subsoiling is necessary for adequate agricultural production. It has worked quite well for this purpose.

Randy Raper, an agricultural engineer at the USDA-ARS National Soil Dynamics Laboratory in Auburn, Alabama, experimented with several different designs. In several trials, he compared the performance of a spiral blade (both clockwise and counterclockwise) compared with a straight blade. The current design consists of several shorter sections that have parallel linkages. This enables the roller to be used in hilly areas, and lessens the vibration and fatigue factor for the farmers using the machine.

Reeves and Raper have worked with cover crops of cereal rye, white and blue lupin, brassicas, wheat, crimson clover, various vetches, sorghum-sudangrass, millet, oats, black oats and ryegrass. Cash crops they've experimented with include field corn, tropical corn, watermelon, sweet corn, southern peas, cotton, peanuts, soybeans, wheat, pearl millet and grain sorghum. For their area, the easiest management system with most benefit is cereal rye with cotton.

In terms of future design modifications, Dr. Wayne Reeves is satisfied with the last design that was developed. He emphasized that many roller designs will work adequately enough to kill cover crops. He points to several other important factors for success that farmers should think about: growing a cover crop with allelopathic activity, timing of the rolling, and growing cover crops to provide enough residue to suppress weed growth.

Black Magic

Michigan State University extension specialist Dale Mutch had this roller built with the help of a MSU Project GREEEN grant, following the basic design of the Rodale Institute's roller/crimper. The design of the roller has proved satisfactory, and Mutch has no plans to modify it.

MSU's Black Magic roller/crimper. Photo courtesy of Dale Mutch.

Mutch has been experimenting since 2004 with treatments of rye and vetch followed by soybeans. Results have been variable over the years, but Mutch has found that rye makes a better mulch for soybeans than either a mix of rye and vetch or vetch alone. He has been working with farmers with new applications for the roller/crimper, such as a cover crop of rye, followed by a cash crop of blueberries, and rye followed by pumpkins.

For a more detailed discussion of Mutch's work as part of the "No-Till Plus" study, see chapter 6.

Steve Groff's Chop-N-Go roller/crimper. Photo courtesy of Steve Groff.

Chop-N-Go

Steve Groff of Cedar Meadow Farm in Pennsylvania uses a rolling stalk chopper to knock down residue on his continuous no-toll farm.

Steve Groff grows 215 acres of crops, about half of which are vegetables. His crops include tomatoes, sweet corn, pumpkins, field corn, wheat, soybeans and alfalfa. He also grows his own seeds for certain crops, including tillage radishes and Early Cover hairy vetch. In Groff's rotation, he pairs a cover crop of vetch with field corn or sweet corn, and a crop of vetch and rye with either pumpkins or tomatoes. He has also grown tillage radishes followed by corn.

Groff has been using a rolling stalk chopper to kill cover crops since 1995. It works well for him and he sees the implement as "an integral part of my management arsenal." He relies on the rolling stalk chopper to get cover crops rolled down, but he also uses small amounts of herbicide to kill cover crops. "Because I'm a vegetable farmer, I do many successive plantings. I need to be able to plant when I need to plant. I use herbicide to kill the cover crops, but a little herbicide goes a long way." The rolling stalk chopper has allowed Groff to reduce his herbicide costs significantly.

The rolling stalk chopper has two rows of rollers, set up in two gangs. Each roller has eight 23-inch blades. When Groff started using the rolling stalk chopper, he made a few different modifications to improve the effectiveness of the implement on his hilly Pennsylvania farm. The rollers have been modified so that they work independently and can cover rough or uneven ground. The rollers are also spring loaded so that they exert more down pressure on the cover crops, increasing the kill rate. He also added collars on the bearings so that they would not get clogged with cover crops, particularly vetch. Groff is so satisfied with the rolling stalk chopper that he hasn't made any modifications for several years, and doesn't plan to make any more.

Chop-N-Go (left) and the Rodale (right) roller/crimper. Photo courtesy of Steve Groff.

Although Groff is completely happy with his system, he concedes that it's not for everyone. There are a number of benefits for farmers who understand how cover crops fit into the big picture of the farm system. "Improving soil quality is like making an investment in the bank. How much is that worth? You can't put a dollar value on it, but you can see the long-term effects, especially in a difficult crop year." Cover cropping has helped Groff lower his nitrogen costs and keep his pumpkins cleaner.

The previous photo is from a trial comparing the effectiveness of the rolling stalk chopper and the Rodale Institute roller/crimper. "The rolling stalk chopper is a bit more aggressive," commented Groff. "You can tell that from the photo. But both did the job of killing the cover crop. When we looked at the site 10 days later, you couldn't tell the difference between the two areas."

Berea College's rolling stalk chopper.

Green Berea

At Berea College in Kentucky, Professor Sean Clark and his team have been rolling rye cover crops for corn with a Bessler rolling stalk chopper. They've been experimenting with the system for the past six years with varying degrees of success. Their best success so far has been in well-drained fields with a moderate amount of rye biomass (2.5-3 tons/acre). In addition, they only plant into fields that do not have a significant problem with Johnson grass. They roll down the cover crop of rye at the soft dough stage, and have had no problems with rye competition. No herbicide is necessary at roll down, though some herbicide is used to control weeds when corn plants are about one foot tall.

The rolling stalk chopper doesn't have any modifications – it is used "as is." Clark notes that when the amount of rye biomass is too high (4 tons/acre or more), it causes problems with the rolling stalk chopper. The cutting device on the rolling stalk chopper doesn't cope well with high amounts of biomass.

For the future, Clark doesn't plan to make any changes to the rolling stalk chopper. However, he has read about the Rodale roller/crimper and would be interested to try it.

To read a study published by Clark entitled "Cover Crop Roll-Down for Weed Suppression in No-Till Crop Production," visit *www.ca.uky.edu/agc/pubs/pr/pr470/pr470.pdf.* In this you'll see a comparison of rye/corn plantings with three treatments: no herbicides, minimal herbicide applications and more extensive herbicide applications.

Winslow Winner

Ernest Winslow grows 1,235 acres of certified organic crops, including corn, beans, wheat and sod. He is planning to phase out sod during the next three years and start growing cowpeas and carrots. Currently he grows several cover crops, including crimson clover, rye and vetch, but only uses his roller on the rye and a rye/clover blend. He also has plans to experiment with a mixture of rye, vetch, clover and radish.

Winslow's other growing practices include using compost tea (he currently holds two patents on compost tea makers) and using chicken manure from a nearby layer farm for his cover crops. He hopes to transition away from the chicken manure and replace it with legumes in his rotation.

A three-roller setup from Ernest Winslow in Scotland Neck, North Carolina.

The three-roller setup is front mounted on the tractor. At the present time, the three rollers together are about 22 feet wide (including a six inch overlap between rollers). Behind the rollers is a spray tank, which Winslow uses to spray a mixture of orange oil and vinegar to increase the kill rate that the roller/crimper provides. The concoction includes one quart of orange oil, four gallons of a 12 percent solution of vinegar and 2.75 gallons of water per acre. The orange oil and vinegar work well together – the orange oil partially dissolves the plant tissue and increases the effectiveness of the vinegar. At a seven gallon per acre spray rate, Winslow isn't applying very much of the organic herbicide. He keeps his particle size very small to provide even coverage. The herbicide improves the kill rate of the roller/crimper and allows him to roll the cover crop at an earlier date, before anthesis. It also helps kill broadleaf weeds.

Winslow has modified the roller/crimper design significantly to suit his needs. He uses a three-roller set up so that the rollers can float independently and follow the contour of the ground. The wing rollers are attached to the top link of his three-point hitch with a chain, which helps them float with the contours of the land. He also made some modifications to the roller shaft, which was having some flexing problems near the end of the drum. That problem is solved now. In general, he is very satisfied with the roller/crimper design. The chevron pattern works well and he can roll along at six miles per hour without any problems. "It makes a nice rolling unit with no chattering," commented Winslow. For the future, he plans to modify the roller so that it will be 30 feet wide, which will make rolling faster and easier.

A small, experimental roller built by technicians at the USDA-ARS National Soil Dynamics Laboratory in Auburn, Alabama. Photo courtesy of Randy L. Raper, USDA-ARS-NSDL.

Captain America

This roller was designed as a class project with students from the University of Alabama. Randy Raper, an agricultural engineer who works with the Agricultural Research Service, said that the design worked very well, and even with subsequent designs it's been hard to beat. Since it is an experimental design, the blades are detachable and can be replaced. The curved blades ensure that each blade is in constant contact with the ground, and little vibration occurs. In contrast, rollers that have straight blades often have problems with vibration and can only be driven at a maximum field speed of two miles per hour. Although this may work on smaller farms, it's just not fast enough for American farmers. The rollers designed by the Soil Dynamics Lab have a goal speed of 10-15 miles per hour.

The Captain America was the first of many rollers designed by the Soil Dynamics Lab at USDA-ARS. They have been tested with cover crops such as rye, wheat and black oats. The researchers are very pleased with the results. "In Alabama, we are always about two weeks away from a drought," explained Randy Raper. The rollers optimize the amount of biomass that can be grown in an area. The rolled cover crop increases infiltration and soil quality, and increases crop yield. By conserving moisture, the cover crop mat protects against drought for an additional 7-15 days.

Penn State University's roller/crimper using the chevron design.

Orange Crush

During a field day in 2004 at Rodale Institute, Bill Curran from Penn State University saw the Rodale roller/crimper in action. He decided that he had to have one for himself. During the winter of 2004-2005, Cory Dillon, agronomy field technician and mechanic, built the Orange Crush following the Rodale design. Since the summer of 2005, they've been using it for trials at the Rock Springs Research Farm, Rock Springs, Pennsylvania.

Curran likes the chevron design. "It allows for a fairly smooth ride without much vibration," he reports. "This is a problem with the straight bar roller designs. I also like being able to add extra weight by filling the tank with water. This allows easier transport when empty and additional weight when rolling."

Bill Curran and graduate students, Steven Mirsky and Ruth Nick have been working on cover crops. Mirsky wrote his thesis on the termination of rye and its possibilities for weed control. In a separate project, Ruth Nick is working with Dave Wilson of the Rodale Institute on the best strategies for terminating hairy vetch. Curran and other researchers are now trialing plantings of rye followed by soybeans or pumpkins, and vetch followed by corn. The roller/crimper works well for both rye and vetch.

For more information, see Penn State's section in chapter 6, or view Curran's website at *www.weeds.psu.edu*.

Big Blue

Dan, Steve and Tony Polter of Polter's Berry Farm in Fremont, Ohio, built this blue roller based on the Rodale Institute's design. They have been using it to plant pumpkins for the past five years. Although getting started was tricky, the system now works so well they wouldn't consider planting pumpkins without it.

The Polters made only one modification to Rodale's design – they changed the width to 17 feet. This works well with their 15-foot wide Monosem planter, allowing some overlap between passes. They also have found that they don't need to fill the roller with water, as the weight of the roller alone is sufficient to kill the cover crop.

The Polters use a cover crop of rye, which they grow to about five feet tall. They then spray it with

The Polter's roller/crimper using the chevron design.

Roundup, and two weeks later roll the cover crop and plant the pumpkins into the killed cover crop with one pass. The benefits from the system are very high quality, clean pumpkins. "You can't tell the top from the bottom," explained Dan Polter. This gives their product a market edge.

Fresh Cut

The knife roller is the granddad of roller/crimpers in the United States, and has been in use since the 1970's. A knife roller is a cover crop roller with parallel crimping bars, such as the one shown above. Rollers like this one are in use all over South America, where they're an important part of no-till agriculture. In areas with high rainfall, cover crops are extremely important to prevent erosion and soil degradation.

There are several different knife roller designs in use in South America, depending on the intended use and the farm size. Some are pulled behind draft animals and are meant for small-scale production, while other tractor-mounted units are in use on larger farms.

For more information, see chapter 10, Roller/Crimpers Around the World.

Front Runner

Georgia farmer Lamar Black built this front mounted roller from his own design. Black constructed the roller from older equipment he had around the farm, including a do-all. The steel drum is mounted on 4 x 4 tubing. He welded angle irons onto the cylinder at 8 inches apart for the crimping bars.

Originally, he used the roller on the front of his tractor, as shown in the photo. Currently, he used the machine on the rear of the tractor. The change in mounting is due to a change in the use of the implement. Now he sprays his rye three to four weeks ahead of planting in order to let the soil moisture recharge. Black is a conventional farmer who uses a post emergent herbicide about two weeks after planting.

Black likes the design he came up with because it was simple and easy to build. He used parts already on hand, and spent a total of about $3,000 for additional materials. The finished roller is 18 feet wide with three sections.

"Rollers are definitely the way to go," says Black. He likes the way that cover crops add organic matter to the soil while providing some weed control.

A knife roller in use on the farm of Erny Schlindwein, president of the Paraguayan No-Till Farmers Association. Photo courtesy of Rolf Derpsch.

A front mounted roller made from recycled equipment by Lamar Black. Photo courtesy of Steve Groff.

Black grows mostly rye (sometimes also ryegrass) as a cover crop. He rolls these and plants cash crops of cotton, soybeans, corn and peanuts. He has also tried planting a cover crop of wheat, but has a hard time getting a good kill rate with his roller. In the past, he has used an airplane to aerial seed rye and the method has worked well for him.

If Black were to redesign his roller, he would add crimping bars in a spiral pattern and make the bars taller. He believes that this would improve the crimping action and enable him to more effectively kill cover crops.

The Multi-Roller

Vaughn Jackson's special design was created by I & J Manufacturing and spreads 30 feet wide to match the width of his planter and no-till drill. Features include a 13-foot front mounted roller that covers the wheelbase of his tractor. The dual rear rollers extend another 9 feet and are mounted on a toolbar attached to a 3-point hitch. Hydraulics lift the two rear rollers for road travel.

During the past year, Jackson has discovered a couple of problems with the design, which he will remedy this winter. Because the tractor, roller and planter combination is quite long, it takes a lot of room to turn around. The rollers are quite heavy, and even when raised the tractor has limited turning capability. Jackson intends to switch to a mid-mount system, which may solve some of his difficulties. Ideally, the mid-mount system would be more compact for travel and storage. He also recommends that the rollers on the back should be slightly wider, allowing for a little more overlap.

Aside from these problems, the roller/crimper worked well on rye this year, and Jackson's soybean yield was as good as his conventional field. Next year, he plans to use a cover crop of field peas and oats, followed by corn. Jackson is currently in transition to organic production, and grows corn, soybeans, and wheat, which are crops that he can market locally. Overall, Jackson is very optimistic about organic no-till farming.

"I am transitioning because of no-till organic which has a lot to do with the roller/crimper. Something on the inside of me said, 'you can do this.' Two truly great ideas such as no-till and organic will eventually come together if they are really great ideas and I believe they are," Jackson stated.

I & J Manufacturing created this 30-foot wide planter and no-till drill.

The End of the Tour

Now that you've seen some different roller designs and had the opportunity to visit with creative innovative farmers and researchers from around the country, perhaps you'll be able to think more concretely about what will work on your own farm. We visited with folks who have shown that roller designs are quite flexible in terms of size and set up. You can either build your own following the Rodale design with the help of the computer aided drawings (CAD) from the resources at the back of the book, or get help from a fabricator. You can design your own now that you know what you're trying to accomplish. With some experimentation, you'll be able to come up with a design that works for you. Or, you might just want to purchase one from a builder like I & J Manufacturing. Whichever path you chose, just get started, be patient, be observant, remember that the cover crops are the real key, and experiment on your own farm.

APPENDIX

GLOSSARY OF TERMS

***Note:** Glossary items marked NOP definition are quoted from the National Organic Program Standards § 05.2 "Terms defined."*

Actinomycete. One of a class of bacteria largely responsible for the decomposition of organic matter in soil, and thus for the production of humus and replenishing soil nutrients.

Aggregates, soil. The building blocks formed when soil minerals and organic matter are bound together.

Agricultural inputs. All substances or materials used in the production or handling of organic agricultural products (NOP definition).

Allelopathic effect. Effect of some plants to suppress the growth or germination of other competing plants.

Annual seedling. A plant grown from seed that will complete its life cycle or produce a harvestable yield within the same crop year or season in which it was planted. (NOP definition)

Available nutrient. The form of a nutrient that is available for plants to use. In the organic system, microorganisms convert non-available nutrients to available ones.

Bulk density. The mass of dry soil per unit volume. This is used as a measure of compaction for agricultural soils.

Cation. A positively charged ion.

Cation exchange capacity (CEC). The ability of a given soil plot to retain and exchange positively charged ions (cations), expressed in milliequivalents per 100 grams of soil (me/100 g).

Chelating. Resulting in a chelate and by which process nutrients are held in the soil and made available for plant uptake.

Compost. The product of a managed process through which microorganisms break down plant and animal materials into more available forms suitable for application to the soil. Compost must be produced through a process that combines plant and animal materials with an initial C:N ratio of between 25:1 and 40:1. Producers using an in-vessel or static aerated pile system must maintain the composting materials at a temperature between 131 F and 170 F for three days. Producers using a windrow system must maintain the composting materials at a temperature between 131 F and 170 F for 15 days, during which time, the materials must be turned a minimum of five times (NOP definition).

Control. Any method that reduces or limits damage by populations of pests, weeds or diseases to levels that do not significantly reduce productivity (NOP definition).

Cover crop. Any crop grown for the purpose of weed control, controlling erosion, amending soil fertility, and building organic matter. Cover crops are usually tilled under in an immature growth stage. Sometimes called a green manure crop.

Crop. A plant or part of a plant intended to be marketed as an agricultural product or fed to livestock (NOP definition).

Crop residue. The plant parts remaining in a field after the harvest of a crop, which include stalks, stems, leaves, roots and weeds (NOP definition).

Crop rotation. The practice of alternating the annual crops grown on a specific field in a planned pattern or sequence in successive crop years so that crops of the same species or family are not grown repeatedly without interruption on the same field. Perennial cropping systems employ means such as alley cropping, intercropping, and hedgerows to introduce biological diversity in lieu of crop rotation (NOP definition).

Crop year. The normal growing season for a crop (NOP definition).

Cultivation. Digging up or cutting the soil to prepare a seed bed; control weeds; aerate the soil; or work organic matter, crop residues, or fertilizers into the soil (NOP definition).

Cultural methods. Methods used to enhance crop health and prevent weed, pest or disease problems without the use of substances; examples include the selection of appropriate varieties and planting sites; proper timing and density of plantings; irrigation; and extending a growing season by manipulating the microclimate with greenhouses, cold frames, or wind breaks (NOP definition).

C:N ratio. The ratio of carbon to nitrogen in any organic material such as crop residue. A high ratio results in low rates of decomposition and can also result in a temporary decrease in nitrogen for the plant, as microorganisms use the nitrogen to break down the plant material.

Disease vectors. Plants or animals that harbor or transmit disease organisms or pathogens which may attack crops or livestock (NOP definition).

Dolomitic. Containing dolomite, a mineral and a sedimentary carbonate rock, both composed of calcium magnesium carbonate, $CaMg(CO_3)_2$.

Exudate. Fluids that ooze from diseased or injured plant tissue.

Fertilizer. A single or blended substance containing one or more recognized plant nutrient(s) which is used primarily for its plant nutrient content and which is designed for use or claimed to have value in promoting plant growth (NOP definition).

Field capacity. The amount of water left in a given soil plot after free drainage has practically ceased, usually two to three days following its saturation.

Forage. Vegetative material in a fresh, dried, or ensiled state (pasture, hay or silage), which is fed to livestock (NOP definition).

Fulvic acid. One of two types of organic acidic polymer contained in humus, its name deriving from the Latin *fulvus,* indicative of its yellow color.

Humic acid. One of two types of organic acidic polymer contained in humus, its name deriving from the Latin *humus,* meaning earth, indicative of its brown color.

Inspection. The act of examining and evaluating the production or handling operation of an applicant for certification or certified operation to determine compliance with the Act and the regulations in this part (NOP definition).

Inspector. Any person retained or used by a certifying agent to conduct inspections of certification applicants or certified production or handling operations (NOP definition).

Manure. Feces, urine, other excrement, and bedding produced by livestock that has not been composted (NOP definition).

Mulch. Any nonsynthetic material, such as wood chips, leaves or straw, or any synthetic material included on the National List for such use, such as newspaper or plastic that serves to suppress weed growth, moderate soil temperature, or conserve soil moisture (NOP definition).

National Organic Program (NOP). The program authorized by the Act for the purpose of implementing its provisions (NOP definition).

Nitrogen fixation. Conversion, by bacteria, of atmospheric nitrogen to a form that plants can use. This function is performed by rhizobia in cooperation with the roots of legumes.

Nonsynthetic (natural). A substance that is derived from mineral, plant or animal matter and does not undergo a synthetic process as defined in section 6502(21) of the Act (7 U.S.C. 6502(21)). For the purposes of this part, nonsynthetic is used as a synonym for natural as the term is used in the Act (NOP definition).

Nontoxic. Not known to cause any adverse physiological effects in animals, plants, humans or the environment (NOP definition).

No-Till. A system of planting crops without the major soil disturbance created by a tillage implement.

Organic. A labeling term that refers to an agricultural product produced in accordance with the Act and the regulations in this part (NOP definition).

Organic matter. The remains, residues or waste products of any organism (NOP definition).

Organic production. A production system that is managed in accordance with the Act and regulations in this part to respond to site-specific conditions by integrating cultural, biological, and mechanical practices that foster cycling of resources, promote ecological balance, and conserve biodiversity (NOP definition).

Organic system plan. A plan of management of an organic production or handling operation that has been agreed to by the producer or handler and the certifying agent and that includes written plans concerning all aspects of agricultural production or handling described in the Act and the regulations (NOP definition).

Pasture. Land used for livestock grazing that is managed to provide feed value and maintain or improve soil, water and vegetative resources (NOP definition).

Penetrometer. A device that measures soil resistance to penetration, an indicator of the degree of compaction.

Pesticide. Any substance which alone, in chemical combination, or in any formulation with one or more substances is defined as a pesticide in section 2(u) of the Federal Insecticide, Fungicide, and Rodenticide Act (7 U.S.C. 136(u) et seq) (NOP definition).

Producer. A person who engages in the business of growing or producing food, fiber, feed, and other agricultural-based consumer products (NOP definition).

Prohibited substance. A substance the use of which in any aspect of organic production or handling is prohibited or not provided for in the Act or the regulations of this part (NOP definition).

Records. Any information in written, visual, or electronic form that documents the activities undertaken by a producer, handler, or certifying agent to comply with the Act and regulations in this part (NOP definition).

Rhizosphere. The narrow region of soil immediately surrounding a plant's roots, that is directly influenced by the roots' secretions and is inhabited by associated soil microorganisms (including mycorrhizae), where most of a plant's nutrient cycling occurs.

Rhizobia bacteria. Bacteria which can fix atmospheric nitrogen into a form that plants can use. Rhizobia live in the roots of legumes and form a mutually beneficial relationship, receiving energy rich molecules from the plant in exchange for nitrogen.

Soil aggregates. The building blocks formed when soil minerals and organic matter are bound together.

Soil and water quality. Observable indicators of the physical, chemical, or biological condition of soil and water, including the presence of environmental contaminants (NOP definition).

Soil colloid. The particles of soil with a large surface-area-to-mass ratio and generally having a net negative charge, essential to the absorption, holding, and release of ions and thus in the processes of nutrient fixation and uptake.

Soil profile. A vertical cross-section of a given soil plot, extending through all its horizons into the parent material.

Soil water. Water suspended in the soil, namely the region from which water is discharged by plant transpiration and evaporation.

Strip cropping. A method of farming employing alternating strips of closely sown crops (usually small grains) with strips of row crops, used when a slope is too steep or long to prevent soil erosion.

Subsoiling. A method of deep plowing used to break up compacted subsoil, or hardpan, produced by many conventional tillage methods.

Synthetic. A substance that is formulated or manufactured by a chemical process or by a process that chemically changes a substance extracted from naturally occurring plant, animal or mineral sources, except that such term shall not apply to substances created by naturally occurring biological processes (NOP definition).

Tillage. The mechanical manipulation of soil, usually to prepare a seedbed, incorporated crop residues and soil amendments, and general soil loosening. Inversion tillage involves inverting soil layers, as when plowing with a moldboard plow. Non-inversion tillage does not mix soil layers, as when disking or harrowing.

Tilth. An indicator of soil health pertaining to its ability to aggregate, allowing for good drainage and air circulation.

Transplant. A seedling which has been removed from its original place of production, transported and replanted (NOP definition).

Zone tillage. Tillage in a limited area of a field to prepare an area for planting. Usually in a narrow band (4-6 inches wide). A modification of no-tillage which is better for cold, wet soils.

APPENDIX B COVER CROP SOURCES

The following is a list of seed sources for cover crops. Always look for local sources, such as farmers' cooperatives. They'll tend to be more affordable, and you'll have a better chance of finding locally adapted seed. Organic farmers will need to try to find organic seed. Companies that provide some organic seed are listed with the designation organic. Because companies change their offerings frequently, you'll need to call or e-mail to verify that the seed is available. The following two organizations offer a database with a search function for organic seed sourcing.

OMRI: Organic Seed Database
P.O. Box 11558
Eugene, Oregon 97440
Phone (541) 343-7600
Fax (541) 343-8971
E-mail *seedfeedback@omri.org*
Website *www.omri.org/seeds*
Free sourcing service from the Organic Materials Review Institute (OMRI). Search their database for seed varieties available from suppliers who pay a fee to be listed.

Organic Seed Sourcing Service
286 Dixie Hollow
Louisa, Virginia 23093
Phone (540) 894-8865
Fax (540) 894-8060
E-mail *cricket@organicseedsourcing.com*
Website *www.happyhippie.net/organicseedsourcing*
Certified organic seed sourcing service helps farmers find the organic seeds they need. Free documentation of your organic seed search.

Companies Offering Seed for Cover Crops

Adams-Briscoe Seed Co.
P.O. Box 19
325 E Second St.
Jackson, Georgia 30233-0019
Phone (770) 775-7826
Fax (770) 775-7122
E-mail *abseed@juno.com*
Website *www.abseed.com*
Organic clovers, winter peas, vetches, cowpeas, wheat, rye, oats, grasses, sorghums, legume inoculants, millet, buckwheat, field peas, sunn hemp, vetch

Agassiz Seed & Supply
445 7th St. NW
West Fargo, North Dakota 58078
Phone (701) 282-8118
Fax (701) 282-9119
Website *www.agassizseed.com*
Sorghum, sudangrass, millet, ryegrass, clovers, oats, wheat, vetch, legume inoculants

Agri-AFC, LLC
P.O. Box 2207
905 Market St.
Decatur, Alabama 35609
Phone (256) 560-2848
Fax (256) 308-5693
Website *www.agri-afc.com*
Wheat, rye, millet, ryegrass, sorghum sudan, oats, clover

Albert Lea Seed House
P.O. Box 127
1414 W. Main St.
Albert Lea, Minnesota 56007
Phone (800) 352-5247
Fax (507) 373-7032
E-mail *seedhouse@alseed.com*
Website *www.alseed.com*
Organic buckwheat, clover, vetch, oats, wheat, rye

A.L. Gilbert – Farmers Warehouse
4367 Jessup Rd.
Keyes, California 95328
Phone (800) 400-6377
Phone (209) 632-2333
Website *www.farmerswarehouse.com*
Forage, grass, clovers, alfalfa, pasture

The American Organic Seed Co.
P.O. Box 385
304 Anson St.
Warren Illinois 61087
Phone (866) 471-9465
Fax (815) 788-4000
E-mail *art@american-organics.com*
Website *www.american-organic.com*
Certified organic seed corn, soybeans, alfalfa, grasses, forages, bulk grains and snack foods

Ampac Seed Co.
P.O. Box 318
Tangent, Oregon 97389
Phone (800) 547-3230
Fax (541) 928-2430
E-mail *info@ampacseed.com*
Website *www.ampacseed.com*
Sudangrass, hairy vetch, clover, ryegrass

Barenbrug USA
33477 Hwy. 99 East
Tangent, Oregon 97389
Phone (541) 926-5801
Phone (800) 547-4101
Fax (541) 926-9435
E-mail *info@barusa.com*
Website *www.barenbrug.com*
Forage legumes, grasses

Blaine's Best Seeds
6020 22nd Ave. NE
Rugby, North Dakota 58368
Phone (701) 776-6023
E-mail *bbestseeds@stellarnet.com*
Organic hard red spring and winter wheat, durum wheat, rye, triticale, spelt, barley, oats, buckwheat, millet, field peas

The Birkett Mills
Transloading Facility
163 Main St.
Penn Yan, New York 14527
Phone (315) 536-3311
E-mail *custserv@thebirkettmills.com*
Website *www.thebirkettmills.com*

Buckwheat

Buckwheat Growers Association of Minnesota
206 Aldrich Ave SE
Wadena, MN 56482
Phone (218) 631-9212
Fax (218) 631-1711
Website *www.buckwheatgrowers.com*
Buckwheat

Cache River Valley Seed, LLC
Hwy. 226 East
Cash, Arkansas 72421
Phone (870) 477-5427
E-mail *crvseed@crvseed.com*
Website *www.crvseed.com*
Wheat, oats

Cal/West Seeds
38001 County Road 27
Woodland, California 95695
Phone (800) 824-8585
Phone (530) 666-3331
Fax (530) 666-5317
Website *www.calwestseeds.com*
Clovers, alfalfa, sudangrass, sorghum

Cedar Meadow Farm
679 Hilldale Rd.
Holtwood, Pennsylvania 17532
Phone (717) 284-5152
Fax (717) 284-5967
E-mail *steve@cedarmeadowfarm.com*
Website *www.cedarmeadowfarm.com*
Forage radish, hairy vetch

Discount Seeds
2411 9th Ave SW
Watertown, South Dakota 57201
Phone (605) 886-5888
Grains, forage/grain legumes, forage grasses

DLF Organic Seeds
P.O. Box 229
175 West H St.
Halsey, Oregon 97348
Phone (800) 445-2251
E-mail *jeromem@intlseed.com*
Website *www.dlforganic.com*
Organic red and white clover, forage peas, organic cover crop mix

Doebler's Pennsylvania Hybrids, Inc.
202 Tiadaghton Ave.
Jersey Shore, Pennsylvania 17740
Phone (800) 853-2676
Phone (570) 753-3210
Fax (570) 753-5302
E-mail *inform@doeblers.com*
Website *www.doeblers.com*
Clovers, grasses, legume inoculants

Ernst Conservation Seeds
9006 Mercer Pike
Meadville, Pennsylvania 16335
Phone (800) 873-3321
Fax (814) 336-5191
E-mail *sales@ernstseed.com*
Website *www.ernstseed.com*
Oats, clovers, buckwheat, ryegrass, alfalfa, barley, winter peas, rye, wheat, hairy vetch, Japanese millet, foxtail millet

Falk's Seed Farm, Inc.
1170 Hwy 9 NE
Murdock, Minnesota 56271
Phone (320) 875-4341
Fax (320) 875-4342
E-mail *falkseed@westtechwb.com*
Website *www.falkseed.com*
Organic oats, wheat, rye. Special order organic items, corn, forage, turf, natives, horse feed

Fedco Seeds
P.O. Box 520
Waterville, Maine 04903
Phone (207) 873-7333
Fax (207) 692-1022
Website *www.fedcoseeds.com*
Organic grains, forage/grain legumes, grasses, clovers, legume inoculants

Forage First
P.O. Box 64589
St. Paul, Minnesota 55164
Phone (651) 644-4254
Website *www.foragefirst.com*
Hairy vetch, sweet clover, berseem clover, red clover, crimson clover, cowpeas, ryegrass, sorghum, sorghum-sudangrass, forage sorghum, fodder radish, rape, turnip, cover crop mixes

Foundation Organic Seeds, LLC
634 13th Ave N
Onalaska, Wisconsin 54650
Phone (800) 495-6647
Phone (608) 781-4076
E-mail *smohr5@charter.net*
E-mail *foundationorganicseeds@hotmail.com*
Organic and untreated seeds.

High Mowing Organic Seeds
76 Quarry Rd.
Wolcott, Vermont 05680
Phone (802) 472-6174
Fax (802) 472-3201
E-mail *Meredith@highmowingseeds.com*
Website *www.highmowingseeds.com*
Organic buckwheat, oats, rye, rye/vetch mix, field peas, clover, legume inoculants

Horstdale Farm Supply, LLC
12286 Hollowell Church Rd.
Greencastle, Pennsylvania 17225-9525
Phone (717) 597-5151
Fax (717) 597-5185
Barley, wheat, rye, oats, crimson clover, winter, vetch

Hytest Seeds
2827 8th Ave. S
Fort Dodge, Iowa 50501
Phone (800) 442-7391
E-mail *jrkrenz@landolakes.com*
Website *www.hytestseeds.com*
Alfalfa

Johnny's Selected Seeds
955 Benton Ave.
Winslow, Maine 04901
Phone (877) 564-6697
Fax (207) 861-8363
E-mail *rstore@johnnyseeds.com*
Website *www.johnnyseeds.com*
Organic chickling vetch, crimson clover, field peas, green manure mix, sudangrass, mustard, sweet clover, legume inoculants

Jung Seed Genetics, Inc.
341 S. High St.
Randolph, Wisconsin 53956
Phone (800) 242-1855 commercial accounts
Phone (800) 297-3123 retail customers
E-mail *skampstra@jungseedgenetics.com*
Website *www.jungseedgenetics.com*
Large variety of untreated seed

Kamprath Seeds, Inc.
205 Stockton St.
Manteca, California 95337
Phone (209) 823-6242
Fax (209) 823-2582
Vetches, bell beans, small grains, brassicas, subterranean clovers, balansa clover, medics, perennial clovers, grasses

Kaufman Seeds, Inc.
P.O. Box 398
Ashdown, Arizona 71822
Phone (870) 898-3328
Phone (800) 892-1082
Fax (870) 898-3302
E-mail *kaufmanseeds@arkansas.net*
Wholesale grains, forage/grain legumes, grasses, summer annuals

Keystone Group Ag. Seeds
RR 1 Box 81A
Leiser Rd.
New Columbia, Pennsylvania 17856
Phone (570) 538-1170
E-mail *keygroupseed@msn.com*
Hairy vetch, rye, wheat, oats, tillage radish, sorghum sudangrass

King's AgriSeeds, LLC
96 Paradise Ln.
Ronks, Pennsylvania 17572
Phone (717) 687-6224
Phone (866) 687-6224
Forage radish, alfalfa, clovers, rye, triticale, ryegrass, hairy vetch

Little Britain AgriSupply Inc.
398 North Little Britain Rd.
Quarryville, Pennsylvania 17566
Phone (717) 529-2196
E-mail *lbasinc@juno.com*
Oats, rye, barley, wheat and clover. Other cover crops available by special order

Missouri Southern Seeds
P.O. Box 699
Rolla, Missouri 65402
Phone (573) 364-1336
Phone (800) 844-1336
Fax (573) 364-5963
Website *www.missourisouthernseed.com*
Wheat, rye, peas, oats, buckwheat, clover, rape, ryegrass, hairy vetch

Moore Seed Farm, LLC
8636 N. Upton Rd.
Elsie, Michigan 48831
Phone (989) 862-4686
Rye

North Country Organics
P.O. Box 372
Bradford, Vermont 05033
Phone (802) 222-4277
Fax (802) 222-9661
E-mail *info@norganics.com*
Website *www.norganics.com*
Organic buckwheat, ryegrass, oats, rye, wheat, barley, clover, field peas, millet, sudangrass, vetch

Peaceful Valley Farm & Garden Supply
P.O. Box 2209
125 Clydesdale Ct.
Grass Valley, California 95945
Phone (888) 784 1722
Phone (530) 272-4769
Fax (530) 272-4794
E-mail *helpdesk@groworganic.com*
Website *www.groworganic.com*
Organic custom cover crop mixes, clovers, sudangrass, sunn hemp, cowpeas, fava beans, legume inoculants

Pennington Seed, Inc.
P.O. Box 290
Madison, Georgia 30650
Phone (800) 285-7333
E-mail *seeds@penningtonseed.com*
Website *www.penningtonseed.com*
Grains, grasses, forage legumes

Plantation Seed Conditioners, Inc.
P.O. Box 398
Newton, Georgia 39870
Phone (229) 734-5466
Fax (229) 734-7419
Lupin, rye, clover, peas, wheat, vetch

Rohrer Seeds - P.L. Rohrer & Bro. Inc.
P.O. Box 250
2472 Old Philadelphia Pike
Smoketown, Pennsylvania 17576
Phone (717) 299-2571
Fax (800) 468-4944
E-mail *info@rohrerseeds.com*
Website *www.rohrerseeds.com*
Pasture mixes

Rupp Seeds, Inc.
17919 County Rd. B
Wauseon, Ohio 43567
Phone (877) 591-7333
Phone (419) 337-1841
Fax (419) 337-5491
Website *www.ruppseeds.com*
Alfalfa, triticale, wheat, other products available through local distributors

Seedway, LLC.
P.O. Box 250
Hall, New York 14463
Phone (800) 836-3710
Fax (585) 526-6832
E-mail *farmseed@seedway.com*
Website *www.seedway.com*
Wheat, clover, forage grasses

Snow Seed Organics
21855 Rosehart Way
Salinas, California 93908
Phone (831) 758-9869
Fax (831) 757-4550
E-mail *info@snowseedco.com*
Website *www.snowseedco.com*
Organic barley, triticale, vetch

Southern States Cooperative, Inc.
P.O. Box 26234
Richmond, Virginia 23260-6234
Phone (800) 868-6273
Website *www.southernstates.com*
Wholesale (retail outlets in six states) supplier of grains, forage legumes, cowpeas, summer annuals, rapeseed, clover, buckwheat, rye

Sweeney Seed Company
110 South Washington St.
Mount Pleasant, Michigan 48858
Phone (989) 773-5391
E-mail *Sweeney@journey.com*
Rye, annual ryegrass, clover, buckwheat, sorghum sudangrass, oats

Talbot Ag Supply
P.O. Box 2252
Easton, Maryland 21601-8944
Phone (410) 820-2388
Wheat, barley, rye, crimson clover

Turtle Tree Seed
Camphill Village
Copake, New York 12516
Phone (888) 516-7797
Fax (678) 202-1351
Website *www.turtletreeseeds.com*
Organic clover, rye, buckwheat, wheat

The Wax Co., Inc.
212 Front St. N
Amory, Mississippi 38821
Phone (662) 256-3511
Annual ryegrass, forages

Welter Seed & Honey Co.
17724 Hwy. 136
Onslow, Iowa 52321-7549
Phone (800) 728-8450
Phone (800) 470-3325
Fax (563) 485-2764
E-mail *info@welterseed.com*
Website *www.welterseed.com*
Organic alfalfa, ryegrass, clover, millets, plowdown mixes, sorghum, sorghum-sudan, sudangrass, vetch, rape, buckwheat, rye, wheat, and legume inoculants

Wisconsin Foundation Seeds
W6618 County Rd. K
Arlington, Wisconsin 53911
Phone (608) 846-9761
Fax (608) 846-9762
E-mail *jcalbert@wisc.edu*
Oats

Wolf River Valley Seeds
N2976 Hwy. M
White Lake, Wisconsin 54491
Phone (800) 359-2480
Fax (715) 882-4405
E-mail *wrvs@wolfrivervs.com*
Website *www.wolfrivervalleyseeds.com*
Alfalfa, wide range of clovers, forage mixes, oats, field peas, vetch, ryegrass, sorghum, sudangrass

Inoculant Suppliers

Agassiz Seed & Supply

445 7th St. NW
West Fargo, North Dakota 58078
Phone (701) 282-8118
Fax (701) 282-9119
Website *www.agassizseed.com*

Becker Underwood

801 Dayton Ave.
Ames, Iowa 50010
Phone (800) 232-5907
Phone (515) 232-5907
E-mail *request@beckerunderwood.com*
Website *www.beckerunderwood.com*

Dakota Frontier Seeds

6520 45th Ave
Flasher, North Dakota 58535
Phone (701) 597-3919
Fax (701) 597-3918
E-mail *dakotafrontierseeds@westriv.com*
Website *www.acgreenfix.com*
Supplier of AC Greenfix – an annual legume to build soil fertility, supply green manure nitrogen and improve crop yields

EMD Crop BioScience

13100 W Lisbon Ave. Suite 600
Brookfield, Wisconsin 53005
Phone (262) 957-2000
Fax (262) 957-2122
Website *www.nitragin.com*
Manufacturer of Nitragin inoculant

HiStick

801 Dayton Ave.
Ames, Iowa 50010
Phone (800) 892-2013
E-mail *Piran.Cargeeg@beckerunderwood.com*
Website *www.histick.com*

APPENDIX

MANUFACTURERS & EQUIPMENT DEALERS

Ag Resource, Inc.
35268 State Highway 34
Detroit Lakes, Minnesota 56501
Phone (800) 288-6650
Fax (218) 847-9351
Roller/crimper distributor

Buckeye Tractor Co.
P.O. Box 97
11313 Slabtown Rd.
Columbus Grove, Ohio 45830
Phone (800) 526-6791
Phone (419) 659-2162
Fax (419) 659-2082
E-mail *buctraco@bright.net*
Website *www.buctraco.com*
Front hitches

Henke Machine/ Buffalo Equipment
P.O. Box 848
2281 16th Ave.
Columbus, Nebraska 68602-0848
Phone (800) 228-1405
Fax (402) 562-5530
Buffalo rolling stalk chopper

Holland Transplanter Co.
P.O. Box 1527 / 510 E 16th
Holland, Michigan 49422-1527
Phone (616) 392-3579
Phone (800) 275-4482
Fax (616) 392-7996
E-mail *hldtrans@iserv.net*
Website *www.transplanter.com*

I & J Manufacturing
5302 Amish Rd.
Gap, Pennsylvania 17527
Phone (717) 442-9451
Fax (717) 442-8305
Website *www.croproller.com*
Cover crop rollers

Kinze Manufacturing
P.O. Box 806
Waynesberg, Iowa 52361
Phone (319) 668-1300
Fax (319) 668-1328
Website *www.kinze.com*
Toolbars

Market Farm Implements
257 Fawn Hollow Road
Friedans, Pennsylvania 15541
Phone (814) 443-1931
Website *www.marketfarm.com*

Martin Industries, LLC
P.O. Box 428
Elkton, Kentucky 42220
Phone (800) 366-5817
Fax (270) 265-9896
E-mail *martin@martintill.com*
Website *www.martinandcompany.com*
Closing wheels

Mechanical Transplanters Co.
1150 Central Ave.
Holland, Michigan 49423-5230
Phone (616) 396-8738
Phone (800) 757-5268
Fax (616) 396-3619
E-mail *mtc@mechanicaltransplanter.com*
Website *www.mechanicaltransplanter.com*

Monosem Inc.
1001 Blake St.
Edwardsville, Kansas 66111
Phone (913) 438-1700
Website *www.monosem-inc.com*
No-till planters

Pequea Planter
561 White Horse Rd.
Gap, Pennsylvania 17527
Phone (717) 442-4406
Residue slicers

Yetter Manufacturing Company
P.O. Box 358
109 S McDonnough Rd.
Colchester, Illinois 62326-0358
Phone (800) 447-5777
Fax (309) 776-3222
E-mail *info@yetterco.com*
Website *www.yetterco.com*
Residue managers

APPENDIX D NEW FARM ARTICLES

Many of these articles can be accessed from *http://newfarm.rodaleinstitute.org/archive/1000_stories/1000stories_archive.shtml*

"Cold-tolerant hairy vetch and late planting can be key factors for successful organic no-till corn in the Northeast." Managing for optimum weed-fighting and fertility contributions from cover crops pushes back plantings into peak risk times from voracious cutworms, but improved stands prove worth the wait at 153 bu./acre. January 17, 2008 *http://newfarm.rodaleinstitute.org/depts/NFfield_trials/2008/0117/notill.shtml*

"Organic no-till leads to updating of Farming Systems Trial." Rodale Institute combines two groundbreaking projects to push the envelope on how agriculture done right can curtail climate change. May 29, 2008 *www.rodaleinstitute.org/20080529/gw1*

"Measuring soil carbon changes would allow farms to offset excess emissions of other enterprises." Cap-and-trade approach, used wisely, could drive carbon-sequestering activities on-farm and beyond. November 16, 2007 *http://newfarm.rodaleinstitute.org/columns/research_paul/2007/1107/soilcarbon.shtml*

"Emerging technology may give farmers instant read in the field on soil-carbon changes." Pennsylvania funds The Rodale Institute to find out whether new system can document agricultural carbon sequestration for carbon-credit trading. November 16, 2007 *http://newfarm.rodaleinstitute.org/depts/NFfield_trials/2007/1116/ziegler.shtml*

"Earlier-flowering hairy vetch a great advance, but northern farmers need more." Winter survivability is the first consideration, and 'Purple Bounty' shows vulnerability. April 12, 2007 *http://newfarm.rodaleinstitute.org/depts/NFfield_trials/2007/0412/purplebounty.shtml*

"Researchers roll out the details of 2006 no-till organic corn numbers." In this above-average rainfall year, using a rolled-down cover crop worked better than tilling organic plots or non-organic comparison fields. March 15, 2007 *www.rodaleinstitute.org/node/207*

"NE-SARE roller research newsletter debuts. Regional farmers and Penn State researchers are working with The Rodale Institute to develop best management practices for use of the no-till cover-crop roller in the Northeast." This regional focus is funded by the USDA's Northeast SARE program. March 15, 2007 *http://www.rodaleinstitute.org/NE-SARE_roller_research_newsletter_debuts*

"Year 2006 is breakthrough for organic no-till corn yield; tops standard organic for first time at Rodale Institute." Roller system creates moisture-saving mulch from cover crop to suppress weeds and build soil as it slashes fuel and labor inputs. January 12, 2007 *http://www.rodaleinstitute.org/2006_is_a_breakthrough_for_organic_no-till_corn*

"No-Till Plus Project first cropping season wraps up." Farmer and researcher collaborators take stock of what worked and what didn't and prepare for improvement in 2007. December 14, 2006 *http://www.rodaleinstitute.org/no-till_plus_project_first_cropping_season*

"Get to know the no-tillers." A regional guide to the participants in The Rodale Institute's No-Till Plus project. December 14, 2006 *http://www.rodaleinstitute.org/get_to_know_the_no-tillers*

"Plans for no-till roller free for the downloading." Rugged yet elegant design lets crafters turn metal into dynamic tool for saving fuel, cutting chemicals and applying crop rotations. *http://www.rodaleinstitute.org/notill_plans*

"Farmers gear up cover-killing rollers for spring no-till planting season." Interest in chemical-free crop systems lead more farmers to seek high-value alternatives. February 16, 2006 *http://www.rodaleinstitute.org/farmers_gear_up_cover-killing_rollers_for_spring*

"Pennsylvania farmer links organic, conventional farming communities." No-Till+ project cooperator Kirby Reichert grows no-till corn, organic hay and specialty rye straw, among other crops–and keeps an open mind. November 10, 2005 *http://rodaleinstitute.org/pennsylvania_farmer_links_organic_conventional*

"Choosing cover crops for no-till organic soybeans." The more biomass the better for weed suppression–but you do have to be able to plant through the stuff. Of the three cover crops used rye, shown above, provided the most biomass. October 13, 2005 *http://www.rodaleinstitute.org/choosing_cover_crops*

"No-Till FAQs." Introducing answers to frequently asked questions about the No-till Plus project. *http://newfarm.rodaleinstitute.org/depts/notill/faqs.shtml*

"One step closer to production." CAD drawings of the cover crop roller nearing completion. June 21, 2005 *http://www.rodaleinstitute.org/one_step_closer*

"Organic no-till research spreading across the Midwest." From Pennsylvania to Michigan to Illinois, organic no-till is gaining ground as part of a revolution in weed management research and extension. June 2, 2005 *http://www.rodaleinstitute.org/organic_no-till_research_spreading*

"The Roller/Crimper Gallery." A collection of photos of cover crop roller/crimper tools from around the United States – and beyond. May 11, 2005 *http://www.rodaleinstitute.org/roller_crimper_gallery*

"It's planting time – do you know where your earthworms are?" Pennsylvania no-till farmer Steve Groff counts the many, wriggling benefits of no-till. May 11, 2005 *http://www.rodaleinstitute.org/its_planting_time*

"Emerging trends surface at national no-till conference." Cover crops were among the hot topics under discussion at the 13th annual National No-Tillage Conference, reports No-Till Farmer editor Ron Perszewski. April 19, 2005 *www.rodaleinstitute.org/2005414/perszewski*

"Frontiers in conservation tillage." International no-till expert Rolf Derpsch shares his views on the current state and future possibilities of reduced tillage systems worldwide. April 19, 2005 *http://www.rodaleinstitute.org/frontiers_in_conservation_tillage*

"Getting started with cover crops." Cover crops can build tilth, stem erosion and deliver nutrients to primary crops. TRI research agronomist Dave Wilson shares selection and establishment tips for on-farm cover crop research. April 19, 2005 *http://www.rodaleinstitute.org/getting_started_with_cover_crops*

"A truly regenerative agriculture." At Anne and Eric Nordell's Beech Grove Farm in north-central Pennsylvania, horses, cover crops, and reduced tillage add up to "bio-extensive market gardening." Imagine assembling a self-contained, regenerative farming system… and making a living doing it. Impossible, you might say – but over the last 20 years Anne and Eric Nordell of Beech Grove Farm in Trout Run, Pennsylvania, have been doing just that. What's their secret? Draft horses, alternative tillage techniques, and a time-tested rotation of cash and cover crops. They call their system "bio-extensive market gardening." January 7, 2005 *http://newfarm.rodaleinstitute.org/features/1204/nordell/index.shtml*

"Planting soybeans into rye." In northwestern Minnesota, Robin Brekken, Lee and Noreen Thomas and other organic farmers are working to perfect a system for no-till planting soybeans into a standing rye cover. Despite ongoing unpredictable weather, the strategy is showing promise. November 23, 2004 *http://www.rodaleinstitute.org/planting_soybeans_into_rye*

"Perfecting organic no-till systems nationwide." The Rodale Institute Experimental Farm receives NRCS Conservation Innovation Grant to build, distribute and test 10 organic no-till assemblies tailored to regional production needs. September 28, 2004 *http://www.rodaleinstitute.org/perfecting_organic_no-till_systems*

"Choosing the best cover crops for your organic no-till vegetable system." A detailed guide to using twenty-nine species. January 29, 2004 *http://www.rodaleinstitute.org/choosing_the_best_cover_crops*

"Organic no-till for vegetable production?" It can be done – Virginia Tech professor Ron Morse has been trialing a wide range of cover crop species for no-till planting of organic brassicas, cucurbits, Solanaceae and more. January 12, 2004 *http://www.rodaleinstitute.org/organic_no-till_for_vegetable_production*

"Rye lessons learned here at The Rodale Institute." We describe our own variation on planting soybeans into rye cover. September 12, 2003 *http://www.rodaleinstitute.org/rye_lessons_learned*

"Weed FREE!" An ode to rye. Minnesota researcher Paul Porter is working with five farmers to figure out the best way to use a rye cover crop as an effective weed suppressant for soybeans. No-till planting in rye is looking really strong as a strategy. September 12, 2003 *http://www.rodaleinstitute.org/weed_free_an_ode_to_rye*

"Let's talk about soil." We want soil to work for us, says soil scientist Ray Weil. We want it to hold water, recycle nutrients and keep diseases at bay. But we pulverize it with plows and expose it to evaporation and erosion. Now, does that make sense? January 6, 2003 *http://www.rodaleinstitute.org/lets_talk_about_soil*

"Organic no-till with cover crop roll-down is viable in Kentucky research." Chemical-free no-till is one of the current frontiers of organic farming. No-till and min-till crop systems' benefits include improved soil moisture retention, reduced erosion, higher soil organic matter levels and, when chemicals are not used, higher microbial diversity.

September 12, 2003 *http://www.rodaleinstitute.org/organic_no-till_with_cover_crop_roll-down*

"New tools for organic no-till." Introducing a cover crop roller without all the drawbacks of a stalk chopper. Here's the story of how good neighbors designed and constructed a front mounted cover-crop roller that allows you to knock down a weed-suppressing mat and plant through it, all in one quick pass! November 28, 2003 *http://www.rodaleinstitute.org/introducing_a_cover_crop_roller*

"The long road to no-till." A pictorial history of building and using a tool that makes organic no-till a reality. Slideshow *http://newfarm.rodaleinstitute.org/depts/NFfield_trials/1103/slideshow/notillroller1.shtml*

"Permanent cover crop stops soil from washing away." Tired of watching two-feet-deep crevices form on the hillsides after every heavy rain, Steve and Sheri Groff began experimenting with no-till to protect and improve the soil. *http://newfarm.rodaleinstitute.org/archive/1000_stories/sare_stories/groff.shtml*

"Conservation tillage sends residue burning up in smoke." Twenty-four years ago, Carter decided he'd had enough. After days of planting when he couldn't even see the front wheels of his tractor from all the smoke and dust, he vowed to find another way. "I looked at all the carbon going up in smoke, and I knew it wasn't right," he says. "Too much was leaving my land." *http://newfarm.rodaleinstitute.org/archive/1000_stories/sare_stories/carter.shtml*

"Covered up: A look at no-till options." The front unit of the sub-surface tiller-transplanter, developed by Dr. Ron Morse for planting vegetable starts and potato seed through mechanically-killed or winter-killed cover crop mulches. Slideshow. *http://newfarm.rodaleinstitute.org/features/0104/no-till/ss1.shtml*

One Farm to Another Columns by Jeff Moyer

"Scrambling to find Plan B after a nasty winter for vetch." In my mind, I saw deep vetch and timely no-tillage. In my fields, I've got dead vetch, bare ground and problems. May 11, 2007 *http://newfarm.rodaleinstitute.org/columns/jeff_moyer/2007/0507.shtml*

"Legumes buffer organic farms from this year's high N costs." Ethanol-fueled high corn prices create ripple effect that touches organic grain outlook. April 12, 2007 *http://newfarm.rodaleinstitute.org/columns/jeff_moyer/2007/0407.shtml*

"Oil price spike creates incentive for real change." Why tinker with fuel and fertilizer efficiencies when innovative organic synergies offer a way to change the whole system? September 14, 2006 *http://newfarm.rodaleinstitute.org/columns/jeff_moyer/2006/0906.shtml*

"Cutworms challenge organic no-till in wet field." Timing and moisture conditions conspire to give cutworms the edge. July 13, 2006 *http://newfarm.rodaleinstitute.org/columns/jeff_moyer/2006/0706.shtml*

"These are exciting times!" Those were the sentiments of a group of researchers and farmers who met during the first week of March at The Rodale Institute's farm in southeastern Pennsylvania to initiate plans for further research into organic no-till. March 17, 2005 *http://www.rodaleinstitute.org/these_are_exciting_times*

"Harvesting more than just crops." It's been a good season for apples, pumpkins, corn and soybeans here at The Rodale Institute, but it's our cover crop roller that's bearing fruit other farmers can use. October 26, 2004 *http://newfarm.rodaleinstitute.org/columns/jeff_moyer/2004/1004.shtml*

Ask Jeff Columns

"Can I plant a rye cover crop in the spring?" December 13, 2007 *http://newfarm.rodaleinstitute.org/columns/jeff_moyer/ask/2007/1207/1213_1.shtml*

"Can you provide more details on planting organic no-till rotations?" September 13, 2007 *http://newfarm.rodaleinstitute.org/columns/jeff_moyer/ask/2007/0907/0913_2.shtml*

"Can I roll my field of monster hairy vetch?" June 15, 2007 *http://newfarm.rodaleinstitute.org/columns/jeff_moyer/ask/2007/0607/0615_1.shtml*

"How can I get no-till soybeans started?" May 11, 2007 *http://newfarm.rodaleinstitute.org/columns/jeff_moyer/ask/2007/0507/0511_1.shtml*

"Can I no-till into 12-year-old CRP weed infested fields?" March 9, 2006 *http://newfarm.rodaleinstitute.org/columns/jeff_moyer/ask/2006/0306/0309_1print.shtml*

"Can I plant soybeans with a 7-inch no-till grain drill?" February 16, 2007 *http://newfarm.rodaleinstitute.org/columns/jeff_moyer/ask/2007/0207/0216_3print.shtml*

"Do you have measurement details for the roller?" February 16, 2007 *http://newfarm.rodaleinstitute.org/columns/jeff_moyer/ask/2007/0207/0216_2.shtml*

"How can I manage weeds in a no-till system without herbicides?" January 12, 2007 *http://newfarm.rodaleinstitute.org/columns/jeff_moyer/ask/2007/0112_1.shtml*

"What are the major challenges of a no-till roller system?" August 10, 2006 *http://newfarm.rodaleinstitute.org/columns/jeff_moyer/ask/2006/0806/0810_1.shtml*

"Can I use the no-till roller on Marshall rye or sorghum sudangrass?" August 10, 2006 *http://newfarm.rodaleinstitute.org/columns/jeff_moyer/ask/2006/0806/0810_3.shtml*

"Can you tell me more about your no-till organic roller?" April 13, 2006 *http://newfarm.rodaleinstitute.org/columns/jeff_moyer/ask/2006/0406/0413_1.shtml*

"Organic no-till project receives overwhelming response." October 26, 2004 *http://newfarm.rodaleinstitute.org/columns/jeff_moyer/ask/1004/1026_1.shtml*

APPENDIX E NEW FARM ONLINE FORUMS

Access these informative online forums from the New Farm website at *http://newfarm.rodaleinstitute.org/talk*

GENERAL TOPICS

An open forum for any farm-related subject including questions and comments about no-till in general, the goals of The Rodale Institute's "No-Till Plus" project, and the setup of this forum.

NEW FARMER

Share your challenges and insights about getting started.

NO-TILL PLUS

Building, buying and modifying no-till planters, cover crop rollers and other implements. Also discussion about the "No-Till Plus" project and your own experiences.

ALL ORGANIC

A place for organic growers to discuss the additional challenges and benefits of organic farming, including certification tips.

WEEDS

Share questions and answers about managing weeds in organic systems.

FARMING FOR CREDIT

Find out what's growing on at a campus near you.

APPENDIX

NO-TILL CONTACTS

▶ GET TO KNOW THE NO-TILLERS

A regional guide to the participants in The Rodale Institute's No-Till Plus project. For the benefit of readers, here's an annotated list, organized by region, of the farmers and researchers working on the project.

Mid-Atlantic

Pennsylvania

Dave Wilson, Collaborator
King's AgriSeeds
96 Paradise Lane
Ronks, Pennsylvania 17572
Phone (717) 687-6224
E-mail *davewilson@kingsagriseeds.com*

Steve Groff, Farmer
Cedar Meadow Farm
679 Hilldale Rd.
Holtwood, Pennsylvania 17532-9636
Phone (717) 284-5152
E-mail *sgroff@epix.net*
E-mail *steve@cedarmeadowfarm.com*

Kirby Reichert, Farmer
311 Farmall Rd.
Grantville, Pennsylvania 17028-9362
Phone (717) 469-2307
E-mail *reichert@paonline.com*

Southeast

Georgia

Juan Carlos Diaz-Perez, Collaborator
Associate Professor, UGA Coastal Plain
226 Horticulture Building
UGA Coastal Plain Experiment Station
CAES Tifton Campus
Tifton, Georgia 31793
Phone (229) 391-6861
Phone (229) 386-3355
Fax (229) 386-3356
E-mail *jcdiaz@uga.edu*

Frederick "Rick" Reed, Assisting Collaborator
502 Fox Hill Rd.
Douglas, Georgia 31535
Phone (912) 384-6252
Phone (912) 393-4164
E-mail *rr_careed@yahoo.com*

Sharad Phatak, Assisting Collaborator
UGA Coastal Plain
100 Horticulture Building / UGA Coastal Plain Experiment Station
CAES, Tifton Campus
Tifton, Georgia 31793-0748
Phone (229) 386-3901
E-mail *phatak@tifton.cpes.peachnet.edu*

Mike Nugent, Farmer
70 Hobby Lane
Willacoochee, Georgia 31650
Phone (912) 384-5355

Mark Vickers, Farmer
2177 Conway Vickers Rd.
Ambrose, Georgia 31512
Phone (912) 384-1217

Virginia

Ron Morse, Collaborator
Department of Horticulture
306-C Saunders Hall
Virginia Polytechnic Institute & State University
Blacksburg, Virginia 24061-0327
Phone (540) 231-6724
E-mail *morser@vt.edu*

Paul Davis, Farmer
Virginia Cooperative Extension
P.O. Box 310, New Kent County Office
Providence Forge, Virginia 23140
Phone (804) 966-9645
Phone (804) 966-7118
Fax (804) 966-5013
E-mail *padavis@vt.edu*

Midwest

Iowa

Kathleen Delate, Collaborator
Organic Specialist
Depts. of Agronomy/Horticulture
Iowa State University
106 Horticulture Hall
Ames, Iowa 50011
Phone (515) 294-7069
Fax (515) 294-0730
E-mail *kdelate@iastate.edu*

Ron Rosmann, Farmer
Rosmann Family Farms
1222 Ironwood Rd.
Harlan, Iowa 51537-4102
E-mail *ronrosmann@fmctc.com*

Michigan

Dale Mutch, Collaborator
Integrated Pest Management
Michigan State University
W. K. Kellogg Biological Station
3700 E. Gull Lake Dr.
Hickory Corners, Michigan 49060
Phone (800) 521-2619 x 224
Phone (269) 671-2412 x 224
E-mail *mutch@msu.edu*
Website *www.ipm.msu.edu/about.htm*

Jim Kratz, Farmer
NRCS
1075 Cleaver Road
Caro, Michigan 48723
Phone (989) 673-8174
Phone (989) 553-0249
E-mail *jim.kratz@mi.nacdnet.net*

Joe Pirrone, Farmer
Yale, Michigan 48097
Phone (810) 395-2673
E-mail joe@mpirrone.com

David Jansma, Farmer
Nashville, Michigan 49073
E-mail *djansma@integrityauditgroup.com*

Dan Schwallier, Farmer
Coopersville, Michigan
Phone (616) 299-2285
E-mail *dan_schwallier@yahoo.com*

Pat Sheridan, Farmer
2101 N. Sheridan Rd.
Fairgrove, Michigan 48733
Phone (989) 673-2984
Phone (989) 550-0072
Fax (989) 673-5984
E-mail *pmsheridan@hotmail.com*

South

Mississippi

Seth Dabney, Collaborator
USDA-ARS National Sedimentation Laboratory
P.O. Box 1157
598 McElroy Dr.
Oxford, Mississippi 38655
Phone (662) 232-2975
Fax (662) 232-2988
E-mail *sdabney@ars.usda.gov*

Perrin Grissom, Farmer
P.O. Box 344
Stoneville, Mississippi 38776
Phone (662) 822-6769
E-mail *perrin@tecinfo.com*

Northern Plains

North Dakota

Steve Zwinger, Collaborator
NDSU Carrington Research Extension Center
P.O. Box 219
663 Hwy 281 N
Carrington, North Dakota 58421
Phone (701) 652-2951
Fax (701) 652-2055
E-mail *szwinger@ndsuext.nodak.edu*

Blaine Schmaltz, Farmer
6020 22nd Ave. NE
Rugby, North Dakota 58368
Phone (701) 776-6023
E-mail *bbestseeds@stellarnet.com*

West Coast

California

Jeff Mitchell, Collaborator
University of California
Kearney Agricultural Center
9240 S. Riverbend Ave.
Parlier, California 93648
Phone (559) 646-6565
Phone (559) 303-9689
Phone (559) 897-2914
Fax (559) 646-6593
E-mail *mitchell@uckac.edu*

Anil Shrestha, Assisting Collaborator
Weed Ecologist
Integrated Pest Management Program
University of California West Side Research and Extension Center
Five Points, California 93624

Paul Muller & Andrew Brait, Farmers
Full Belly Farm
Capay, California 95607

Tom and Denesse Willey, Farmers
Madera, California 93637
Phone (559) 706-9552
Phone (559) 673-9058

No-Till Project Advisors

Bill Curran
Penn State University
210 ASI Bldg
University Park, Pennsylvania 16802
Phone (814) 863-1014
E-mail *wsc2@psu.edu*

John Teasdale
USDA ARS-Beltsville Research Center
5601 Sunnyside Avenue
Beltsville, Maryland 20705
Phone (301) 504-5504
E-mail *teasdale@ba.ars.usda.gov*

APPENDIX G WEB RESOURCES

▶ ARTICLES & WEBSITES

Articles

"Brassica Cover Crops to Alleviate Soil Compaction" Discusses the oilseed radish and its role in alleviating soil compaction. *http://enst2.umd.edu/weilbrassicacovercrops.pdf*

"Conservation Tillage Methods" Dr. Mary Peet, North Carolina State University. Sustainable Practices for Vegetable Production in the South. *http://www.cals.ncsu.edu/sustainable/peet/tillage/cons_til.html*

"Conservation Tillage and Cover Crop Systems for Organic Processing Tomato Production (Year 2) (OFRF)" Interesting information for tomato growers. *http://ofrf.org/funded/reports/cahn_01f21.pdf*

"Evaluation of Frost-Killed Cover Crop Mulches for Organic No-Till Production of Spring Vegetables on Small Farms (OFRF)" Discusses wide range of cover crops followed by vegetables. *http://ofrf.org/funded/reports/schonbeck_04s12.pdf*

"Farmscaping to Enhance Biological Control" Provides information on pest control with beneficial insects. *http://attra.ncat.org/attra-pub/PDF/farmscaping.pdf*

"No-Till Drilling Cover Crops after Wheat Harvest and their Influence on next Season's Corn" Reviews the effects of oilseed radish, clover, and hairy vetch seeded as cover crops. *http://web2.msue.msu.edu/bulletins/Bulletin/PDF/E2897.pdf*

"No-Till Production of Irish Potato on Raised Beds" Summary of trials at Virginia Tech and recommendations for potato growers. *http://www.ag.auburn.edu/auxiliary/nsdl/scasc/Proceedings/1997/Morse.pdf*

"A No-Tillage Tomato Production System Using Hairy Vetch and Subterranean Clover Mulches" Compares tomato crops grown following vetch and clover to conventional mulches. *http://www.sarep.ucdavis.edu/newsltr/v7n1/sa-11.htm*

"No-Till Vegetable Production: Non-Chemical Methods of Cover Crop Suppression and Weed Control" Appropriate Technology Transfer for Rural Areas (ATTRA) document on no-till vegetable production. *http://attra.ncat.org/downloads/notill_veg.doc*

"Nutrient Quantity or Nutrient Access? A New Understanding of How to Maintain Soil Fertility in the Tropics" Review of The Ecological Management of Soils by Ana Primavesi. h*ttp://ppathw3.cals.cornell.edu/mba_project/moist/RolandB.html*

"On-Farm Research Guide (OFRF)" Information on how to conduct your own research projects. *http://ofrf.org/grants/on-farm_research_guide.pdf*

"Overview of Cover Crops and Green Manures" Excellent source of information on cover crops and their uses. *http://attra.ncat.org/attra-pub/covercrop.html*

"Pursuing Conservation Tillage Systems for Organic Production" Overview of the potential for conservation tillage systems. *http://attra.ncat.org/attra-pub/organicmatters/conservationtillage.html*

"Smart Cover Cropping" Uses of cover cropping on the Steve Groff farm in Pennsylvania. *http://www.ibiblio.org/farming-connection/covercro/groff/coverman.htm*

"Soil Management: The Key to Sustainability." Aref Abdul-Baki, USDA-ARS Vegetable Laboratory. *http://californiaagriculture.ucanr.org/landingpage.cfm?article=ca.v063n01p35&abstract=yes*

"Sorghum-sudangrass Grown as a Cover Crop for Organic No-till Vegetable Production, and as a Hay Crop for the Organic Market (OFRF)" Evaluates potential of sorgum-sudangrass to provide weed suppression for fall plantings of cabbages. *http://ofrf.org/funded/reports/finney_03f15.pdf*

"Sustainable Production of Fresh-Market Tomatoes and Other Vegetables With Cover Crop Mulches" Use of vetch as a mulch with various kinds of vegetables. *http://www.ars.usda.gov/is/np/SustainableTomatoes2007/SustainableTomatoes2007Intro.htm*

"Sustainable Soil Management (ATTRA)" Covers basic soil properties and management steps toward building and maintaining healthy soils. *http://attra.ncat.org/attra-pub/PDF/soilmgmt.pdf*

"Transplanter and Stalk-Chopper Modifications" Steve Groff feature, Sustainable Farming Connection website *http://www.ibiblio.org/farming-connection/covercro/groff/equiip.htm*

U.S. No-Till Websites

American Journal of Alternative Agriculture
http://eap.mcgill.ca/MagRack/AJAA/ajaa_ind.htm
This is a great resource to search for organic no-till articles.

ATTRA
http://attra.ncat.org
ATTRA, The National Sustainable Agriculture Information Service is managed by the National Center for Appropriate Technology (NCAT) provides information and other technical assistance to farmers and others involved in sustainable agriculture in the United States.

Cedar Meadow Farm (Steve & Cheri Groff)
www.cedarmeadowfarm.com
Information on Pennsylvania no-tiller Steve Groff, and his work with vegetable production.

Conservation Tillage Information Center (CTIC)
www.ctic.purdue.edu
Search on "no-till" for additional information and links.

Dakota Lakes Research Farm
www.dakotalakes.com/Publications.htm
Good resource for no-till farming in dry conditions in the Central and Northern plains.

No-Till Farmer
www.no-tillfarmer.com
Homepage for newsletter on no-till farming. Information on the national no-till conference.

No-Till on the Plains
www.notill.org
Web page for No-Till on the Plains, Inc., a non-profit educational organization providing information to farmers on adopting No-till and other sustainable production methods

Organic Seed Sourcing
www.organicseedsourcing.com/index.htm
Use this free resource to search for organic seeds.

Organic Farming Research Foundation
http://ofrf.org/index.html
OFRF funds and publishes original research on organic farming methods, including no-till. This is an excellent source of information on topics of all kinds.

Penn State University, Soil Management
http://soilmanagement.psu.edu/smdefault.cfm
Penn State's soil management website.

Reduced Tillage Systems for Vegetables
www.hort.cornell.edu/reducedtillage/index.htm
Cornell program that focuses on reduced tillage systems for the cool northeastern climates.

South Dakota No-Till Association
www.sdnotill.com
Resources for no-tillage on the prairie. Provides cover crop info and seed sources.

Southern Conservation Tillage Conference for Sustainable Agriculture (SCTCSA)
www.ag.auburn.edu/auxiliary/nsdl/scasc/
Information about the Southern Conservation Agricultural Systems Conference.

UC SAREP Cover Crop Resource Page
www.sarep.ucdavis.edu/ccrop/
The UC SAREP Cover Crop Database includes over 5,000 items gleaned from more than 600 separate sources, including journal articles, conference proceedings, standard textbooks, unpublished data, and personal communications from researchers and farmers.

USDA-SARE
www.sare.org
Research projects and publications on a range of topics, including no-till.

International No-Till Websites

African Conservation Tillage Network (ACT)
www.act.org.zw
The African Conservation Tillage work (ACT) promotes and facilitates sharing of information and experiences across sectors, disciplines and geographical boundaries among players and stakeholders involved in promoting adaptation and adoption of conservation farming principles and practices in Africa.

Animal Traction Network for Eastern and Southern Africa (ATNESA)
www.atnesa.org/contilworkshopcontents.htm
Information on the book Conservation tillage with animal traction edited by Pascal Kaumbutho and Timothy Simalenga.

European Conservation Agriculture Federation (ECAF)
www.ecaf.org
Website provides interesting information about no-till in Europe.

Food and Agriculture Organization of the United Nations
www.fao.org/ag/ca
Information on worldwide conservation tillage initiatives.

Manitoba-North Dakota Zero-Tillage Farmers Association
www.mandakzerotill.org
A website to facilitate the exchange of ideas and disseminate information regarding zero-tillage.

No-Tillage
www.rolf-derpsch.com/notill.htm
Website for Rolf Derpsch, no-till consultant in Paraguay.

South Australian No-Till Farmers Association (SANTFA)
www.santfa.com.au
SANTFA aims to promote the role of no-till systems as an economic and environmentally sustainable farming practice and to help facilitate the sharing of information between farmers on applying successful no-till cropping systems.

WANFTA (Western Australian No-Tillage Farmers Association)
www.wantfa.com.au
WANFTA is driving adoption of sustainable and profitable broadacre cropping systems by sharing farmer experiences and innovations from our research and field trials.

WASWC (World Association of Soil and Water Conservation)
www.waswc.org
Click on "no-till" for a number of interesting publications

APPENDIX

"NO-TILL PLUS" TRIALS INFORMATION

▶ RESULTS FOR THE RODALE INSTITUTE

Results and summary of practices from the trials of no-till corn planted in rolled hairy vetch for the year 2006. The no-till corn plots were harvested on November 21, 2006.

In August of 2005, production field No. 60 was measured and divided into replications for the purpose of collecting data about hairy vetch and a subsequent no-till corn crop in 2006. The following data comes from this production field that was converted into randomly replicated plots in order to scientifically collect, quantify and run statistics on the data. Each experimental plot was 20 feet wide x 50 feet long, in four replications with 25-foot buffers between replications. The treatments consisted of hairy vetch from different seed tag origins (Minnesota, Wisconsin, two Oregon sources and Pennsylvania farmer-grown, labeled Steve Groff (Early Cover) vetch). The previous crop in the field was winter wheat, which was planted in the fall of 2004 and harvested in July of 2005. The wheat was combined for grain and the straw was baled and removed. Compost was applied to the wheat stubble at the end of the summer of 2005 at the rate of approximately 10 tons/acre (wet weight), which is approximately 4 to 4.5 tons of dry material solids. The field was moldboard plowed in late August to incorporate the compost and wheat stubble, and disking and culti packing were done in early September to prepare the seedbed for drilling the hairy vetch.

The hairy vetch was planted on September 8, 2005 at the rate of 25 lbs./acre.

There were 62 days after planting before the first killing frost, and 47 to 49 days after emergence of the vetch before the first killing frost. The general recommendation is that sowing be at least 40 days (preferably 50 or 60 days) before the first killing frost. This is important because the hairy vetch needs enough time to produce aboveground biomass, crowns, and reserves of carbohydrates in the root systems. These factors, along with the genetic selection of the cultivar, contribute to winter survivability of the hairy vetch. Our first killing frost (32 F) was November 19, 2005, followed by November 25 (30 F) and November 26 (25 F).

The hairy vetch emerged 15 days after the September 8 planting, and was growing until the roll/crimp kill on June 9. There were 260 days between planting and kill of the hairy vetch.

In the spring, aboveground biomass cuts were taken in all the replicated plots on April 21 and June 9, 2006. The average aboveground biomass dry matter weight on April 21 was 3,531 lbs./acre (this ranged from 2,679 lbs./acre to 5,470 lbs./acre among the five different seed sources of hairy vetch). The average aboveground biomass dry matter weight on June 9 was 6,146 lbs./acre (this ranged from 5,997 lbs./acre to 6,648 lbs./acre among the five different seed sources of hairy vetch). The dry biomass was sampled and sent to the Pennsylvania State University lab for nitrogen analysis.

▶ TABLE 1: HAIRY VETCH BIOMASS ON APRIL 21, 2006 & JUNE 9,2006

Hairy Vetch Evaluation for No-Till Corn, Five Hairy Vetch Populations, The Rodale Institute, Field 60 (center portion).

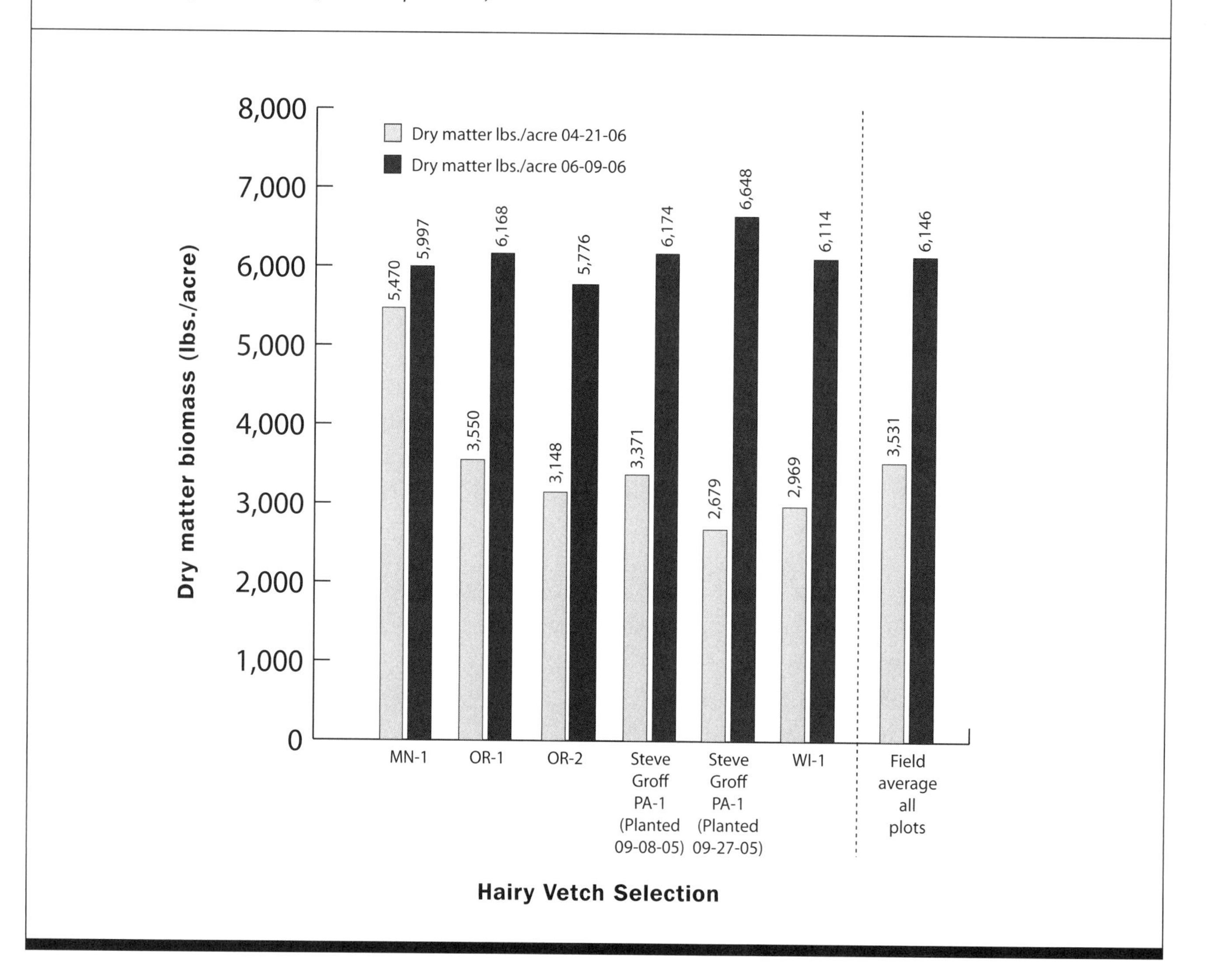

Samples of the biomass cuts on both dates were analyzed for percent nitrogen. On April 21, 2006 the average percent nitrogen from the aboveground biomass was 4.77 percent with a range of 3.85 to 5.66 percent, on June 9, 2006 the average percent nitrogen from the aboveground biomass was 3.31 percent, with a range of 2.84 to 3.81 percent among the different seed tag origins of hairy vetch. The amount of nitrogen in the aboveground biomass at time of rolling ranged from 170-253 lbs./acre, with an average of 203 lbs./acre.

The hairy vetch cover crop was mechanically killed with the front mounted roller/crimper on June 9, which created the killed cover crop mulch. In the same pass, the corn was planted with a no-till planter into the rolled-down mat of hairy vetch.

The no-till planter was a Monosem Air Seeder on a Kinze toolbar with a heavy residue coulter, double-disk openers and cast iron closing (press) wheels to close the seed furrow. Extra weight is added to the planter in order to facilitate cutting down through the thick rolled-down hairy vetch

▶ TABLE 2: HAIRY VETCH NITROGEN IN ABOVEGROUND BIOMASS
Hairy Vetch Evaluation for No-Till Corn, Five Hairy Vetch Populations, The Rodale Institute, Field 60 (center portion).

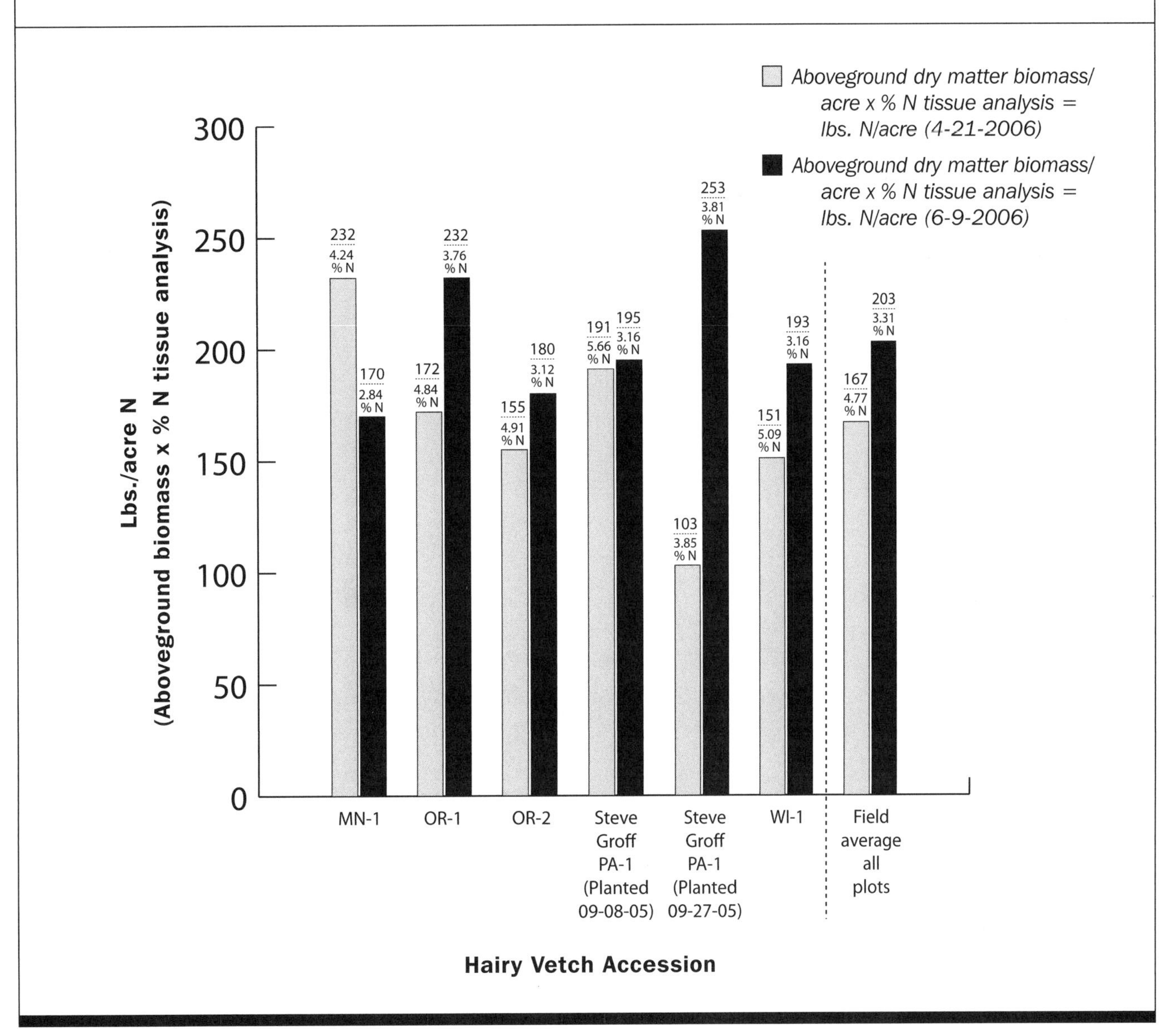

mat and into the soil surface to an adequate planting depth of 1.5-2 inches.

The corn variety was Blue River 68F32 Corn (113 day relative maturity). There were 2,140 growing degree days for the growing season (June 9 through the end of September). The accumulated rainfall for June through the end of September was 26.54 inches, 10.44 inches over the average rainfall for that period over the past 30 years.

On September 18, 2006 weed biomass was taken in the plots and separated between in-row and between row biomass.

The in-row dry matter weed biomass ranged from 106-455 lbs./acre, with an average of 232 lbs./acre. The between-row dry matter weed biomass ranged from 408 to 1,360 lbs./acre, with an average of 938 lbs./acre. It should be noted that the critical period for weed control in corn is from the third to eighth leaf stage. During this period of time,

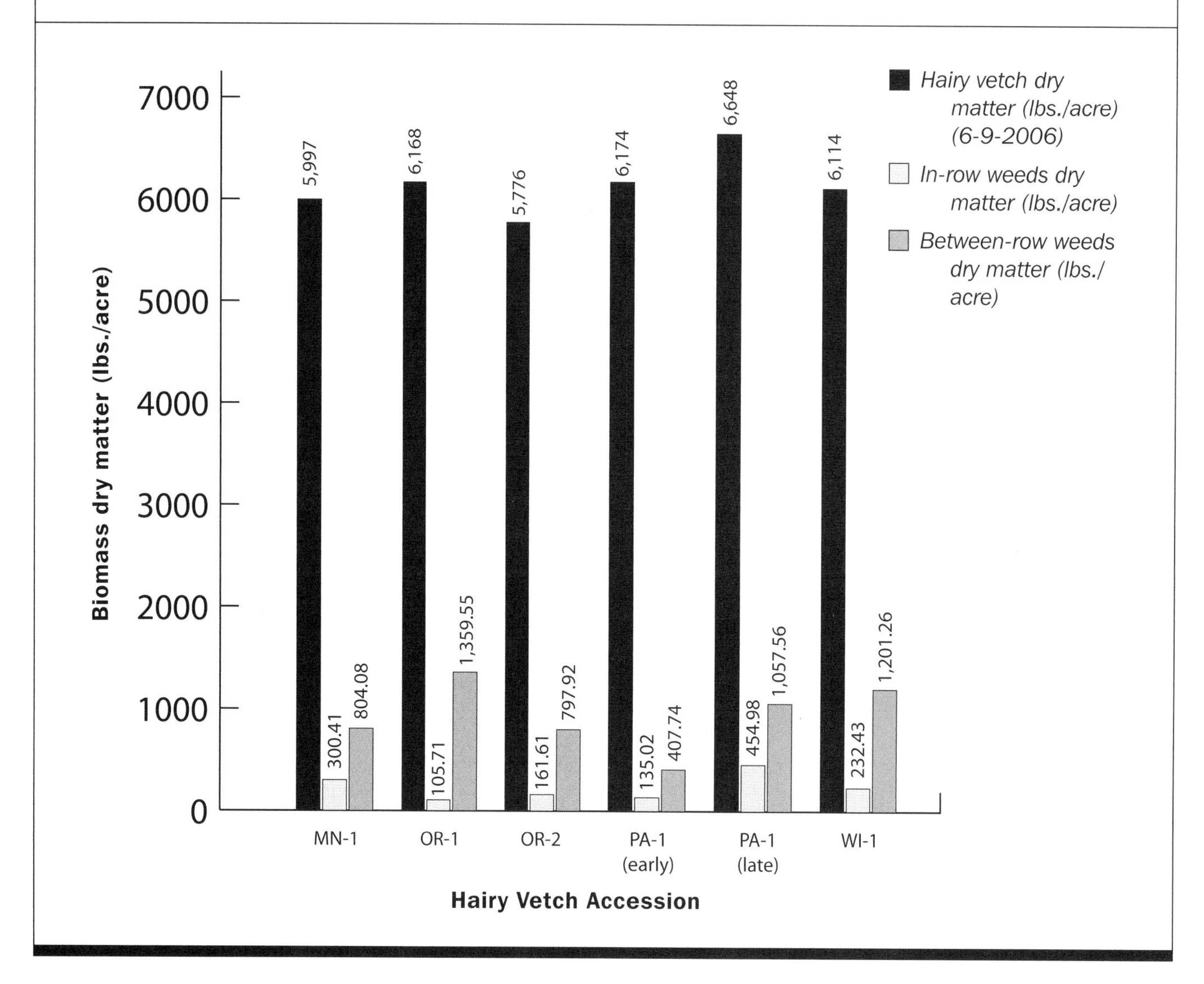

TABLE 3: HAIRY VETCH & WEED BIOMASS
The Rodale Institute, Field 60 (center portion); Hairy Vetch biomass taken at September 6, 2006 (time of kill). Weed biomass taken at September 18, 2006 (before corn harvest).

the rolled-down hairy vetch mat prevented many weeds from germinating and growing. Competitive in-row weeds were amounts were very low from the combination of the early weed suppressing mat of hairy vetch and the subsequent canopy of the corn. In addition, because the organic nitrogen becomes slowly available, it is not available for early competitive weed growth. Eventually, some of the weeds break through the mat and grow, but since they germinate later, they are not as detrimental to corn yields. Because the mat gives a continuous soil cover that is sliced with a double disk opener for planting, there are vastly fewer of the competitive in-row weeds, those that grow in the corn root zone and therefore more closely compete with the corn plant for nutrients and water.

The corn was harvested on November 21, 2006. The average yield across all the hairy vetch plots was 146 bu./acre at 15.5 percent moisture, with a range of 139-152 bu./acre. As points of comparison, the Berks County, Pennsylvania average yield for 2006 was 130 bu./acre, and the southeastern region of Pennsylvania average was 147 bu./acre.

▶ **TABLE 4: ORGANIC NO-TILL CORN YIELDS**

The Rodale Institute, Field 60 (center portion); Corn cv. Blue River 68F32 (113 day maturity).

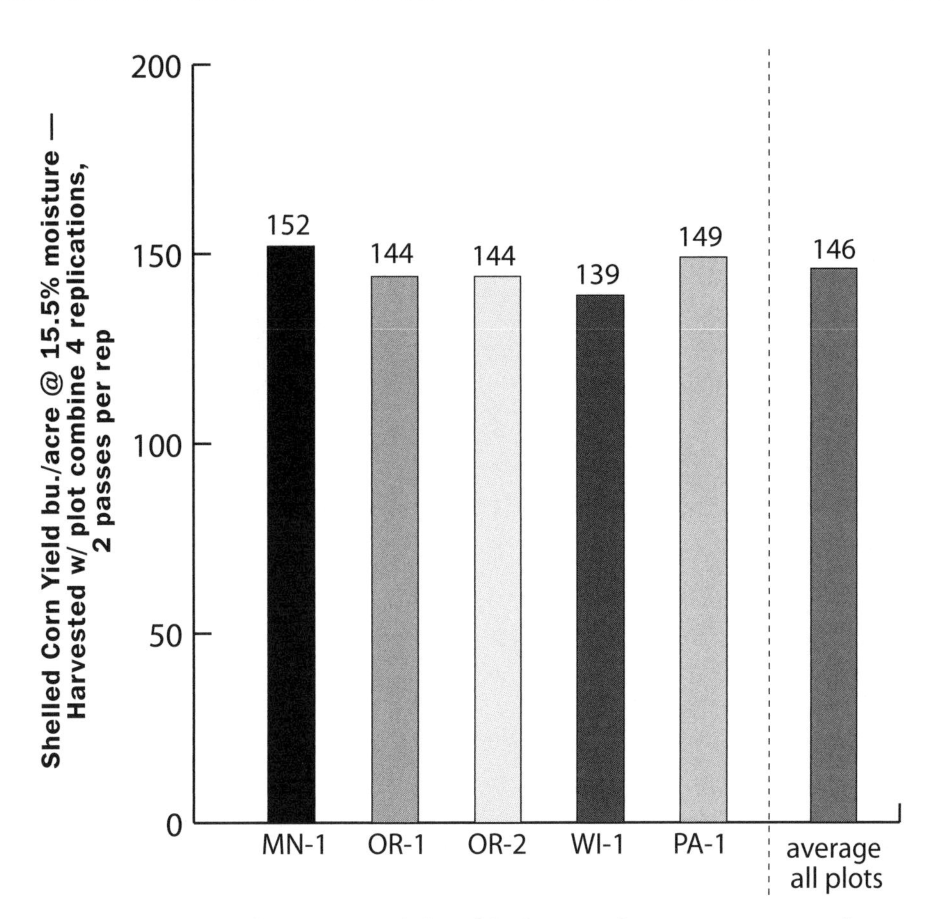

Corn no-till planted on June 9, 2006 into rolled hairy vetch from different seed tag origins.

The corn had been planted at a population of 32,000 plants/acre. The average pre-harvest population count was 24,533 and ranged from 22,971 to 25,295 plants/acre. Much of the reduction in population was attributed to cutworm damage (one disadvantage of the no-till system is that the mat provides shelter for the cutworms). During the pre-roll biomass cut we evaluated for cutworm, we counted the cutworms and we extrapolated from 33,000 to 34,000 cutworms per acre. More than one worm per corn plant per acre at our corn planting rate. As a result of the cutworm numbers at that time the planting and rolling was delayed. The hairy vetch plots were ready from May 19 to June 2, 2006 and could have been rolled with an effective kill on the hairy vetch, but the cutworm population was high. The delay let the cutworms mature and develop into moths. When we went back in after the corn was emerging we still had some cutworm damage but we also found many moths emerging from the seed furrow slits as we did our counts and

▶ **TABLE 5: 2006 ORGANIC NO-TILL CORN YIELDS**

The Rodale Institute, Field 60 (center portion); Corn cv. Blue River 68F32 (113 day maturity), Corn no-till planted on June 9, 2006 into rolled hairy vetch from five different seed tag origins.

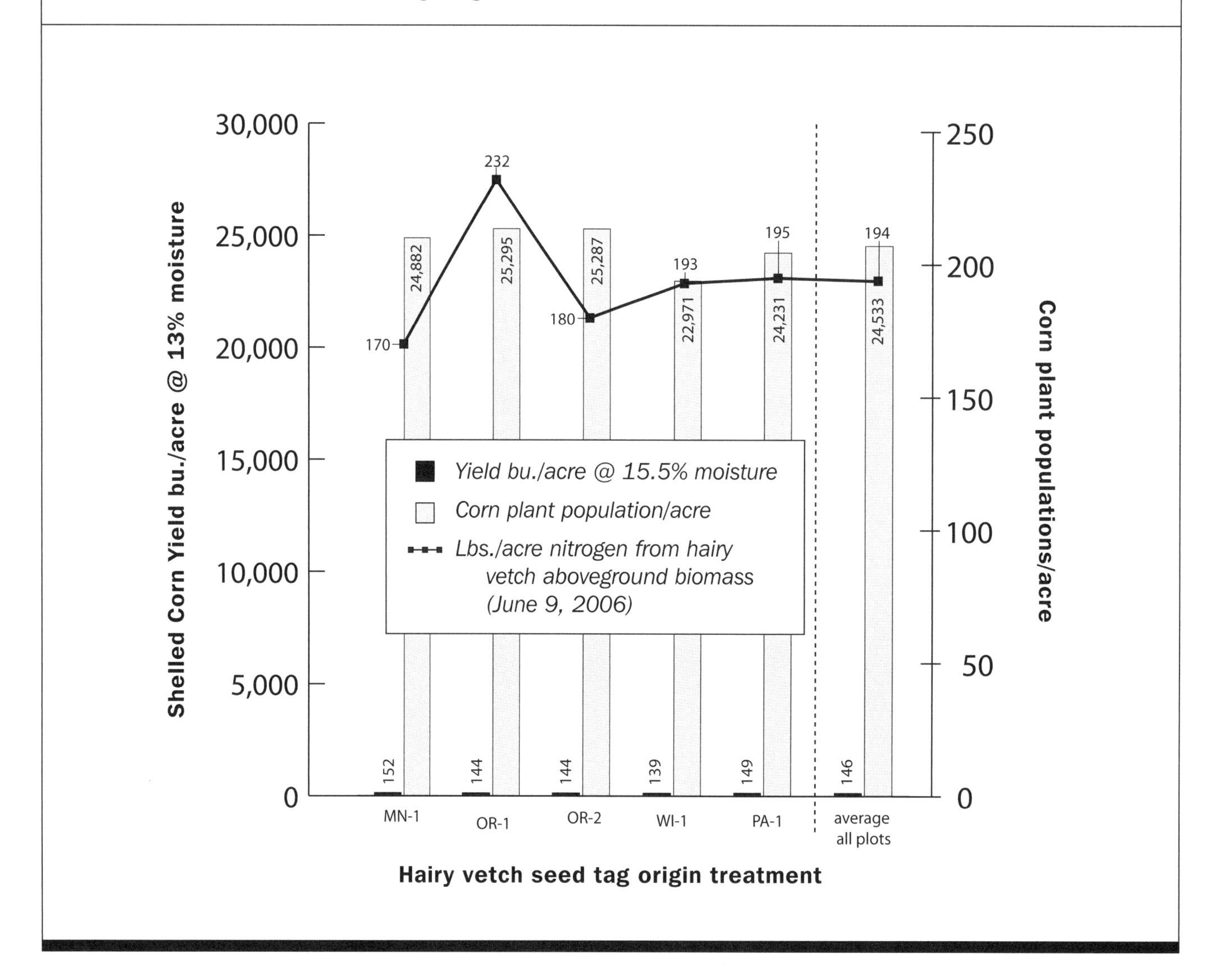

examination. Many moths had already emerged and left. I think in this case the delayed planting let the majority of the cutworms mature to the moth stage where they did not pose a chewing threat to the corn seedlings. This will be a continued challenge for us in the future, dependant on timing and will certainly vary from year to year with the environmental conditions.

The nitrogen fertility for the corn yield came from various sources including long-term accumulated organic matter in the soil. Stores of organic matter built up from a combination of crop residues, including soybean crop residue, hay crop residue (alfalfa/red clover/timothy mix, which is grown two to four years, typically three years in succession in the rotation), winter annual cover crops and compost applications.

The other major nitrogen source is the winter annual legume hairy vetch that was planted in the fall before the no-till corn crop. As stated earlier, in 2006 we measured an average of 194 lbs./acre from aboveground dry hairy vetch biomass.

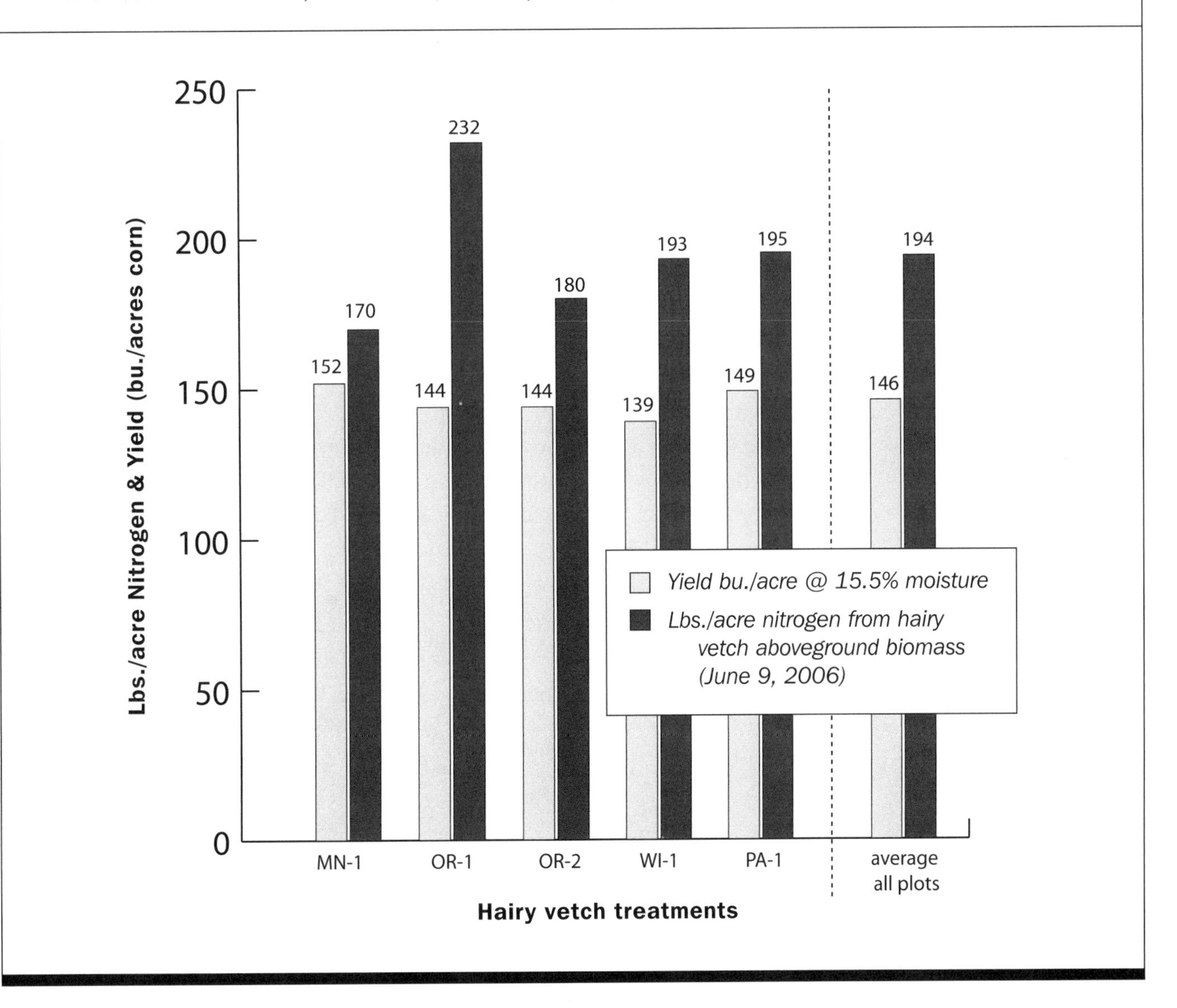

▶ TABLE 6: 2006 HAIRY VETCH NITROGEN IN ABOVEGROUND BIOMASS & NO-TILL CORN YIELDS

The Rodale Institute, Field 60 (center portion).

When this was rolled and crimped, it serves as a multi-purpose killed mulch mat. The purposes are to suppress weeds, and, as it decays, to make nitrogen available to the corn crop. In addition, the mat acts to conserve moisture by preventing evaporation and keeping the soil temperature cooler. The mat also harbors beneficial insects, and as it decays, nourishes soil microorganisms that in turn recycle nitrogen.

After the no-till corn was harvested, the field was disked and the winter annual cereal rye cover crop was planted into the disked corn stalk stubble and remaining hairy vetch residue.

Considerations for this organic no-till corn system include:

• Establishment of the hairy vetch cover crop, having a seeding date early enough to produce adequate aboveground and root biomass before the first killing frost.

• For no-till grown in northern zones the use of hairy vetch varieties that are winter hardy (look for seed tag origins from hairy vetch seed produced in the Northern states instead of Southern warm-winter states).

• Also selecting a hairy vetch variety that is an earlier flowering variety and still produces adequate biomass for weed suppression and nitrogen production is important and will be advantageous for an earlier rolling-mechanical kill date of the hairy vetch and thus an earlier corn planting date.

• Successful mechanical roll/crimp kill depends on the hairy vetch cover crop being at full bloom, rolling before that time will not give effective kill and the hairy vetch will grow back. Timing and patience is very important, this date varies somewhat from year to year depending on growing conditions.

• Shorter season corn varieties, corn with relative maturity ratings that are lower than the typical corn planted in the local growing zone will do better and will reach full maturity with the shorter growing season due to the late planting waiting for the hairy vetch to bloom.

• The no-till planter has to be adjusted, for this system to get a successful corn stand.

• The hairy vetch cover crop biomass is much thicker than this and adjustments on the no-till planter need to be made to manage this biomass appropriately.

• An aggressive coulter to cut through the thick hairy vetch mat, the planter depth of the gage wheels and double disk openers need to be adjusted for proper planting depth.

• In this past years case a set of cast iron closing wheels were added and successfully closed the seed furrow slice.

• In addition extra weight was added to the planter unit to give the additional ballast to the planter to get adequate downward pressure to slice and plant in this heavy residue mat.

Rodale Institute On-Farm Research Field Plots in Progress During the Fall and Winter of 2006-2007

Trial: Hairy vetch adaptation for winter survivability and early rolling in a no-till system

Hairy vetch established during the time from mid-August to mid-September grows until deep killing frosts and then goes dormant. Winter surviving vetch grows aggressively in April and May to produce nitrogen for the corn crop. The biggest problem with this system has been the winterkilling of hairy vetch. Trials from 2005 to 2007 show that hairy vetch varieties vary substantially in their ability to survive winterkill under Pennsylvania conditions.

For a second year in a row field plots were established and planted for this hairy vetch evaluation. In collaboration with Dr. Thomas Devine, USDA ARS, six hairy vetch accessions received from USDA as well as six other commercially available hairy vetch populations from various seed tag origins were planted and established in the fall 2005.

Evaluations of Hairy Vetch from the Fall 2006 through Winter 2007

Included in the evaluations were six hairy vetch accessions (common, population 26, K-12, B-35, Steve Groff 2006 and AUEC 2006) and five other commercially available populations (Oregon origin (Early Cover), Nebraska origin, Steve Groff 2005 (Early Cover), AUEC 2003, and Minnesota origin). All the seeds were planted on September 8, 2006 with the exception of the Minnesota seed origin. The Minnesota origin seed was planted on September 19, 2006 due to the late arrival of the seed to our location.

▶ TABLE 7: HAIRY VETCH SEED SOURCES

Population	Experimental Hairy Vetch Populations 06/07 Code	Seed Sources		
1	K-12	These populations were received from Tom Devine, USDA, ARS		
2	Population 26			
3	B-35			
4	Common			
5	2006 Steve Groff			
6	2006 AUEC			
		Purchased Lot #'s	**Origin**	**Supplier**
7	OR-1	W6-6-HV-603	Oregon	F.M. Brown & Sons
8	NE-1	HV02-05	Nebraska	Ernst Conservation Seeds
9	MN-1	AKHVW606	Minnesota	Albert Lee Seed House
10	2005 Steve Groff		Pennsylvania	Farmer/grower Steve Groff
11	2003 AUEC	A.U. Early Cover		F.M. Brown & Sons

▶ **TABLE 8: HAIRY VETCH PERCENT EMERGENCE, NUMBER OF PLANTS EMERGED**
The Rodale Institute, September 25, 2006 (17 days after planting) Field 14-15 (Eastern Section)

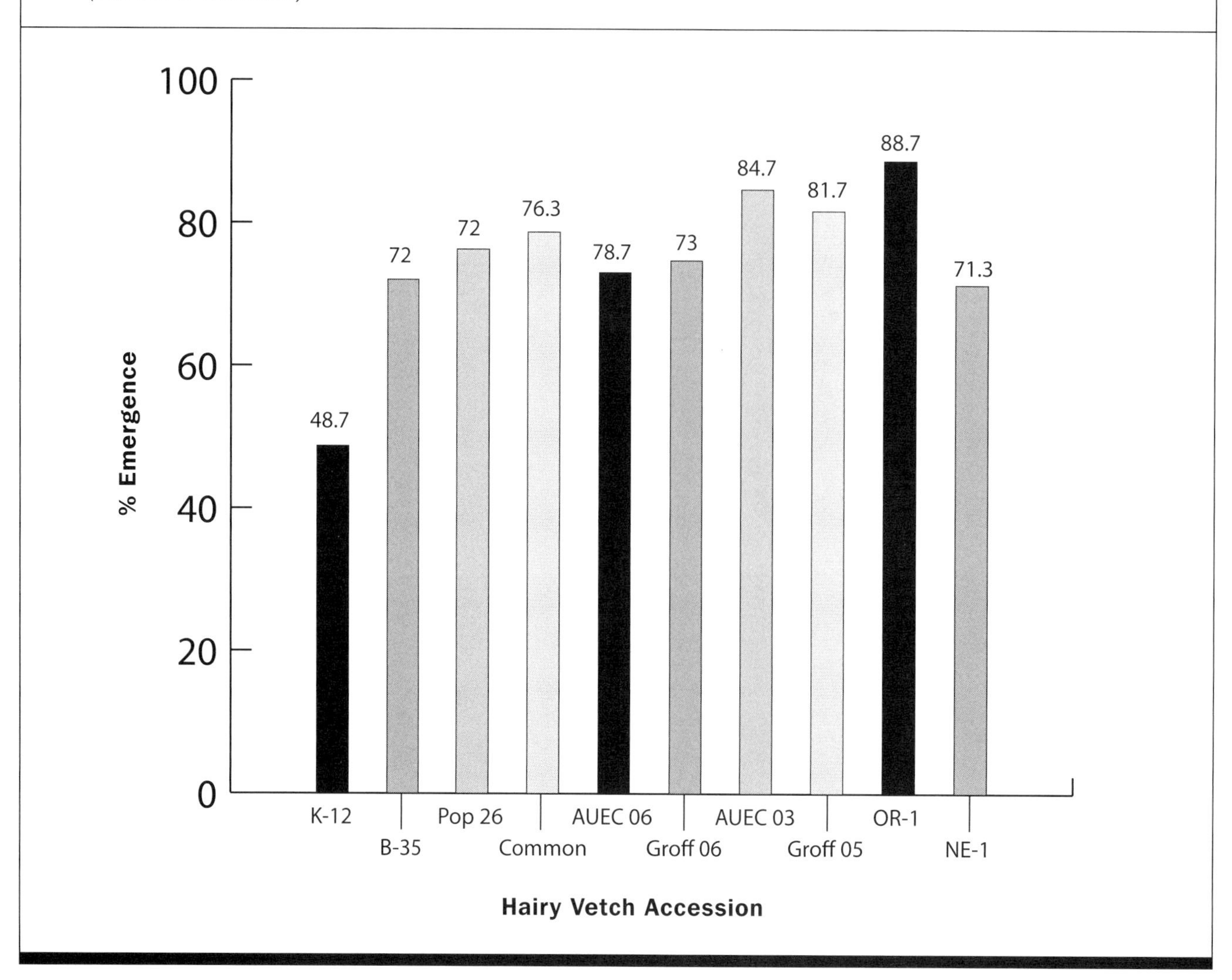

Before planting, the samples of seeds were counted and weighed to determine the number of seeds per gram, seeds per pound, to compare the relative size of the seeds between the populations and for future reference.

The seed samples were planted in three replications, each replication in tilled plots 5 feet wide by 10 feet 6 inches long rows planted 1.5 to 2 inches apart in the row.

On September 25, 2006 the number of plants that had emerged were counted in the plots.

On January 24, 2007 the plots were evaluated for percent ground cover, using a 0.5 m^2 quad placed at approximately one foot in from the east end of the row and then again one foot in from the west end of the row, two evaluations were made for each row in each replication. The percent ground cover is the percent of ground inside the 0.5 m^2 quadrate that was covered by the hairy vetch plant. Since the row length of the plot is 126 inches two quadrants (0.5m^2) are approximately 55.7 inches in row length, combined total represents 44 percent of the plot row.

▶ TABLE 9: HAIRY VETCH SEEDS PER GRAM, SEEDS PER POUND

Accession	Seeds per gram	Seeds per pound
Population 26	50.50	22,906
Groff 2006	43.20	19,595
K-12	42.95	19,482
B-35	40.47	18,359
AUEC 2003	39.60	17,962
Groff 2005	36.68	16,501
Oregon origin (Early Cover)	35.68	16,182
AUEC 2006	34.85	15,807
Common	29.73	13,485
Nebraska origin	29.67	13,458
Minnesota origin	27.79	12,605

▶ TABLE 10: HAIRY VETCH EMERGENCE RATE (DESCENDING ORDER, 9/25/06)

Accession	Emergence Rate Percentage
OR-1	88.7
AUEC 03	84.7
Groff 05	81.7
Common	78.7
Pop 26	76.3
Groff 06	74.7
AUEC 06	73
MN-1	73
B-35	72
NE-1	71.3
K-12	48.7

TABLE 11: HAIRY VETCH PERCENT GROUND COVER EVALUATION

The Rodale Institute, 01/24/07, 138 days after planting Field 14-15 (Eastern Section)

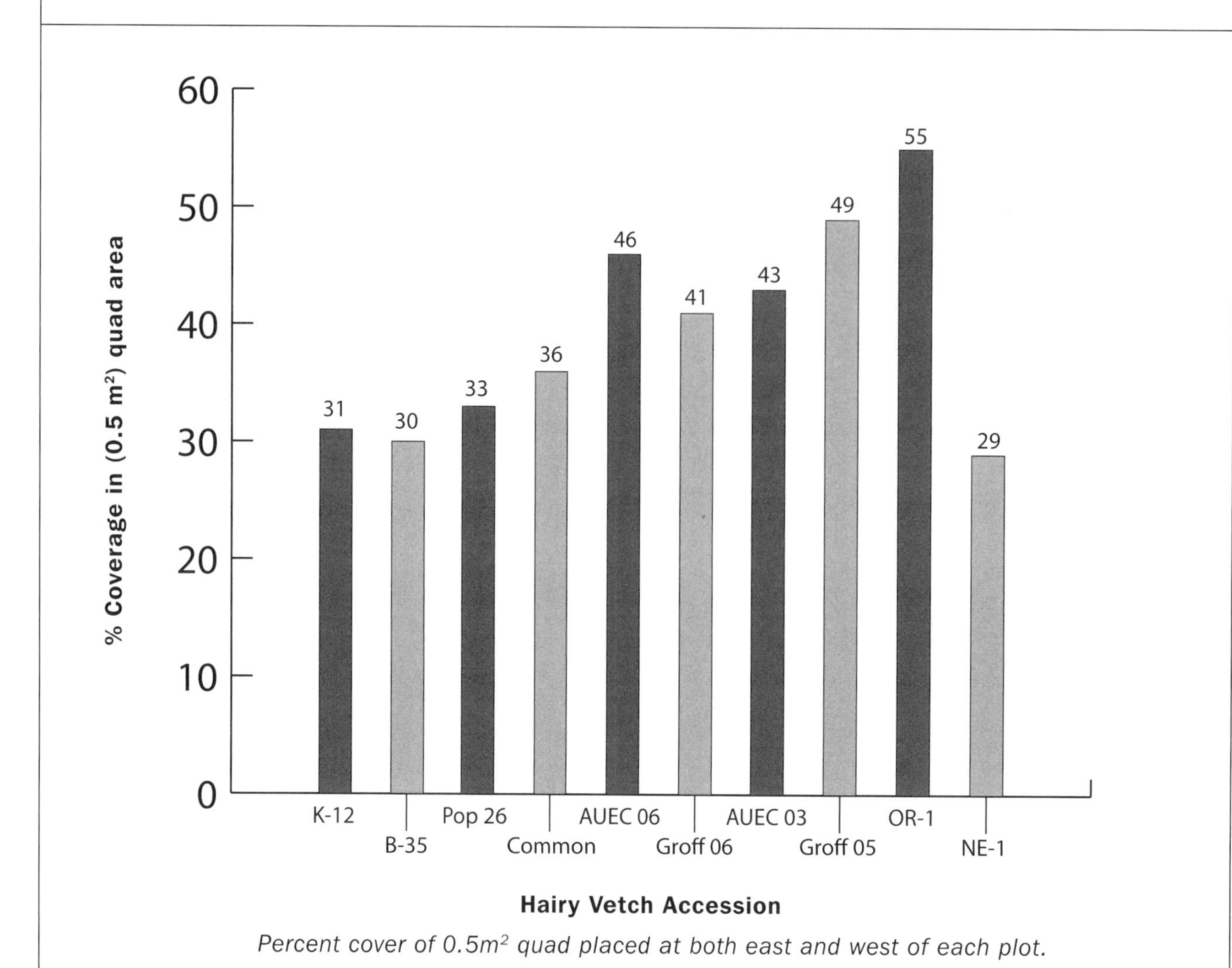

Percent cover of 0.5m² quad placed at both east and west of each plot.

TABLE 12: HAIRY VETCH PERCENT PLOT COVERAGE (DESCENDING ORDER, 1/24/07)

Accession	% Coverage in 0.5 m^2 quad
OR-1 (early cover)	55
Groff 05 (early cover)	49
AUEC 06 (early cover)	46
AUEC 03 (early cover)	43
Groff 06	41
Common	36
Pop 26	33
K-12	31
B-35	30
NE-1	29
MN-1	18

On February 12, 2007, a second evaluation for percent ground cover was conducted, and the first evaluation for percent kill was conducted on this date. Using a 0.5 m^2 quad placed at approximately one foot in from the east end of the row and then again one foot in from the west end of the row, two evaluations were made for each row in each replication. The percent ground cover is the percent of ground inside the 0.5 m^2 quad that was covered by the hairy vetch plant. The percent kill was quantified by the amount of the plant in the 0.5 m^2 quad that showed discoloration (brown or yellowing) but not green growth that was wilting.

First major kill was at 15 F on January 26, 2007, then low temperatures stayed below 15 F between February 2, 2007 and February 9, 2007. The hairy vetch was exposed and there was no snow cover.

▶ **TABLE 13: HAIRY VETCH PERCENT GROUND COVER & PERCENT WINTERKILL COMPARISON, FEBRUARY 12, 2007.**

The Rodale Institute (157 days after planting), Field 14-15 (Eastern Section).

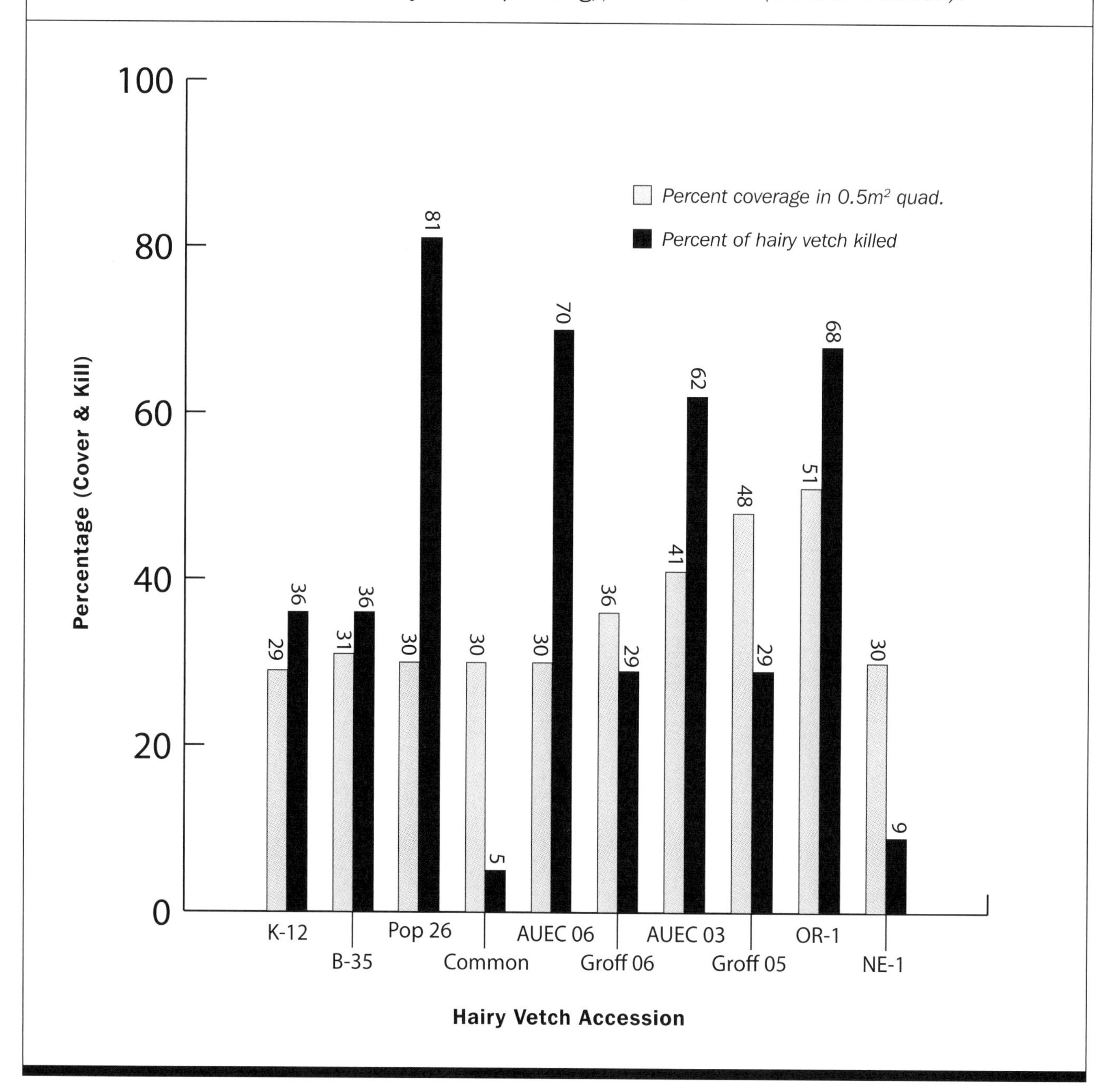

▶ TABLE 14A: HAIRY VETCH PERCENT PLOT GROUND COVERAGE (DESCENDING ORDER, 2/12/07)

Accession	% Ground Coverage in 0.5 m^2 quad
OR-1 (early cover)	51
Groff 05 (early cover)	48
AUEC 03 (early cover)	41
Groff 06 (early cover)	36
B-35	31
Pop 26	30
Common	30
AUEC 06 (early cover)	30
NE-1	30
K-12	29
MN-1	18

▶ TABLE 14B: HAIRY VETCH PERCENT KILL (ASCENDING ORDER, 2/12/07)

Accession	% Ground Coverage in 0.5 m^2 quad
MN-1	0
Common	5
NE-1	9
Groff 06 (early cover)	29
Groff 05 (early cover)	29
K-12	36
B-35	36
AUEC 03 (early cover)	62
OR-1 (early cover)	68
AUEC 06 (early cover)	70
Pop 26	81

On February 12, 2007, the Nebraska origin, the common, and the Minnesota origin, hairy vetches all had less than 10 percent kill with the common and the Minnesota having 5 percent and 0 percent kill respectfully. In this same field to the west of the evaluation, both the Nebraska origin and the Oregon origin (Early Cover) were planted on Sept 7, 2006 in large plots that were drill planted for the upcoming 2007 no-till roller trial. These large replicated field plots were planted in combination with oats as a "nurse crop." The percent kill of these two types of vetch on the large scale also confirms 60 to 70 percent kill for the Oregon origin (Early Cover) and about 10 percent kill for the Nebraska origin hairy vetch. In another field was Minnesota origin hairy vetch planted on September 21, 2006 in replicated plots on a large scale. In these plots the Minnesota origin hairy vetch has less than 5 percent kill.

▶ TABLE 15: EMERGENCE RATE, PERCENT COVER & PERCENT KILL OF HAIRY VETCH
The Rodale Institute, Field 14-15 (Eastern Section).

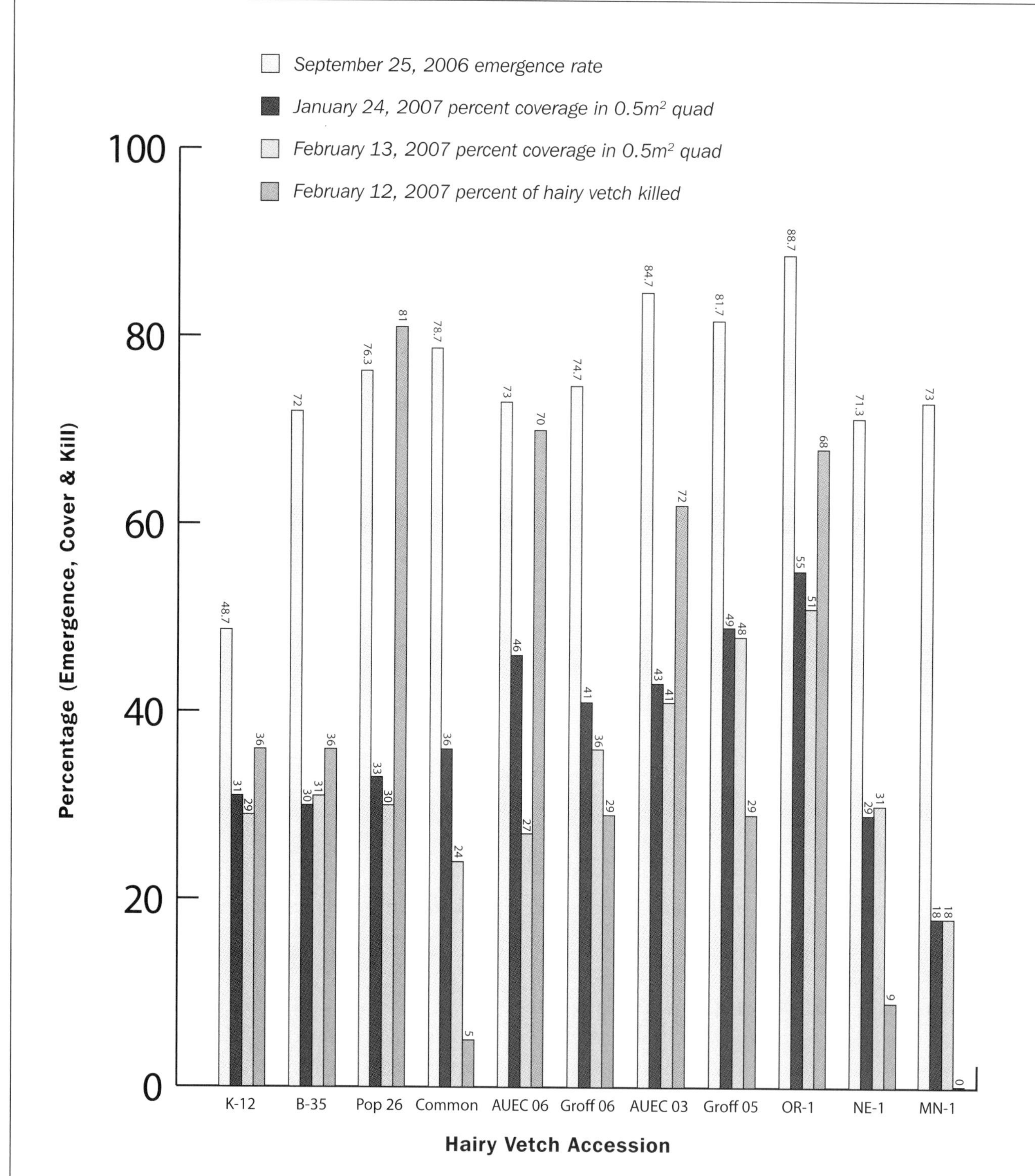

Hairy vetch planted September 8, 2006 (MN-1 planted September 16, 2006)

▶ TABLE 16: DAILY LOW TEMPERATURES FOR THE PERIOD OF SEPTEMBER 8, 2006 TO FEBRUARY 28, 2007

The Rodale Institute, Field 14-15 (Eastern Section).

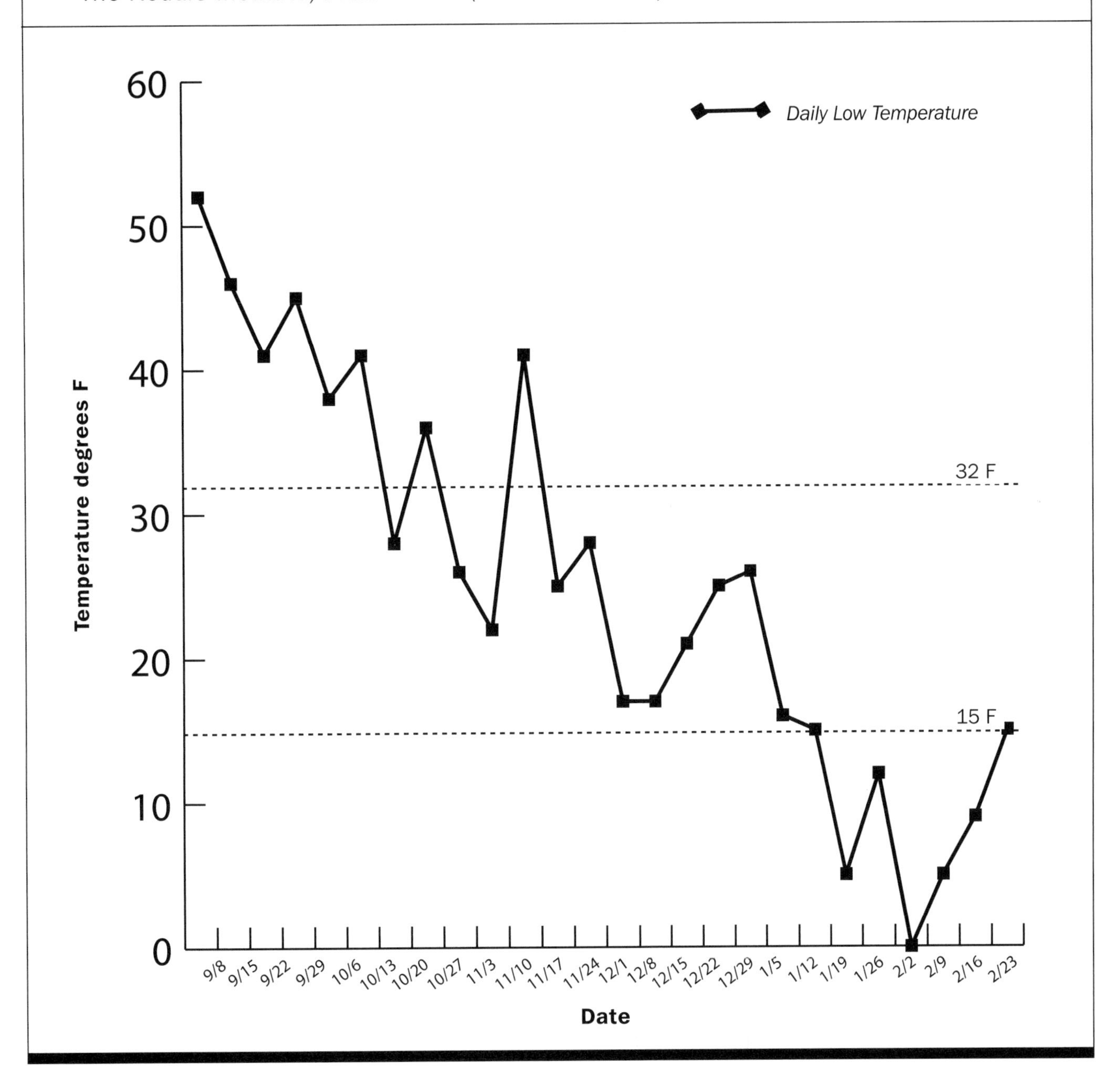

The first frost occurred on October 13, 2006 with a low temperature of 28 F (-2.2 C), 35 days after planting the hairy vetch, (24 days after planting for MN-1).

Most of the hairy vetch kill took place during the nights on January 26 and 27, 2007, when the minimum temperatures at our location were 5 F (-1.1 C) and 7 F (-3.3 C), respectively. Prior to that date on January 11 the daily low temperature was 16 F (-8.8 C), on January 17 the daily low temperature was 15 F (-9.4 C), and on January 21 the daily low temperature was 15 F (-9.4 C). On the January 24 evaluation there was no kill observed in the plots, from this observation, it is

▶ **TABLE 17A: HAIRY VETCH PERCENT GROUND COVER IN 0.5m² QUAD SAMPLES ON 03/27/2007 (DESCENDING ORDER)**

Accession	% Coverage in 0.5 m² quad
OR-1 (early cover)	42
AUEC 06 (early cover)	42
Groff 05 (early cover)	40
Groff 06 (early cover)	35
AUEC 03 (early cover)	34
Common	33
B-35	31
Pop 26	28
NE-1	26
K-12	26
MN-1	17

▶ **TABLE 17B: PERCENT HAIRY VETCH KILL IN 0.5m² QUAD SAMPLES ON 03/27/2007 (DESCENDING ORDER)**

Accession	% of hairy vetch killed (brown, yellow die-back)
MN-1	5
Common	28
NE-1	48
Groff 06 (early cover)	66
Groff 05 (early cover)	83
B-35	83
OR-1 (early cover)	95
K-12	96
AUEC 03 (early cover)	98
AUEC 06 (early cover)	100
Pop 26	100

estimated that the killing temperature for the vetch began somewhere below 15 F (-9.4 C), since this was the lowest the temperature had dropped on three dates prior to the January 24 evaluation date without any evidence of kill. During this period of time the hairy vetch plants were exposed with no snow cover present.

On March 27, 2007, a third evaluation to measure percent ground cover was conducted (see table 17a and 17b), and the second evaluation for percent kill was conducted on this date. Using a 0.5 m² quad placed at approximately one foot in from the east end of the row and then again one foot in from the west end of the row, these two evaluations were made for each row in each replication. The percent ground cover is the percent of ground inside the 0.5 m² quad that was covered by the hairy vetch plant. The percent kill was quantified by the amount of the plant in the

0.5 m² quad that showed discoloration (brown or yellowing) but not green growth that was wilting.

On March 27, 2007, the Minnesota seed tag origin hairy vetch had the least amount of kill (approximately 5 percent), the common hairy vetch had approximately 28 percent kill and the Nebraska seed tag origin had approximately 48 percent kill. Steve Groff's 2006 (Early Cover) had approximately 66 percent kill. Noteworthy is that in this same field to the west of the evaluation is both the Nebraska origin and the Oregon origin (Early Cover) planted on Sept 7, 2006 in large plots that were drill planted for an upcoming 2007 no-till trial. These large replicated field plots were planted in combination with oats as a "nurse crop." The percent kill of these two types of vetch on the large scale again also confirms 98 to 100 percent kill for the Oregon origin (Early Cover) but only about 10 percent kill for the Nebraska origin hairy vetch.

In the larger field plots the hairy vetch was planted with spring oats as a nurse crop, the spring oats winterkilled and provided cover for the hairy vetch. In the case of the Oregon origin (Early Cover) there was 98 to 100 percent winterkill even with the presence of the dead oat stubble. In the case of the Nebraska origin hairy vetch the percent kill in the large plots with the dead oat stubble present was much less, only about 10 percent kill, compared to the small test plots which had about 48 percent kill for the Nebraska hairy vetch where the hairy vetch was planted by itself with no oat nurse crop.

Also, in another field the Minnesota origin hairy vetch was planted on September 21, 2006 in replicated plots on a large scale, this was planted with winter cereal rye and with winter cereal rye and mammoth red clover, in these field plots the Minnesota origin hairy vetch has less than 5 percent winterkill.

Greenhouse Trials

Greenhouse trials of the commercially available hairy vetch population trials were conducted in conjunction with the field trials of these populations. The hairy vetch populations were evaluated for germination, plant height, shoot length, leaf length and timing of crown development in these legumes. These characteristics will be compared to how the hairy vetch populations respond in the field for winter survivability. This information is being

TABLE 18: AVERAGE PLANT HEIGHT OF POTTED HAIRY VETCH
December 20, 2006, 16 days after planting, The Rodale Institute.

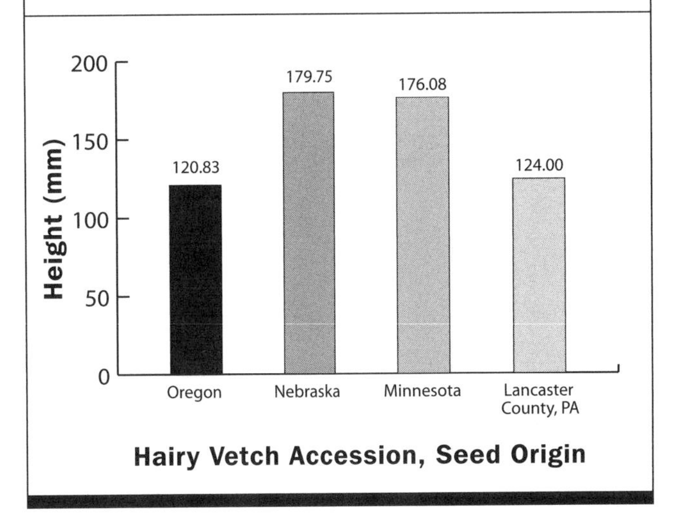

TABLE 19: AVERAGE LEAF LENGTH OF POTTED HAIRY VETCH
December 20, 2006, 16 days after planting, The Rodale Institute.

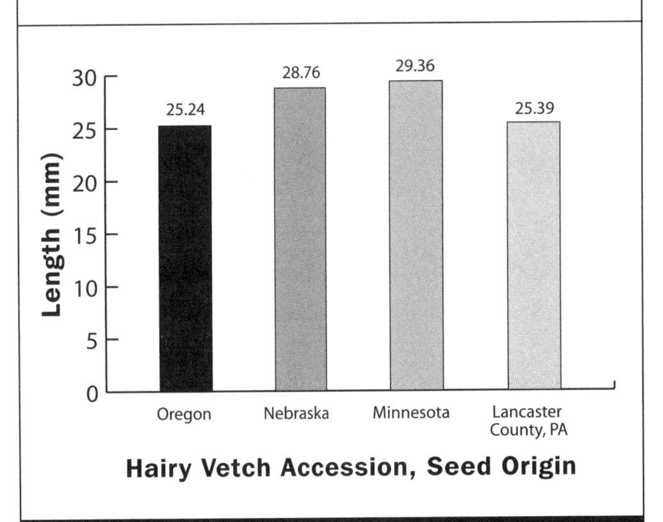

▶ TABLE 20: AVERAGE LEAF WIDTH OF POTTED HAIRY VETCH

December 20, 2006, 16 days after planting, The Rodale Institute.

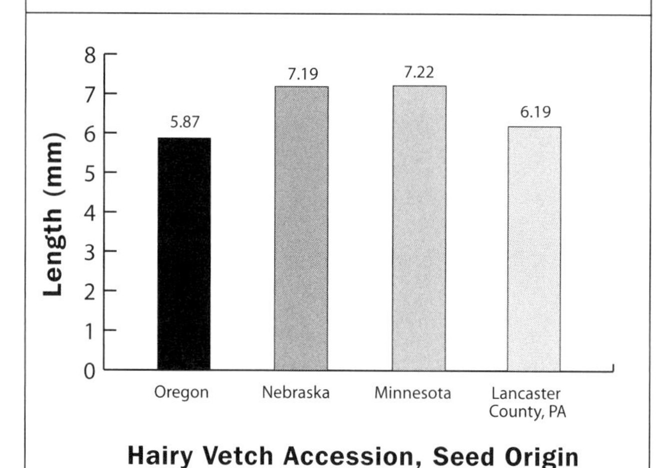

▶ TABLE 21: AVERAGE LEAF AREA OF POTTED HAIRY VETCH

December 20, 2006, 16 days after planting, The Rodale Institute.

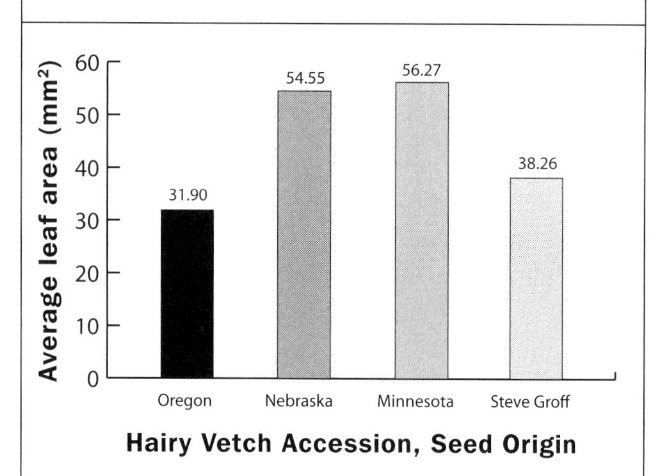

collaborated with Dr. Devine USDA – Beltsville to determine advantageous characteristics for selection of hairy vetch for winter survivability.

OBSERVATIONS FROM THE GREENHOUSE TRIAL The hairy vetch with the Minnesota seed tag origin had the most mature plants with many of the plants crowning and having four to five crown extensions. Leaves on the crowns were much rounder than on crowns of other accessions. The hairy vetch with the Nebraska seed tag origin had plants with about three crowns, some almost as long as the main stem. Early crowning increased plant height, increased shoot length, leaf length and leaf width, resulting in a greater leaf area. These characteristics were observed with the hairy vetch from both the Minnesota and Nebraska seed tag origins. In the field these two were the most winter hardy with the least amount of winterkill. The hairy vetches of Oregon seed tag and farmer-produced Lancaster County origin were both the Early Cover type of vetch and had similar traits. In the field the Oregon origin hairy vetch had a more extreme winterkill (95 to 100 percent) with very little spring re-growth and the Lancaster County, Pennsylvania produced Early Cover had about 50 to 60 percent winterkill with spring re-growth.

Evaluations of Cover Crop Treatments Rolled for No-Till Corn

DATE OF ROLLING AND HAIRY VETCH KILL COMPARISONS. Large-scale field plots of oats and hairy vetch plots were planted on September 7, 2006. Four consecutive rolling/planting dates of the hairy vetch in the spring of 2007 will be evaluated to determine the correlation of growing degree days and stage of flowering with the effectiveness of the roller to mechanically kill the hairy vetch at these dates.

This trial was duplicated utilizing commercially available hairy vetch seed with a seed tag from Oregon and Nebraska. The hairy vetch from Oregon winterkilled under the winter conditions mentioned and graphed previously under the "Hairy vetch adaptation for winter survivability and early rolling in a no-till system" section earlier in this appendix. As a result of the winterkill of the Oregon seed tag origin hairy vetch, these Oregon plots will not produce adequate biomass to be rolled and this section of the trial will be modified. The Nebraska seed tag plots did not winterkill and will be utilized for this trial. The initial rolling date will be at 50 percent bloom stage, the next four consecutive dates will be at approximately one week intervals after that date.

Total trial size= 32,270 ft^2 (0.740 acre)

Four replications, two cover crop origins, four plots per replication, total sixteen plots

Plot size 20 feet x 50 feet (1,000 feet^2) = 0.0229 acre

Oats and hairy vetch cover crops planted Fall 2006 (two pass drilling operation)

Cover crop mix A: 'Blaze' oats and hairy vetch (variety not stated) seed tag origin: Oregon

Cover crop mix B: 'Blaze' oats and hairy vetch (variety not stated) seed tag origin: Nebraska

Treatment 1: 50 percent bloom (typically May 15 to May 30)

Treatment 2: 1 week after 50 percent bloom

Treatment 3: 2 weeks after 50 percent bloom

Treatment 4: 3 weeks after 50 percent bloom

TABLE 22: FALL SEEDED HAIRY VETCH COMPARISON

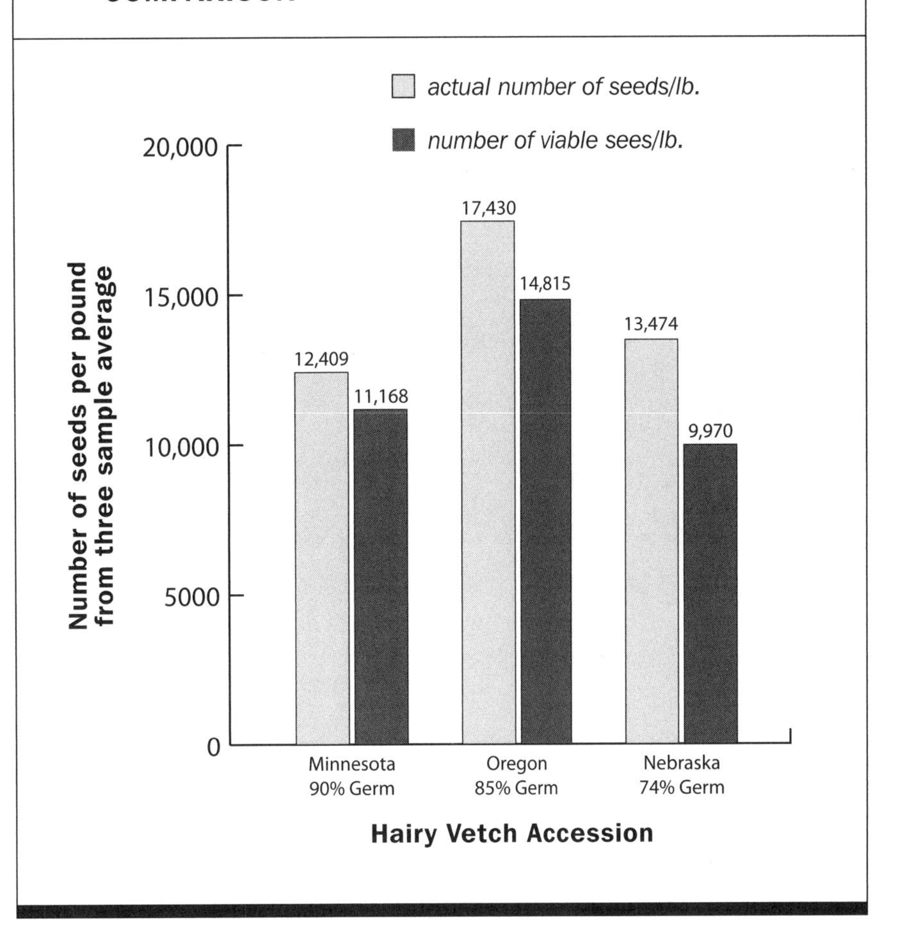

No-Till Corn Trial

Evaluation of reduced seeding rates by spatial manipulation of hairy vetch planted with a nurse crop of oats

Large-scale plots for this trial were planted on September 8, 2007. This trail will continue as a multi-year evaluation of a reduced seeding rate of hairy vetch for the rolled no-till system. This is accomplished by using a grain drill that was modified with baffles placed in the grain box to enable a planting configuration of every other row of hairy vetch and oats. The 10-foot drill has 15 drops at 8-inch row spacings. Baffles were made to separate the grain box into 15 individual seed boxes. In an every-other row configuration the boxes are filled with the oats and hairy vetch cover crops; 9 out of 15 drilled rows of oats and 8 out of 15 drilled rows of hairy vetch. This configuration results in a 53 percent seeding rate of hairy vetch by utilizing the every other row configuration. Past evaluations have shown that the reduced seeding rate in this configuration will still produce adequate hairy vetch biomass and nitrogen in the spring for adaptation in the rolled no-till system. Therefore reducing seeding costs of the oats and hairy vetch cover crop. This also allows the establishment of a cover crop bi-culture of nurse crop oats and winter annual hairy vetch with a

TABLE 23: WINTER DRY MATTER BIOMASS OF HAIRY VETCH & FROST KILLED OATS NURSE CROP
Field 14-15 (Western Section), Planted September 8, 2006

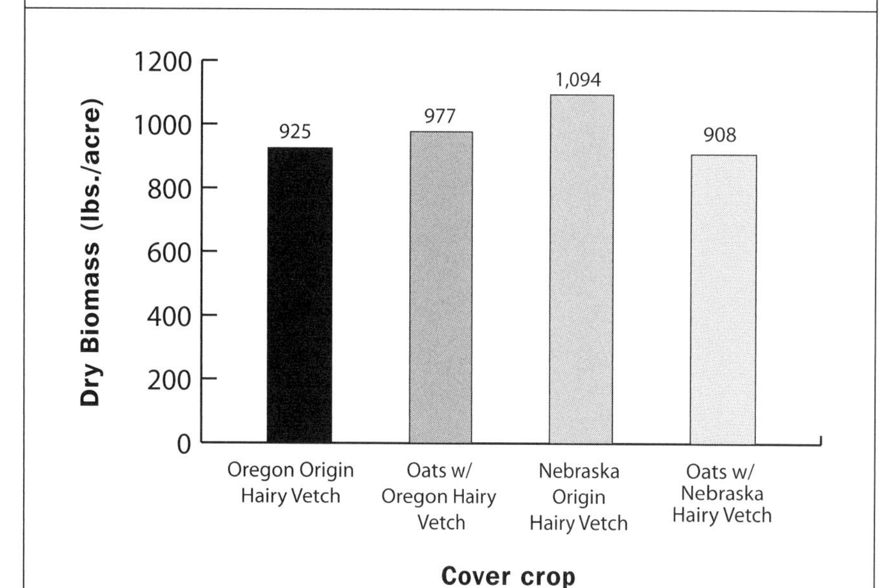

Hairy vetch from two seed origins (Oregon and Nebraska) planted with one pass Tye Stubble drill. Hairy vetch and oats planted in every other row configuration.

Oats and hairy vetch cover crops planted fall 2006 (one pass drilling operation with every other row configuration)

Cover crop mix A: 'Blaze' oats and hairy vetch (variety not stated) seed tag origin: Oregon

Cover crop mix B: 'Blaze' oats and hairy vetch (variety not stated) seed tag origin: Nebraska

one-pass operation reducing time and energy costs.

Four consecutive rolling/planting dates of the hairy vetch in the spring of 2007 will be evaluated to determine the correlation of growing degree days and stage of flowering with the effectiveness of the roller to mechanically kill the hairy vetch at these dates.

This trail was also duplicated with hairy vetch seed from a seed tag origin from both Oregon and Nebraska. The Oregon hairy vetch winterkilled so as mentioned above these plots will be modified.

Total trial size= 32,270 ft^2 (1.0 acre)

Four replications, four plots per replication, total sixteen plots

Plot size 20 feet x 50 feet (1,000 feet^2) = 0.0229 acre

No-Till Soybean Trial

SMALL GRAIN COVER CROPS FOR NO-TILL SOYBEANS. Treatment plots of winter annual small grains were planted on October 9, 2006. Treatments included winter annual small grain cereal crops rye, triticale and spelt, drill planted at a high seeding rate (target three million viable seeds /acre) and a low seeding rate (target 1.5 million viable seeds/acre). Seeding rates were adjusted and the drill was calibrated by calculating a seed count of seeds per pound of seed and factoring that by the percent germination to determine viable seed per acre rates. The grain drill was calibrated for each small grain cultivated variety or seed tag origin. Evaluations will include recording the rate of tillering and uniformity of maturity and biomass measurements.

Treatments:

On-farm produced winter cereal rye (1.4 bu./acre and 2.7 bu./acre)

Commercially available winter cereal rye, (variety not stated) (1.8 bu./acre and 3.4 bu./acre)

'Aroostook' cereal rye (1.6 bu./acre and 3.0 bu./acre)

▶ TABLE 24: WINTER DRY MATTER BIOMASS OF HAIRY VETCH & COVER CROP BIOMASS
Field 14-15 (Center Section), Planted January 12, 2007

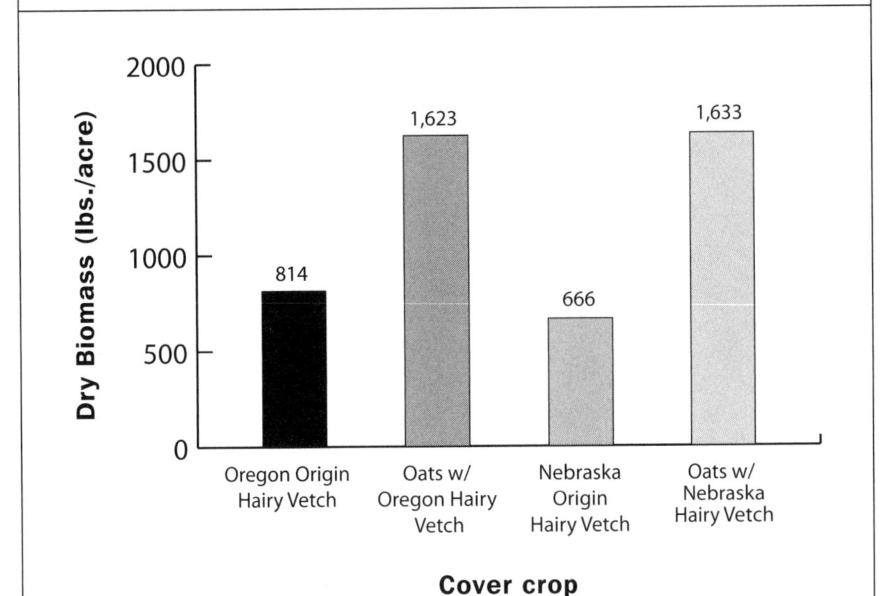

Hairy vetch from two seed origins (Oregon and Nebraska) planted September 7, 2006 with a double pass using a JD drill.

On Oct 11, 2006 the following treatment plots were established:

'Balboa' cereal rye, origin Canada, (1.3 bu./acre and 2.67 bu./acre)

'Oberkulmer' winter spelt, (spikelets planted at 3.27 bu./acre, 2.52 bu./acre naked seed)

Triticale, (2.12 bu./acre and 'Colonel' oilseed radish at 11.58 lbs./acre

Triticale, (2.12 bu./acre and 'Daikon' forage radish at 12.79 lbs./acre)

No-Till Soybean Trial

Evaluation of rolling cover crop and no-till planting in a perpendicular direction from the direction of planting small gain cover crops

For evaluating the effectiveness in weed suppression rolling and no-till planting of soybeans perpendicular to the direction that the cover crop was planted. Additional winter cereal rye treatments were planted in the North-South direction to establish the cover crop for rolling and no-till planting of soybeans in the East-West direction.

For this trial seven replications of three treatments were established.

On-farm produced winter cereal rye (2.7 bu./acre)

Commercially available winter cereal rye, (variety not stated) (3.4 bu./acre)

'Aroostook' winter cereal rye (3.0 bu./acre)

No-Till Soybean Trial

Evaluation of the rolling of winter annual small grain cover crops for no-till soybeans

This trial is designed to evaluate cover cropping practices and the row spacing effect on weed control in no-till soybeans. This mat of killed mulch will be evaluated for weed control with no-till soybeans planted at 7.5 inches with a no-till drill and at 30 inch row spacing with a no-till planter. Plots with tritcale planted at two seeding rates were established on September 28, 2007. The seeding rates targeted a seeding rate of 1.5 million viable seeds/acre and 3 million viable seeds per acre to evaluate and compare the rate of tillering and uniformity of maturity and biomass measurements.

In this same field, winter cereal rye 'Aroostook,' 'Balboa,' and two populations with the "variety not stated" (VNS) designation were planted at two seeding rates to evaluate. 'Oberkulmer' winter spelt was also included in the evaluation.

TABLE 25: COMPARISON OF HAIRY VETCH BIOMASS (DRY MATTER) ON FOUR ROLLING DATES

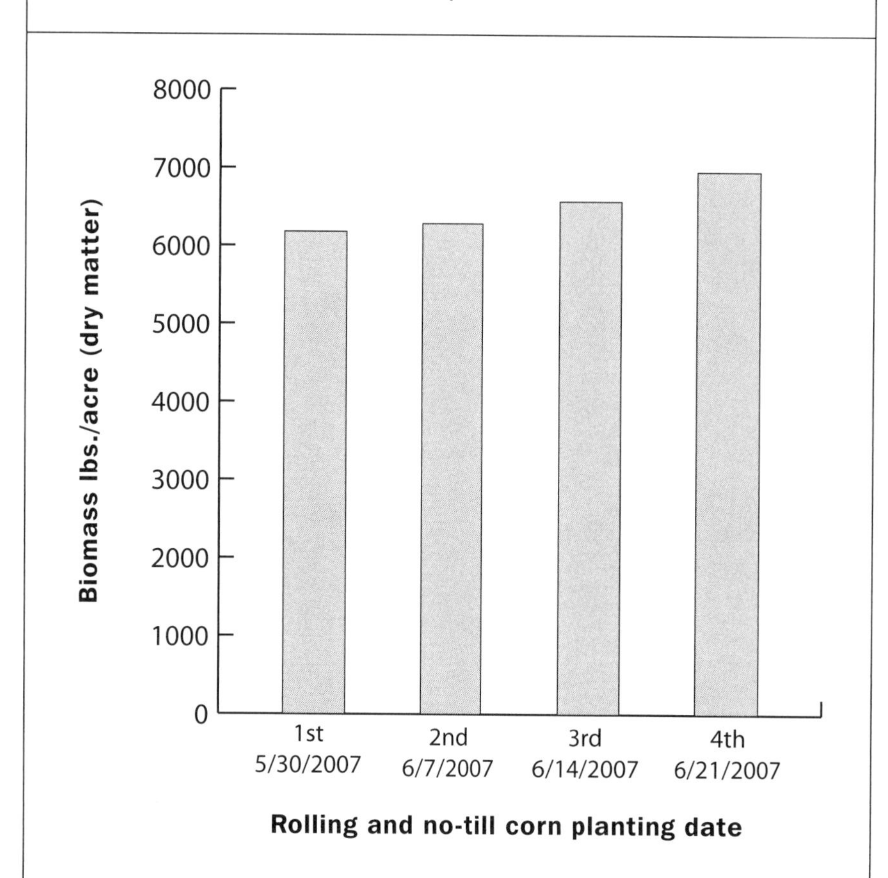

every year they may contribute to increased weed suppression.

The rye seed Peter used was from Seedway LLC, I had Peter ship two bags to The Rodale Institute location so an evaluation of this variety from that seed tag origin could be made in a side-by-side replicated trial where it could be more closely evaluated for growth, biomass and maturity and subsequent weed suppression of the cover crop compared with several other treatments.

Peter also showed his subsoiler and discussed the use of this as a treatment and as a pre-plant cultural practice as a comparison.

In the fall of 2006, Peter planted a field with this Seedway winter rye (seed tag origin from Canada). Although it could not be verified by variety type according to the seed tag label because it is listed as VNS (variety not stated), Peter said that this variety is a "Balboa-type" variety of rye.

Upon a phone discussion with Peter he planted the field on September 4, 2006 with a seeding rate of 3 bu./acre.

In the spring of 2007 this field will be measured out and replicated plots set up for evaluation of this rye cover crop for no-till soybeans at his location. Mechanical rolling to kill the rye will be compared to an herbicide treatment. In addition, the use of a subsoiler before planting will be evaluated in this comparison.

No-Till Soybean Trial

On-farm research with collaborating farmer Peter Schuster, Seneca Falls, New York. Evaluation of small grain rye cover crop treatment rolled for no-till soybeans 2006-2007

An initial farm visit with Peter was made to discuss collaboration of a trial on his farm. Peter had a field of soybeans planted into rye that was surveyed. This rye was a heavy stemmed (thick stemmed) variety that Peter said was a "balboa variety type." Review of past on-farm research results from other locations show that the "Balboa" rye variety may out yield other varieties of rye although these values may not be significant

No-Till Soybean Trial

▪ *On-Farm Research with Collaborating Farmer Bill Mason, Queen Anne, Maryland*

ROLLED SMALL GRAINS FOR NO-TILL SOYBEANS. An initial farm visit with Bill to survey his no-till planted soybeans in rolled down rye was accomplished and at that time plans were discussed for research plots to be established on his farm. The trial is to evaluate rolled small grains for no-till soybeans and a trial to evaluate rolled crimson clover alone and crimson clover with wheat for no-till corn. Subsequent trips to Bill's farm were accomplished to establish these two trials.

▪ *Evaluation of cover crop treatments rolled for no-till corn 2006-2007*

This trial will compare the practices of broadcasting (aerial seeding) the cover crops into standing soybeans versus drilling the cover crops into soybean stubble. The broadcast treatments were established to accomplish in replication the same seeding rate and seeding date as the actual aerial seeding practice that occurs on the rest of the adjacent production field.

Total trial size: 128,000 ft^2 (2.94 acres)

Four replications, four plots per replication, total sixteen plots

Plots size 20 feet x 400 feet (8000 $feet^2$)= 0.183 acre

Cover crops planted fall 2006

Treatment 1: Broadcast (aerial seeded) crimson clover

Treatment 2: Broadcast (aerial seeded) crimson clover and wheat

Treatment 3: Drilled crimson clover

Treatment 4: Drilled crimson clover and wheat

No-Till Soybeans

▪ *Evaluation of small grain cover crop treatments rolled for no-till soybeans 2006-2007*

This trial will compare two different winter rye varieties with triticale in this system.

Total trial size: 108,000 $feet^2$ (2.48 acres)

Four replications, three plots per replication, total twelve plots

Plots size 30 feet x 300 feet (9000 $feet^2$)= 0.21 acre

Small grain cover crops planted fall 2006

Treatment 1: 'Wheeler' rye

Treatment 2: 'Aroostook' rye

Treatment 3: Trical 815 Triticale

No-Till Corn and Soybeans Trial

▪ *On-farm research with collaborating farmer Kirby Reichert, Grantville, PA*

Kirby Reichert farms several different farm locations in the Grantville area, the trials will be held at two different locations. At the Casper Kohler, Seek No Further Farm location we will look at cover crop applications for no-till corn.

▪ *Evaluation of cover crop treatments rolled for no-till corn in 2006-2007*

Winter survivability of the legume cover crop and subsequent aboveground biomass production for weed suppression and nitrogen production are critical considerations for a successful rolled no-till system for corn. Most available hairy vetch seed is labeled as VNS (variety not stated). Preliminary research at The Rodale Institute has shown that hairy vetch seed that is produced in different locations may have varying winter survivability characteristics. In addition, seed viability (percent germination) and seed size varies from seed grown in different locations that when contributed together all affect the resulting plant population of the cover crop.

This trial will compare hairy vetch seed (VNS) from three different seed tag locations; Nebraska, Minnesota and Oregon. Replications of these treatments were planted all with oats as

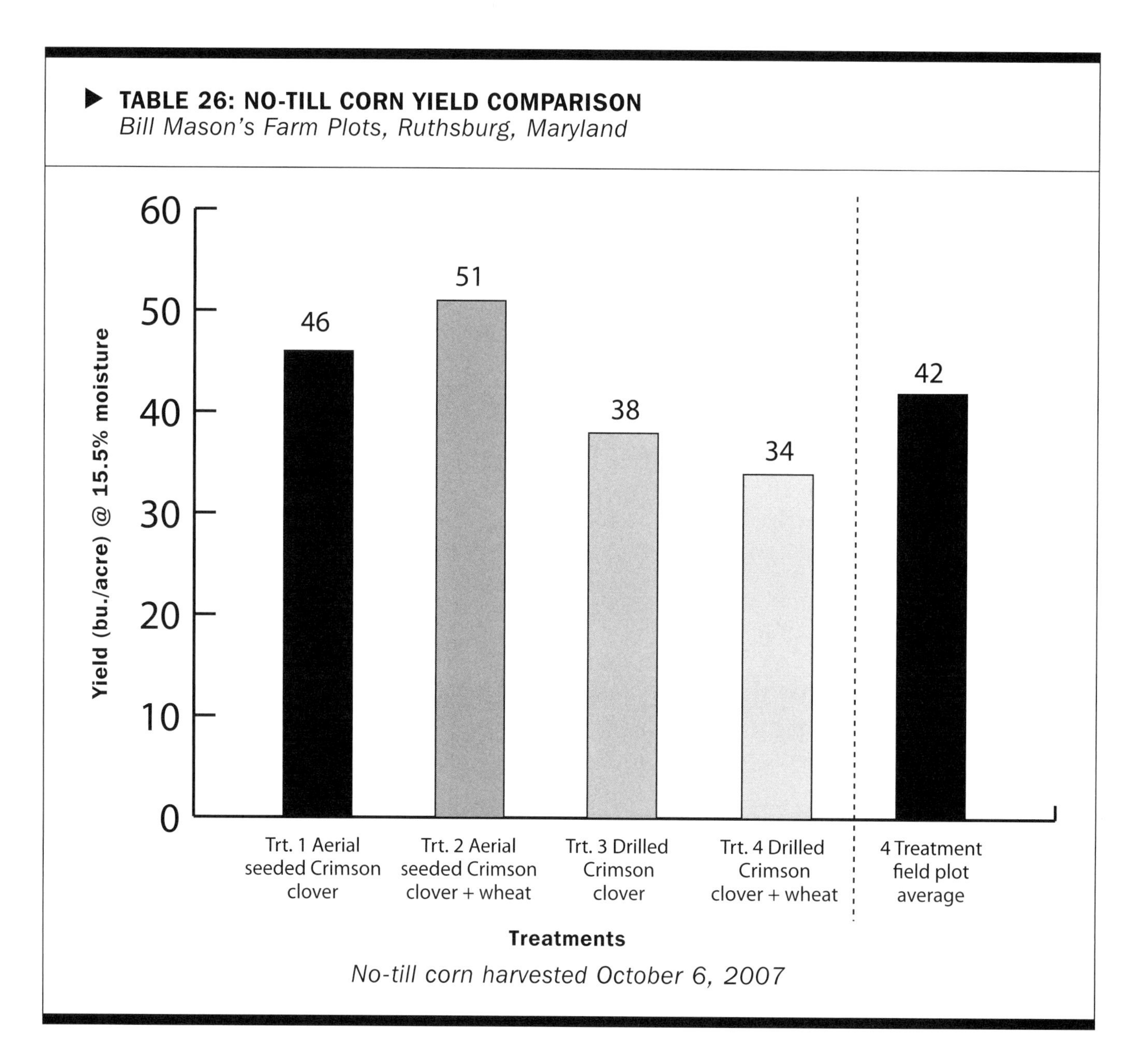

a nurse crop to evaluate the seeding rate, winter hardiness, biomass and related weed suppression and nitrogen production, for rolling and no-till planting of organic corn in 2007. An additional treatment of oats and crimson clover was included as another comparison.

Another consideration for successful no-till planting is the engineering of the no-till planter in this killed cover crop mulch system. Factors of the planter specifics of weight, coulter design, double disk openers and correct seed furrow closers all need to be taken into consideration. Kirby has two White no-till planters. While working with Kirby in 2006 we initially rolled and planted a short pass of the hairy vetch for a trail run. We were using Kirby's older model White planter, which worked well. One of the sprockets broke on the older model planter so the rest of the field was planted with the newer model no-till planter. The weight and closer wheel design on the newer model is not the same. As a result the corn stands were not satisfactory for the system. We will be working with Kirby this winter to make modifications to the no-till planter to try next year to get adequate corn populations in the no-till system.

Total trial size= 28,250 feet^2 (0.65 acre)

Five replications, four plots per replication, total twenty plots

Plots size 20 feet x 50 feet (1000 feet^2)= 0.0229 acre

Cover crops planted fall 2006

Treatment 1: Oats and hairy vetch (Nebraska origin)

Treatment 2: Oats and hairy vetch (Minnesota origin)

Treatment 3: Oats and hairy vetch (Oregon origin)

Treatment 4: Oats and crimson clover

At the Green Hill Road farm site we will evaluate cover crop applications for no-till soybeans.

No-Till Soybeans

■ *Evaluation of small grain cover crop treatments rolled for no-till soybeans 2006-2007*

This trial will compare 'Aroostook' rye, two VNS ryes from different seed sources, Triticale and 'Oberkulmer' winter spelt. Four of these treatments will also be compared at The Rodale Institute to have multi-location data available for the cover crop.

Total trial size= 22,500 feet^2 (0.516 acre)

Four replications, five plots per replication, total twenty plots

Plots size 20 feet x 50 feet (1000 feet^2)= 0.0229 acre

Small grain cover crops planted fall 2006

Treatment 1: 'Aroostook' rye, origin PA

Treatment 2: Cereal rye (VNS) 91 percent Germination, origin PA

Treatment 3: Cereal rye (VNS) 83 percent Germination, origin Canada

Treatment 4: Trical 815 Triticale

Treatment 5: 'Oberkulmer' winter spelt

ON-FARM RESEARCH WITH COLLABORATING FARMERS JOHN AND AIMEE GOOD OF QUIET CREEK FARM CSA, KUTZTOWN, PENNSYLVANIA

■ *Evaluation of winter annual cover crop combinations in rotation before winter squash*

On September 21, 2006, field preparations included, disking the field twice with the heavy disk to incorporate mixed vegetable crops and prepare the soil for planting cover crops. All cover crops were planted the same day after disking with the John Deere 450 grain.

Replicated plots of cover crop combinations including (rye and hairy vetch) and (rye, Austrian winter peas and crimson clover) were established and cover crop progression and growth is being evaluated. These strips will be rolled in June for no-till planting of winter squash.

No-Till Corn Trial

ON-FARM RESEARCH WITH COLLABORATING FARMER BILL MASON, QUEEN ANNE, MARYLAND.

■ *Evaluation of cover crop treatments rolled for no-till corn 2006-2007.* No-till planter considerations at planting of time to establish a uniform stand of corn were the main challenges at Bill Mason's Farm. In all the treatments over all, corn stands were not adequate for optimal yields. In the treatments where the cover crops were drilled instead of aerial seeded the covers established well and were heavier in these plots, but these plots had stands with low populations due to not having the equipment adjusted properly to establish optimum stands which led to reduced yields. The primary challenge was having the equipment set up to properly cut into the mat, and getting good seed to soil contact.

▶ **TABLE 27: EVALUATION OF THIRTEEN HYBRID CORN VARIETIES**

Company	Variety	Relative Maturity	Lot #	Germination Rate	Seed Count/ Size
1. Blue River Hybrids	17B16	83 days	1B17-3	95%	MF
2. Blue River Hybrids	30B19	90 days	Test Plot Seed		2,305
3. TA Seeds	TA302-00	90 days	708TACUT	95%	
4. Blue River Hybrids	2R10	91 days	1B32-7	95%	SF
5. Blue River Hybrids	42A32	96 days	1542201C	95%	2,230
6. Great Harvest	38T4	98 days	916SA	95%	
7. Blue River Hybrids	4437	99 days	Test Plot Seed		1,567
8. TA Seeds	TA5100	101 days	722TAUT	94%	F1
9. Blue River Hybrids	49M37	102 days	1B49-3C	95%	MF
10. Blue River Hybrids	51B31	103 days	Test Plot Seed		1,738
11. Great Harvest	44X2E	104 days	916MS	95%	
12. Blue River Hybrids	56M32	106 days	1B561	95%	LF
13. Blue River Hybrids	68F32	113 days	Test Plot Seed		1,491

ON-FARM RESEARCH WITH COLLABORATING FARMER KIRBY REICHERT, GRANTVILLE, PENNSYLVANIA.

■ *Evaluation of small grain cover crop treatments rolled for no-till soybeans 2006-2007.*

At Kirby Reichert's farm extremely dry conditions in spring led to poor cover crops stands of biomass in both the hairy vetch/ crimson clover for corn trials and in the small grains for Soybean trials. In the legume for corn trials there were a few plots that looked adequate for rolling but because of the scientific design (replicated randomized plots) that were also laid out in a field on the contour of a slope these plots were scattered throughout the field and if planted would have caused the participating farmer much trouble to get no-till corn established and tilled corn established in the cover crop plots that did not do well and would need to be plowed. This was primarily due to the consideration of space needed for the equipment to turn and conduct tillage practices. Therefore we decided because of production constraints we would sacrifice the plots and Kirby plowed this field for clean tillage.

As a result of this, we modified the design of the plots for the upcoming year cover crop trial and we established strip trails instead of replicated random plots.

No-Till Corn Trial

■ *On-Farm Research at The Rodale Institute, Kutztown, Pennsylvania*

This trial focused on determining the correlation between growing degree days and stage of flowering (physiological stage of the cover crop) with the effectiveness of the roller to mechanically kill the hairy vetch at these dates. This was coordinated with the Pennsylvania State University research team. At The Rodale Institute site we replicated this with hairy vetch seed with seed tag origins from Oregon and Nebraska.

The hairy vetch in the plots that were planted with the seed from Oregon origin which was an Early Cover type of hairy vetch had winterkilled, as a result these plots had to be dropped from the trial due to winterkill resulting in inadequate stands of hairy vetch for rolling.

The hairy vetch with a seed tag origin from Nebraska overwintered well and these plots were rolled and planted starting on May 30, 2007 with three subsequent rolling dates in one week intervals until the final date of June 21, 2007. To date these plots have not been harvested but data concerning biomass and plant population in relation to time of rolling and planting was taken. Cutworms in the earlier planted dates reduced the stand of corn, this was measured and evaluated and will be compared to final yields. The cutworm population will be one of major consideration and cultural practices.

No-Till Corn Trial

■ *Evaluation of Thirteen Hybrid Corn Varieties (90 day RM to 113 day RM) for Adaptation into the Rolled No-Till System*

Hybrids provided by Blue River Hybrids Organic Seeds, TA Seeds and Great Harvests Seeds.

This trial was planted and has not been harvested as of this date. We will evaluate these thirteen hybrid corn varieties in the no-till system.

Cover Crop Roller/Crimper Results 2004-2005

The first year with the roller/crimper was a very good year. The cereal rye had excellent growth, and the hairy vetch had good growth. Hairy vetch was planted at 45 lb./acre on Aug. 15 and winter rye planted at 2 bu./acre on Sept. 9, 2003 into a replicated complete block field design consisting of four replications. The covers were rolled at flowering on June 4, 2004, and dark hilum feed-grade soybeans were drilled into the crimped mat four days later in 7.5-inch rows at 180,000 seeds/acre. No additional tillage or supplemental weed control methods were used. Weed control throughout the season was excellent. The soybeans were harvested Oct. 7, 2004. Soybean yields of 58 bu./acre and 62 bu./acre were harvested for hairy vetch and rye, respectively. In comparison, the average soybean yields in the surrounding area were 40 bu./acre in 2004.

The cover crops and following soybean crop did not do well in 2005. The rye plants were short and thin, and the vetch was short with a thin stand. The decision to plant before cover crop flowering because of dry soil resulted in the rye and vetch not dying as expected. The growing season was also short on moisture. Cover crops of hairy vetch and rye were planted at various rates and combinations for seven treatments on Aug. 25, 2004 as part of a randomized complete block design consisting of four replications. Two additional cover crops were planted on Sept. 14th, and a no cover crop control rounded out the experiment of ten treatments.

Treatments consisting of three treatments of rye (1, 2, and 3 bu./acre), two treatments of vetch (30 lb./acre), and three treatments of a cover crop mix (3 bu./acre rye plus 15 lb./acre vetch, 2 bu./acre rye plus 20 lb./acre vetch, and 1 bu./acre rye plus 30 lb./acre vetch) were drilled to soybeans. A single treatment of rye (3 bu./acre) and a single treatment of vetch were seeded Sept. 14, and were planted to corn and soybeans, respectively. Covers were rolled/crimped May 23, 2005, prior to rye pollination and vetch flowering, in an effort to plant soybeans earlier. As a result, the cover crops continued to grow and stood back up. Poor cover crop kill resulted in a second rolling/crimping on June 16. The 2 and 3 bu./acre rye only and corn treatments were not rolled/crimped a second time. The corn treatment and the 2 bu./acre rye only treatment were flail mowed. 'Vinton' clear hilum soybeans (which traditionally yield up to ten bushels lower than newer varieties) were drilled into the covers May 24 at 220,000 seeds/acre and were harvested Sept. 27. The no cover crop control treatment was rotary hoed May 31 and cultivated June 24 and 28, 2005. Yields were much lower than in 2004, with the highest yields coming from the rye only treatments at an average of 20.3 bu./acre. The cover crop mix treatment yielded an average of 16.3 bu./acre. The vetch only treatments yielded 13.5 bu./acre (early) and 5.8 bu./acre (late). The cover-free control yielded 18.9 bu./acre, while the corn treatment yielded an unacceptable 24.5 bu./acre. Complicating the research process was a six-week drought, which reduced soybean yield (including conventional) throughout Southwest Michigan.

APPENDIX I: A RESOURCE FOR TRANSITIONING TO ORGANIC

▶ THE RODALE INSTITUTE ONLINE TRAINING GUIDE

As you consider the process of transitioning to an organic farming system that meets the USDA certification standards you will find there are many new skills to learn and concepts to master. One resource to help with this is the Transitioning to Organic training guide that Rodale Institute has created to help hone skills and address these new concepts. By reading through the text and sidebars, you'll have the opportunity to learn from the staff of the Institute and other farmers just like yourself. These folks and the knowledge they share will help speed up the transition process and avoid many of the pitfalls that could trip you up.

Transitioning to organic

The Rodale Transitioning to Organic course is a 15-hour online program designed to help understand the National Organic Standards and use them as your framework for making the transition to organic production. It's perfect for farmers who are ready to make the complete transition to certified organic, and for those interested in simply integrating more sustainable methods into their current farming system. Just want to learn more about how certified organic farming works? The course can help there, too.

The course includes everything you need to know to grow and sell certified organic products, including:

- The fundamental principles of organic agriculture
- Practical details about organic crop and livestock production
- Marketing opportunities available to organic producers
- Recordkeeping and other specific requirements of organic certification

The Transitioning to Organic course can be taken anywhere you have access to a computer connected to the Internet, even the public library. There are no set course hours, registration fees or tests to take. The time it takes depends on the individual. You can start and stop each module at your convenience. You can also bookmark a page and return at a later time. There are no specific start or stop dates and the course is available to you at your convenience.

The development of organic certification and the USDA story

In the early days of the organic farming movement in the 1960s, most organic farmers' production was sold locally to people who knew and trusted them. As demand increased in the 1970s, the supply chain grew, with processors and distributors buying up large quantities of organic commodities and then selling them for use in processed products or to retail outlets far from the fields where the food had been grown. The need arose for some kind of verification that the products had indeed been grown on farms following recognized organic practices.

The third-party certification system was developed to meet this need. By the 1980s, dozens of certification groups – many of them founded by farmers – had been created both here in the U.S. and in other countries. Robert Rodale and the Rodale Institute were instrumental in these early efforts and helping to write and administer one of the first organic certification programs in the United States.

All of these early, regional organic standards had a lot in common in terms of basic principles, but they sometimes differed when it came to details. Consistent international standards were needed, especially for exporters and food processors. European importers were balking at buying U.S. products not certified to European standards. Concern was also growing about fraudulent organic labels on products that were actually not organic at all.

In 1990, in response to widespread demand from the organic sector, Congress passed the Organic Foods Production Act, charging the U.S. Department of Agriculture (USDA) with creating a federal system for organic certification. After prolonged debate, the National Organic Program Standards were finally implemented in 2002.

Once the USDA's National Organic Program (NOP) – the culmination of the Organic Foods Production Act of 1990 – went into effect, all products labeled as "organic" were required to carry the USDA Certified Organic label. Farmers who generate less than $5,000 annually in sales are exempt from certification and inspection to save costs but still must follow the NOP Standards (just as if they were certified) in order to market their products as organic.

The NOP Standards require organic producers to manage soil fertility through the use of rotations, cover crops, and the application of plant and animal materials or low-solubility natural minerals. These practices must either maintain or improve soil organic matter content, manage deficient and excess plant nutrients, and control erosion.

Organic certification requirements

Producers must use preventive practices to manage crop pests, weeds and disease. Organic livestock must have access to the outdoors, shade, shelter, exercise areas, fresh air and direct sunlight as is appropriate for the type of animal and the local climate. Organic livestock may not be given antibiotics or hormones and must be fed 100 percent organically grown feed. Ruminant livestock must have access to open pasture.

Here are a few notes about the certification requirements and process:

- An Organic System Plan that must be filed with an accredited certifier as the first step in obtaining an organic certificate.
- A farm can be certified field-by-field, so you can literarily ease your way into the process over time.
- Organic products must be grown on land that has not used prohibited substances for a minimum of three years prior to the harvest of the crop.
- All synthetic materials are prohibited unless they are included on the National Organic list.
- All natural materials are allowed unless they are specifically prohibited on the National List.
- Organic farming requires a proactive management system based on ecologically sound practices. Organic farmers must:
  - § Build organic matter and soil tilth continuously.
  - § Balance soil nutrients using natural and allowed products.
  - § Develop and implement a good crop rotation with cover cropping.
  - § Work to protect and expand the biodiversity of the farm and soil.
- Use weed management practices including cover cropping, crop rotation, equipment like rotary hoes, tine weeders, row cultivators, flame weeders, and now roller/crimpers.
- Each organic field must have clear boundaries and maintain an adequate buffer with adjoining non-organic land.
- Organic seeds and transplants must be used, both for crops and cover crops.
- Farmers must document their management practices and have their farms inspected once

yearly to verify that they are following their approved organic system plan.

- It is possible to do organic and non-organic production in different fields on the same farm. However, this requires extra documentation and steps to maintain organic integrity.

Here's a course outline to get you started and provide a sneak preview into the course content. To access the full course information, visit *www.rodaleinstitute.org*.

Getting started

This section helps you get started, even if you are not completely computer literate. It's easy to find your way through the course materials with the navigation bar. The navigation area consists of a series of buttons located in the left column on the screen. Two areas are secure and password-protected to guard your information – the Organic System Plan and Crop Conversion Calculator.

Getting started displays all instructions on what you need in order to take the course, how to navigate through the course and the tools linked to it.

Why organic? is a discussion of some of the benefits of organic agriculture as well as a brief history of the Rodale Institute.

Soils is a discussion of healthy soil as the foundation of your success in organic farming.

Crops is a discussion of organic crop production.

Livestock is a discussion of basic livestock practices and information for various species.

Marketing is a discussion of overall organic market trends and opportunities. In this module you will be introduced to the second course tool, the Crop Conversion Calculator.

Certification is a discussion of the actual process of organic certification of your operation.

Wrap-up is the last unit. It holds your Certificate of Completion. Visit this unit for a few suggestions about how to stay in touch with the organic community and the Rodale Institute.

In the ***Organic System Plan*** is a secure, password-protected area. You will have the option to register upon your first time here. If you register, you will have access to an interactive tool that lets you fill out, save and print the forms required by certifying agents to start the process of organic certification.

The ***Crop Conversion Calculator*** is also a password-protected area that allows you to calculate various scenarios of your farm operations and see the economic results of an organic alternative.

In the ***Glossary*** is an explanation in alphabetical order of terminology used in the course that may not be very familiar to you.

Why organic?

This section gives a broad overview of organic agriculture. It's good to read for basic information. It will provide some background on how to make good decisions for your farm. You'll need to decide whether becoming certified organic is the best choice for you. An introductory section outlines several considerations in the argument for transitioning to organic agriculture from an environmental, economic and community perspective.

From an environmental standpoint, organic agriculture builds life in the soil while avoiding the use of toxic chemicals that can accumulate in soil, water, food and people. Non-organic farming relies on dwindling fossil fuel resources, while organic farmers build their own fertility into their systems, which improve over time and do not rely on outside inputs.

From an economic point of view, organic farming has been one of the fastest-growing sectors of agriculture for more than a decade, with 20 to 24 percent increases annually since 1990. Organic farming allows farmers to reap up to three times the profit margins of non-organically raised meat and produce. (U.S. sales of organic food and beverages grew from $1 billion in 1990 to nearly $17 billion in 2006, and the Agricultural Marketing Service expects this trend to continue.)

From the perspective of community, organic food and agriculture are a means of supporting local and regional businesses. This builds the vitality and strength of our communities. The growth of both farmers markets and the community supported agriculture (CSA) movement serve as a testament to the ability of organic farming to revitalize downtown centers and reestablish partnerships between regional agricultural and urban areas.

Understand that there may be some roadblocks along the way to conversion to organic agriculture. According to the Economic Research Service of the U.S. Department of Agriculture, "obstacles to adoption by farmers include high managerial costs and risks of shifting to a new way of farming, limited awareness of organic farming systems, lack of marketing and infrastructure and inability to capture marketing economies."

Still, the USDA reports that many U.S. producers are embracing organic farming in order to lower input costs, conserve non-renewable resources, capture high-value markets, and boost farm income.

By breaking the process into manageable steps, you will probably find the transition from non-organic to organic management to be both profitable and rewarding. Many farmers who have made this transition have told us that their organic management practices have brought a new sense of fun and satisfaction to their work and to their lives as a whole.

Growers who sell most of their crops directly to the end consumer via a farm stand, farmers market or community supported agriculture (CSA) may consider organic certification unnecessary because their customers know them and trust their farming practices. Keep in mind, however, that if you intend to sell any of your products through a third party, such as a grocery retailer, certification is imperative to ensure customer confidence (and a grocer can't label your product as "organic" unless it is certified). One of the strongest arguments for uniform federal organic standards was that consumers would be able to rest assured that "organic" meant something specific. A federal standard also makes organic interstate commerce a lot less of a headache.

Soils: An introduction

In this module of the Transitioning to Organic course is an explanation of the importance of building the soil as the foundation of your organic future. Investing in a healthy soil ecosystem creates a hospitable and beneficial environment that accumulates and pays dividends over time.

This module has four lessons: healthy soil, soil monitoring, soil management practices and composts. The soils section will help farmers identify healthy soil and see its relationship to healthy crops, understand soil testing, and recognize soil management practices.

No matter what soil type or types you have, a sound soil-building program that includes the wise use of tillage, attention to soil organic matter, and the use of crop rotations, cover crops, soil amendments and compost will improve the health of the soil. Furthermore, this improved soil health will translate into more predictable yields, higher-quality products and greater returns.

Your soil is the foundation of your organic future. The beauty of "farming the soil" is twofold: you increase your ability to succeed year after year, and you leave a legacy of fertility and resilience for the next generation of farmers.

By the end of this lesson, you should appreciate the importance of soil biodiversity and know how to develop a soil fertility plan in keeping with NOP Standards. Understanding soil biodiversity and fertility is critical to how you will meet your obligation to improve soil under the USDA organic standards.

Organic regulations direct farmers to use practices that will sustain or improve soil conditions without causing pollution of crops, soil or water by contaminants or prohibited substances.

Section §205.203 of the NOP Standards identifies objectives that serve to protect the soil and the environment. These include:

- Select and implement tillage and cultivation practices that maintain or improve the physical, chemical and biological condition of soil and minimize erosion.
- Manage crop nutrients and soil fertility through rotations, cover crops, and the application of plant materials.
- Manage plant and animal materials to maintain or improve soil organic matter content in a manner that does not contribute to contamination of crops, soil, or water by plant nutrients, pathogenic organisms, heavy metals, or residues of prohibited substances.

Under NOP Standards, cover crops need to be part of your plan to build the soil. Section §205.203 of the Standard clearly states that plant materials must be managed to maintain or improve soil organic matter.

Covered fields conserve topsoil and nutrients. For example, in Pennsylvania, a winter crop of vetch or rye works well with the principle crops of corn and soybeans: Vetch provides nitrogen for the corn, while rye soaks up nutrients and helps manage weeds in the soybeans.

Much of what you know about tillage from non-organic farming also applies to organic farming. Most conscientious farmers are careful to restrict tillage activities. However, because of the explicit NOP requirement to protect and build soil quality, organic farmers must plan their tillage regime before the season begins and document the actual tillage that occurs.

Tillage is like fire in a forest. Both have to be managed wisely, and both generate inevitable physical changes to achieve their benefits. However, tillage has risks in that it:

- Accelerates the rate and extent of decline in soil quality
- Increases subsoil compaction
- Increases fossil fuel use and labor costs
- Can lead to soils that are too wet, and crusting of bare soils

You'll learn lessons like these and so much more as you begin to experience the power of your soil and its ability to regenerate itself.

Crops

In the first two modules of this course, the basic principles of organic farming and how the USDA's National Organic Program (NOP) certification system works are the focus. Also covered are some fundamentals of soil science and how in organic agriculture, the focus is on building and caring for the soil. If your soil is in good shape, chances are your crops, livestock and your bottom line will be, too.

In the Crops module, more details of organic crop management are discussed: planning crop rotations and working with cover crops; sourcing seeds and other planting materials in accordance with organic regulations; and developing effective weed and pest management strategies. Also discussed briefly is the harvesting and certification of wild crops, known as wildcrafting.

As in previous modules, discussed are what has been learned over the years under the organic farming systems research done at the Rodale Institute, including the practices followed in the production fields. And there are plenty of examples and tips from organic farmers and researchers in other parts of the country.

Crop rotations vary widely according to region and farm type. You need to develop a rotation based on available resources, including soil, equipment, labor, market opportunities and storage capacity. Good organic crop rotations include both cash crops and cover crops. If you've got plenty of land, you can include long periods of hay or pasture to break weed cycles and build fertility. If you're pressed for space, you may need to rely more heavily on composts or other soil amendments to supply fertility.

Generally speaking, your certifier will expect to see a rotation sequence of three to five crops suitable to your part of the country. You will need to outline your basic rotation sequence (or sequences) when you fill out your Organic System Plan. The best cropping plans are flexible so you can respond to changing conditions. The plans can be different for various fields.

Seeds and planting stock are the building blocks of any rotation, and special care must be taken to ensure that your seeds are sourced and your planting stock is propagated in keeping with organic regulations. Another key feature of most vegetable operations is greenhouse production, particularly in northern climes. Quality seed and healthy planting stock grown in a responsibly managed greenhouse is the best head start you'll get against the challenges that await out in the field.

The organic approach to dealing with weeds is best described as ecologically-based weed management or integrated weed management (IWM). IWM brings together a wide variety of strategies from well-designed crop rotations to adjusting planting methods to novel techniques like flame weeding. These together offer an effective weed management program. Iowa State University weed ecologist Matt Liebman refers to this as the "many little hammers" approach – going after weeds with many small, varied strategies instead of a one-shot approach, as with herbicides.

IWM emphasizes an ecological understanding of how weeds behave in farming systems. Virtually every field activity you engage in – from soil amendments to crop selection to tillage methods, can have an impact on your weed levels and how they interact with crops.

There are a few basic principles of integrated weed management to keep in mind.

Don't let weed populations get out of hand. This means if you see a patch of weeds developing or if you notice that a certain field has become weedy, you need to increase the intensity of management in that area. This can be as simple as scouting and targeting patches of problem weeds or rotating a field into a weed-suppressive crop.

Don't let weeds get adapted to your operation. This means using multiple and diverse tactics to manage weed populations. Weeds can easily survive and persist if the same management practices are done at the same time of year every year.

The amount of damage weeds can do to a crop can vary. There are many ways to make crop plants more competitive so the negative impact on crop yield from weeds is reduced. Just as every field operation can affect weed levels, weed-crop competition can be affected as well. The key is to manage your system so that the crops are given as much of an advantage as possible over the weeds.

Livestock

This module gives basic information about livestock, but also touches on some of the hot button issues for those interested in raising organic livestock. These include pasture for ruminants, as well as organic feeds.

Organic animal husbandry represents one of the strongest growth areas in agriculture today. Consumer demand for organic meat, milk and eggs continues to increase, and as a result, organic commodity buyers are actively recruiting farmers in many parts of the country.

Having animals on an organic farm fosters integrated farming systems in which nutrients are cycled through animals, and manures (composted or uncomposted) are returned to pastures and fields to maintain soil fertility. Grazing or browsing livestock can make use of marginal land not suitable for row crop production, assist with weed management and help distribute income and workload throughout the year. Livestock can also add flexibility to your operation, enabling you to sell crops directly or feed them through animals as market conditions or other factors shift.

This module explains the National Organic Program (NOP) Standards as they apply to livestock production. Here we discuss the transition process, feed requirements, living conditions, health care practices and basic processing rules. At the end of this module, you'll have the opportunity to complete your Organic Livestock Plan using the customized online tool.

Even if you don't have livestock now, I encourage you to read through this module. You may choose to acquire livestock later, you may wish to sell organic livestock feed or you may rent pasture to another organic farmer. In any case, it's important to understand organic livestock regulations.

Shifting to organic livestock production requires careful planning. You may need to make changes to your infrastructure, marketing strategies and recordkeeping systems as well as to your crop and livestock management methods. Talk to other producers, sustainable agriculture education groups and certification agencies before beginning your transition.

There are a number of different USDA regulations that you'll want to keep in mind. Poultry must be managed organically from their second day of life to be sold as organic. Larger livestock must be managed organically from the last third of gestation. Existing dairy herds may be converted with the farm on a one-time-only basis, with a full year of organic management elapsing prior to the sale of any organic dairy products. Male breeder stock (bulls, rams, etc.) do not need to be managed organically and/or can be transitioned at any time. Be sure to obtain necessary documentation of organic status for any organic animals you purchase.

NOP Standards require that organic livestock be fed 100 percent organic feed. Have a backup plan for alternate organic feed sources in case of a crop failure or other emergency. Any feed additives used must be in compliance with the Standards. Milk replacers, synthetic silage preservatives and growth-promoting hormones are all prohibited.

If you are planning on seeking certification for an organic livestock operation, now would be a great time for you to start filling out your Organic Livestock Plan using our electronic Organic System Plan tool. (Some certifiers combine organic crop and livestock information into a single set of forms, but many ask you to complete both forms if you intend to sell both crops and livestock products as organic.)

NOP Standards require producers to "establish and maintain livestock living conditions which accommodate the health and natural behavior of the animals" (§205.239). Specific requirements stipulate that:

• All animals must have "access to the outdoors, shade, shelter, exercise areas, fresh air, and direct sunlight" as appropriate for "the species, the climate and the environment." Confinement of animals is allowed only on a temporary basis based on weather conditions, health or the animal's stage of production.

• Ruminants must have access to pasture.

• Bedding must be kept clean and dry. If livestock typically eat the bedding, it must be organically produced, like any other part of their feed.

Livestock housing or shelter must be designed to give animals:

- Room for exercise and other natural behaviors such as grooming and lying down
- Protection from extreme temperatures
- Ventilation and fresh air
- Protection from injury

Marketing

With careful marketing you can achieve the premium prices associated with organics and improve your bottom line. This module will show you how to get started. So far, the course has looked at how to produce crops and livestock organically to give you a certifiably different product. To capture the value of your investments in going organic (and the environmental benefits that will result), you need to be able to maintain that difference when you take your products to market. To do that, you'll want to have a business plan that includes a marketing plan and a thorough understanding of costs and pricing.

This module will introduce you to overall organic market trends and the opportunities they provide for you, given your capacity to produce, your location and your desired level of "adding value" to what you grow. Whether you produce field-run soybeans or farm-processed yogurt in a private-label container, a good plan will help you become a successful enterprise by connecting to a solid market for your products.

Here we suggest strategies and tactics to help you manage and market your business in your part of the country. The emphasis is on providing value by optimizing the marketing mix (product, place, price and promotion).

By the end of this module, you will be better able to understand general organic marketing trends and opportunities; identify regional marketing options for what you wish to market; use the Crop Conversion Calculator (this course's crop enterprise budgeting tool); and determine why business and marketing plans are important for your business, and how they can help you decide if organic farming is right for you at this time.

Organic producers are penetrating virtually every market sector where health, environmental and food-quality attributes are valued. These range from neighborhood farmers markets selling fresh produce to contracts for railcars of organic small grains for pasta and bread; from semi-trailers of #2 yellow corn for livestock feed to pricey ounces of dried mushrooms.

Consumer interest in certified organic products includes a range of attributes. In September 2007, a Harris Poll revealed that large majorities of the public believe that organic food is safer for the environment (79 percent) and healthier (76 percent). Almost all frequent organic food buyers believe these values to be true (92 percent and 98 percent, respectively).

Global organic sales of organic food and drink hit an estimated $40 billion in 2006, with fresh produce accounting for about one-third of the sales, according to *Organic Monitor.*

How are farmers responding to this demand? An August 2007 report from the USDA shows that there were 4 million acres of organically certified land – about 2,330,000 acres in pastures and 1,700,000 acres in cropland – as of 2005, the latest year with complete statistics for these land-use indicators. At the other end of the spectrum, the number of farmers markets hit 3,700 that year, doubling from the 1,775 markets of 1994.

Whether you're raising #2 yellow corn, alfalfa hay or tomatoes, the last thing you want to be doing come harvest time is sitting on a surplus of organic produce destined for the conventional market – or even the compost pile. With demand for organics far outpacing supply, there's no reason for this to happen. But you need to be proactive in lining up your markets.

If you're marketing through a CSA, you should have a pretty good idea of how much you need to produce to fulfill that segment of your customer base. (Start by multiplying the number of members you have by what you intend to include in each weekly share.) If you grow grains, consider growing a portion of your crop on contracts rather than depending on the spot market to handle your entire crop.

Farmers markets and drive-up farm stand sales can be trickier to project, but experience will soon inform you. Retail and restaurant customer sales are similar to farmers market and farm stand sales, but perhaps a little more predictable. Gauging the volume of retail and restaurant customer sales will depend on the relationships you can build and maintain.

The amount of produce, grain or livestock you raise to fulfill a contract with a wholesaler or retailer may fluctuate from year to year. You should have a good idea of your obligations within any one season. As you move into organic production, try to balance your new investments in time, land and capital as much as you can. In other words, grow your markets by taking risks you are comfortable with.

It is so important to know the market you're growing for, so you can position yourself to best meet the needs of that market ahead of time. Farmers have so many other factors they can't control, such as weather, pests and market conditions, that you need to give yourself the strongest possible starting point.

Certification

Many transitioning farmers view certification paperwork with some trepidation. This section will show you how to transform a challenge into a tool for business management. Completing this course will give you a big head start on the certification process, but you'll still have to follow the basic steps required of anyone seeking to produce and sell certified organic products.

In this module, we'll discuss certification in more detail – from choosing a certifying agent to filling out the forms to having your farm inspected. We'll review organic regulations concerning materials and inputs, describe recordkeeping systems to facilitate the certification process and underline the importance of maintaining organic integrity from planting to post-harvest handling. We'll also talk briefly about certified organic processing rules.

At the end of this module, you are invited to complete the final sections of your electronic Organic Systems Plan. If you're planning on doing any value-added processing of farm products for the organic market, you may want to complete the electronic Organic Handling Plan as well. Here are the basic steps for anyone seeking to produce and sell organic products:

1. Obtain and review application documents from one or more certifiers.
2. Read the NOP Standards.
3. Document land-use practices and create a farm map. Get soil and water tests, if needed.
4. Develop an Organic System Plan (including an Organic Livestock Plan and/or Organic Handling Plan if necessary).
5. Submit your complete application packet, including payment.
6. Go through the initial inspection.
7. Correct any non-compliances as requested by your certifier.
8. Renew your certification annually by updating your Organic System Plan, paying your fees and getting re-inspected.

In this lesson we'll review key elements of the NOP Standards, consider the different factors that go into choosing a certification agent and outline the organic farm inspection process. We'll suggest ways to make your first inspection go smoothly and discuss procedures for complaints and other issues within the certification regulation.

Additional resources

These online tools can be accessed by visiting *www.rodaleinstitute.org*. There are a number of resources that can help you transition to organic farming, or help you to become a better organic farmer.

Organic system plan

The purpose of this tool is to help you assemble the necessary documentation to apply for organic certification through an accredited certifying agent. Although designed to be used in conjunction with the Rodale Institute's Transitioning to Organic online course, this tool can also be used independently. The Organic System Plan should take between two to eight hours to fill out the first time.

There are a number of different sections, as well as additional tools:

- Organic Farm Plan: the basic plan for farms raising crops.
- Organic Livestock Plan: for farmers who would like to get certified for livestock.
- Organic Handling Plan: for those who will be doing additional handling of products, such as processing into value-added products.

- Farm Plan Update: to fill out for subsequent years after you gain certification.
- Demos: sample system plans based on imaginary farms.

The Organic System Plan requires you to register on the site, and then guides you through a series of questions. Clicking on the information symbol by various questions will provide more information about the topic.

Crop conversion calculator

The Crop Conversion Calculator is a tool that lets you easily do a side-by-side comparison of conventional and organic management on your own farm, using numbers from your own farm. You can also compare the input costs of conventional tillage, organic tillage and no-till operations. This will enable you to prepare a transition to organic no-till.

The calculator shows you a line-by-line comparison of the two systems so you can see just how they would stack up on your farm, in your own climate. The whole process, beginning to end, takes less than a minute.

Farming for credit directory

This is a list of hands-on and classroom-based sustainable agriculture education opportunities. It's organized by region, and includes links to other directories for even more information. *www.rodaleinstitute.org/ffc_directory*

No-till revolution

This page contains the latest information on organic no-till from the Rodale Institute, including over 30 articles and a list of resources for further reading.

www.rodaleinstitute.org/no-till_revolution

INDEX

Index topics for information found in tables are indicated in ***bold type.***

Also from Acres U.S.A.

Eco-Farm: An Acres U.S.A. Primer

BY CHARLES WALTERS

In this book, eco-agriculture is explained — from the tiniest molecular building blocks to managing the soil — in terminology that not only makes the subject easy to learn, but vibrantly alive. Sections on NP&K, cation exchange capacity, composting, Brix, soil life, and more! *Eco-Farm* truly delivers a complete education in soils, crops, and weed and insect control. This should be the first book read by everyone beginning in eco-agriculture . . . and the most shop-worn book on the shelf of the most experienced. *Softcover, 476 pages. ISBN 978-0-911311-74-7*

Weeds: Control Without Poisons

BY CHARLES WALTERS

For a thorough understanding of the conditions that produce certain weeds, you simply can't find a better source than this one — certainly not one as entertaining, as full of anecdotes and homespun common sense. It contains a lifetime of collected wisdom that teaches us how to understand and thereby control the growth of countless weed species, as well as why there is an absolute necessity for a more holistic, eco-centered perspective in agriculture today. Contains specifics on a hundred weeds, why they grow, what soil conditions spur them on or stop them, what they say about your soil, and how to control them without the obscene presence of poisons, all cross-referenced by scientific and various common names, and a new pictorial glossary. *Softcover, 352 pages. ISBN 978-0-911311-58-7*

The Biological Farmer

A Complete Guide to the Sustainable & Profitable Biological System of Farming

BY GARY F. ZIMMER

Biological farmers work with nature, feeding soil life, balancing soil minerals, and tilling soils with a purpose. The methods they apply involve a unique system of beliefs, observations and guidelines that result in increased production and profit. This practical how-to guide elucidates their methods and will help you make farming fun and profitable. *The Biological Farmer* is the farming consultant's bible. It schools the interested grower in methods of maintaining a balanced, healthy soil that promises greater productivity at lower costs, and it covers some of the pitfalls of conventional farming practices. Zimmer knows how to make responsible farming work. His extensive knowledge of biological farming and consulting experience come through in this complete, practical guide to making farming fun and profitable. *Softcover, 352 pages. ISBN 978-0-911311-62-4*

Hands-On Agronomy

BY NEAL KINSEY & CHARLES WALTERS

The soil is more than just a substrate that anchors crops in place. An ecologically balanced soil system is essential for maintaining healthy crops. This is a comprehensive manual on soil management. The "whats and whys" of micronutrients, earthworms, soil drainage, tilth, soil structure and organic matter are explained in detail. Kinsey shows us how working with the soil produces healthier crops with a higher yield. True hands-on advice that consultants charge thousands for every day. Revised, third edition. *Softcover, 352 pages. ISBN 978-0-911311-59-4*

Hands-On Agronomy Video Workshop

DVD Video

BY NEAL KINSEY

Neal Kinsey teaches a sophisticated, easy-to-live-with system of fertility management that focuses on balance, not merely quantity of fertility elements. It works in a variety of soils and crops, both conventional and organic. In sharp contrast to the current methods only using N-P-K and pH and viewing soil only as a physical support media for plants, the basis of all his teachings are to feed the soil, and let the soil feed the plant. The Albrecht system of soils is covered, along with how to properly test your soil and interpret the results. *80 minutes.*

Science in Agriculture

BY ARDEN B. ANDERSEN, PH.D., D.O.

By ignoring the truth, ag-chemical enthusiasts are able to claim that pesticides and herbicides are necessary to feed the world. But science points out that low-to-mediocre crop production, weed, disease, and insect pressures are all symptoms of nutritional imbalances and inadequacies in the soil. The progressive farmer who knows this can grow bountiful, disease- and pest-free commodities without the use of toxic chemicals. A concise recap of the main schools of thought that make up eco-agriculture — all clearly explained. Both farmer and professional consultant will benefit from this important work. *Softcover, 376 pages. ISBN 978-0-911311-35-8*

To order call
1-800-355-5313
or order online
at www.acresusa.com

Agriculture in Transition

BY DONALD L. SCHRIEFER

Now you can tap the source of many of agriculture's most popular progressive farming tools. Ideas now commonplace in the industry, such as "crop and soil weatherproofing," the "row support system," and the "tillage commandments," exemplify the practicality of the soil/root maintenance program that serves as the foundation for Schriefer's highly-successful "systems approach" farming. A veteran teacher, lecturer and writer, Schriefer's ideas are clear, straightforward, and practical. *Softcover, 238 pages. ISBN 978-0-911311-61-7*

From the Soil Up

BY DONALD L. SCHRIEFER

The farmer's role is to conduct the symphony of plants and soil. In this book, learn how to coax the most out of your plants by providing the best soil and removing all yield-limiting factors. Schriefer is best known for his "systems" approach to tillage and soil fertility, which is detailed here. Managing soil aeration, water, and residue decay are covered, as well as ridge planting systems, guidelines for cultivating row crops, and managing soil fertility. Develop your own soil fertility system for long-term productivity. *Softcover, 274 pages. ISBN 978-0-911311-63-1*

The Non-Toxic Farming Handbook

BY PHILIP A. WHEELER, PH.D. & RONALD B. WARD

In this readable, easy-to-understand handbook the authors successfully integrate the diverse techniques and technologies of classical organic farming, Albrecht-style soil fertility balancing, Reams-method soil and plant testing and analysis, and other alternative technologies applicable to commercial-scale agriculture. By understanding all of the available non-toxic tools and when they are effective, you will be able to react to your specific situation and growing conditions. Covers fertility inputs, in-the-field testing, foliar feeding, and more. The result of a lifetime of eco-consulting. *Softcover, 236 pages. ISBN 978-0-911311-56-3*

Bread from Stones

BY JULIUS HENSEL

This book was the first work to attack Von Liebig's salt fertilizer thesis, and it stands as valid today as when first written over 100 years ago. Conventional agriculture is still operating under misconceptions disproved so eloquently by Hensel so long ago. In addition to the classic text, comments by John Hamaker and Phil Callahan add meaning to the body of the book. Many who stand on the shoulders of this giant have yet to acknowledge Hensel. A true classic of agriculture. *Softcover, 102 pages. ISBN 978-0-911311-30-3*

Alternative Treatments for Ruminant Animals

BY PAUL DETTLOFF, D.V.M.

Drawing on 36 years of veterinary practice, Dr. Paul Dettloff presents an natural, sustainable approach to ruminant health. Copiously illustrated chapters "break down" the animal into its interrelated biological systems: digestive, reproductive, respiratory, circulatory, musculoskeletal and more. Also includes a chapter on nosodes, with vaccination programs for dairy cattle, sheep and goats. An information-packed manual from a renowned vet and educator. *Softcover, 260 pages. ISBN 0-911311-77-7*

Grass, the Forgiveness of Nature

Exploring the miracle of grass, pastures & grassland farming

BY CHARLES WALTERS

In this wide-ranging survey of grass forages and pastureland, Charles Walters makes the case that grass is not just for cows and horses — that in fact it is the most nutritious food produced by nature, as well as the ultimate soil conditioner. You will learn from traditional graziers who draw on centuries of wisdom to create beautiful, lush, sustainable pastures, as well as cutting-edge innovators who are using such methods as biodynamics and sea-solids fertilization to create some of the healthiest grasslands in the world. Leading agronomists not only explain the importance of grasses in our environment, they also share practical knowledge such as when to look for peak levels of nutrition within the growing cycle and how to use grass to restore soil to optimum health. A must-read for anyone interested in sustainable, bio-correct agriculture, this information-packed volume is a comprehensive look at an essential family of plants. *Softcover, 320 pages. ISBN 0-911311-89-0*

Soil, Grass & Cancer

BY ANDRÉ VOISIN

Almost a half-century ago, André Voisin had already grasped the importance of the subterranean world. He mapped the elements of the soil and their effects on plants, and ultimately, animal and human life as well. He saw the hidden danger in the gross oversimplification of fertilization practices that use harsh chemicals and ignore the delicate balance of trace minerals and nutrients in the soil. With a volume of meticulously researched information, Voisin issues a call to agricultural scientists, veterinarians, dietitians and intelligent farmers to stand up and acknowledge the responsibilities they bear in the matter of public health. He writes as well to the alarmed consumer of agricultural products, hoping to spread the knowledge of the possibilities of protective medicine — part of a concerted attempt to remove the causes of ill health, disease and, in particular, cancer. *Softcover, 368 pages. ISBN 0-911311-64-5*

Fertility Farming

BY NEWMAN TURNER

Fertility Farming explores an approach to farming that makes minimal use of plowing, eschews chemical fertilizers and pesticides, and emphasizes soil fertility via crop rotation, composting, cover cropping and manure application.

Turner holds that the foundation of the effectiveness of nature's husbandry is a fertile soil — and the measure of a fertile soil is its content of organic matter, ultimately, its *humus*. Upon a basis of humus, nature builds a complete structure of healthy life — without need for disease control of any kind. In fact, disease treatment is unnecessary in nature, as disease is the outcome of the unbalancing or perversion of the natural order — and serves as a warning that something is wrong. The avoidance of disease is therefore the simple practice of natural law. Much more than theory, this book was written to serve as a practical guide for farmers. Turner's advice for building a productive, profitable organic farming system rings as true today as it did sixty years ago when it was written. *Softcover, 272 pages. ISBN 978-1-601730-09-1*

Herdsmanship

BY NEWMAN TURNER

In this book, Turner explains that livestock illness is a result of bad farming practices and that real livestock health begins with true natural farming disciplines such as composting, biodiverse pastures with deep-rooted forages and herbs, and sub-soiling, as well as the avoidance of supposed panaceas that ignore or marginalize these fundamentals such as vaccines, pesticides, antibiotics and artificial fertilizers. He teaches that the cornerstones of profitability are rooted in herd health, which in turn is rooted in: soil fertility and animal nutrition, cattle breeding for better feed efficiency, and cattle breeding for longevity. Longevity, he holds, is the most critical factor for success in livestock breeding and production. *Softcover, 272 pages. ISBN 978-1-601730-10-7*

Fertility Pastures

BY NEWMAN TURNER

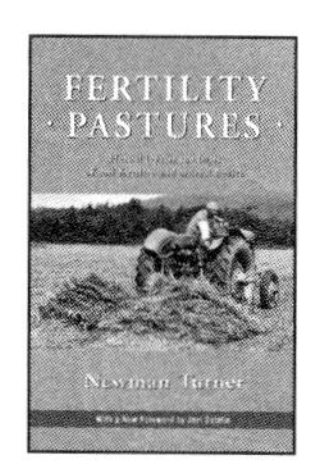

In *Fertility Pastures*, Turner details his methods of intensive pasture-based production of beef and dairy cows in a practical guide to profitable, labor-saving livestock production. He developed a system of complex "herbal ley mixtures," or blends of pasture grasses and herbs, with each ingredient chosen to perform an essential function in providing a specific nutrient to the animal or enhancing the fertility of the soil. He explains his methods of cultivation, seeding and management. There are also chapters on year-round grazing, making silage for self-feeding, protein from forage crops, and pastures for pigs and poultry. He also details the roles individual herbs play in the prevention and treatment of disease. *Softcover, 224 pages. ISBN 978-1-601730-11-4*

Treating Dairy Cows Naturally

By Hubert J. Karreman, V.M.D.

A dairy practitioner describes how cows can be treated for a wide variety of problems with plant-derived and biological medicines. Drawing upon veterinary treatments from the days before synthetic pharmaceuticals and tempering them with modern knowledge and clinical experience, Dr. Karreman bridges the world of natural treatments with life in the barn in a rational and easy to understand way. In describing treatments for common dairy cow diseases, he covers practical aspects of biologics, botanical medicines, homeopathic remedies, acupuncture and conventional medicine. This book will serve as a useful reference for years to come. *Hardcover, 420 pages. ISBN 978-1-60173-000-8*

Holistic Veterinary Care

BY JERRY BRUNETTI
& HUBERT J. KARREMAN, V.M.D.

Dr. Hubert J. Karreman, author of the compendium *Treating Dairy Cows Naturally*, is joined by renowned animal nutrition expert Jerry Brunetti to present an overview of the strategies and tools available for successful holistic herd health management. The emphasis is on natural alternatives for the treatment of common dairy cow problems, including complications in reproduction, birth and lactation. This video will provide you with a basic understanding of the power and the limitations of herbs, how to treat the whole cow, and how to build a herbal medicine kit for your farm. Drawing on actual case studies, which are examined, diagnosed, and treated using holistic protocols, this video serves as a virtual hands-on course in holistic herd health that will prove invaluable to every dairy producer, from the micro-scale family farmer to commercial-scale operations. *VHS & DVD format, 90 minutes. PAL format for Europe, Australia, etc.*

Homeopathy for the Herd

BY C. EDGAR SHAEFFER, V.M.D.

Subtitled *A Farmer's Guide to Low-Cost, Non-Toxic Veterinary Cattle Care,* this new information-packed book by *Acres U.S.A.'s* Natural Vet will tell you what you need to know to get started in the use of homeopathic medicines with cows. Using case studies and practical examples from both dairy and beef operations, Dr. Shaeffer covers such topics as: creating a holistic operation; organics and homeopathy; prescribing; mastitis and fertility-related problems; and the *Materia Medica,* keynotes and nosodes. Also includes a convenient section that lists specific conditions and remedies. *Softcover, 222 pages. ISBN 978-0-911311-72-3*

To order call 1-800-355-5313
or order online at www.acresusa.com